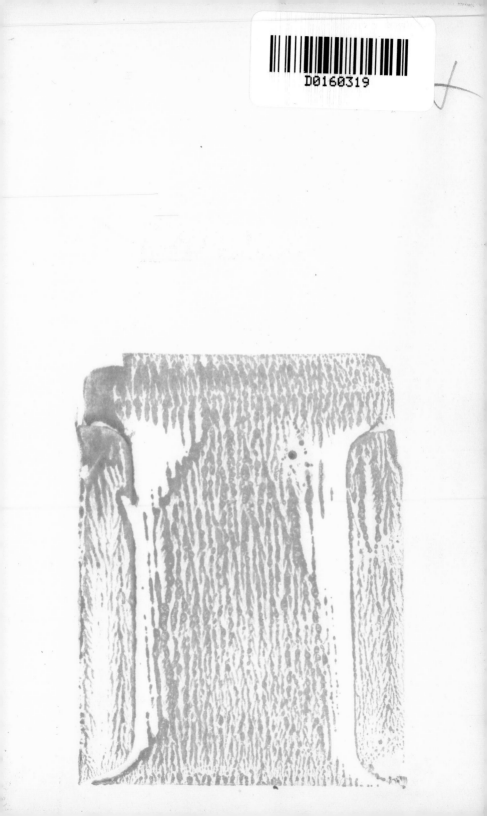

VIBRATIONS AND WAVES

ENGLAND: BUTTERWORTH & CO. (PUBLISHERS) LTD.
                 LONDON: 88 Kingsway, W.C.2

AFRICA: BUTTERWORTH & CO. (AFRICA) LTD.
                 DURBAN: 33–35 Beach Grove

AUSTRALIA: BUTTERWORTH & CO. (AUSTRALIA) LTD.
                 SYDNEY: 6–8 O'Connell Street
                 MELBOURNE: 473 Bourke Street
                 BRISBANE: 240 Queen Street

CANADA: BUTTERWORTH & CO. (CANADA) LTD.
                 TORONTO: 1367 Danforth Avenue, 6

NEW ZEALAND: BUTTERWORTH & CO. (NEW ZEALAND) LTD.
                 WELLINGTON: 49/51 Ballance Street
                 AUCKLAND: 35 High Street

U.S.A.:   BUTTERWORTH INC.
                 WASHINGTON, D.C.: 7235 Wisconsin Avenue, 14

VIBRATIONS
AND
WAVES

R. V. SHARMAN
M.Sc., Ph.D.

Head of Physics and Mathematics Department,
Norwood Technical College, London

LONDON
BUTTERWORTHS
1963

Suggested **U.D.C.** number: 534

Suggested additional number: 538·56

Made and Printed in Great Britain by C. Tinling & Co. Ltd.
Liverpool, London and Prescot

7/6√

CONTENTS

v

5. MODES OF VIBRATION

6. WAVE PROPERTIES

7. ACOUSTICAL WAVE PHENOMENA

8. ELECTRO-MAGNETIC WAVES

9. WAVE VELOCITY

PREFACE

In the following pages an attempt has been made to assemble a coherent account of vibrations and waves, in support of the current trend to treat them as a whole and not in a piecemeal fashion in various parts of physics, methematics and engineering. A central theme is unification—the joining together of these various parts. The main reason is to help the student to understand properly and to be able to 'think around' various topics, in the hope that he will translate such an approach into his later career.

Economy in mathematical treatment is hardly a significant reason for unification because two practical situations that can be exactly described by the same equation have yet to be found. Furthermore, as far as I am aware, one practical situation that can be described exactly by an equation has also yet to be found. Until this is done there would usually seem to be little point in solving exactly and rigorously an equation that is itself an approximation. Hence I see, in accord with Rayleigh*, no need to make an apology for some of the treatment not having the rigorous formal shape that is, or used to be, demanded in pure mathematics. Even so, my experience is that students view with suspicion the 'intuitive' solution which is justified by substitution in the equation to be solved. Where possible solutions of equations have been obtained by the usual methods of pure mathematics, but occasionally space limitation has necessitated the use of other methods. I also make no apology for using vectors freely. The physicist or engineer who has not a working knowledge of vector analysis is doing himself a disservice.

The symbols employed are very largely conventional and the use of the same symbol for vastly different quantities has been avoided where possible. For a work covering such a wide field a list of symbols used throughout the book was not found practicable within alphabetic limitations if complex subscripts were not to be used. Definitions of symbols are given where necessary in the text. References to other works are few because a student can rarely afford the time to consult many references. A consideration of wave-particle dualism and wave mechanics is omitted only because space limitation precludes an appropriate treatment.

While I am certain that the teaching of mathematics is very

* Rayleigh, *The Theory of Sound*: Dover, 1945 (Reprint).

difficult, if not impossible, without the use of many examples, I am inclined to doubt whether the teaching of physics, particularly that of about degree level, is aided significantly by the solution of numerical problems which are, at best, a statement of data all of which are not physically realizable or accurately ascertainable and, at worst, so far from experimental results as to be devoid of physics although perhaps of mathematical interest. Happily the tendency is being shown, in some examinations, to depart from the classical 'book-work, numerical problem, rider' kind of question towards those which demand rather more thought and initiative from the student. Although the present book might have been improved by placing some such problems at the end of certain chapters, the improvement resulting was thought to be negligible when balanced against the vast amount of work and space required for answers, as problems without answers are of little use to a student. Furthermore a resulting tendency of the book to become tied to particular examination syllabuses would be very difficult to avoid and is here undesirable.

I am indebted to C. A. Hogarth, B.Sc., Ph.D., who suggested that this book be written, and to the following who also diligently read parts of the typescript and made some valuable suggestions: J. Crank, D.Sc.; G. F. Lewin, B.A., D.Phil; Professor P. Lewis, B.Sc., Ph.D. Any errors that remain are, of course, my responsibility.

R. V. Sharman

April, 1963.

FREE VIBRATIONS

1.1. Simple Harmonic Motion

If a particle P, shown in *Figure 1.1*, moves in a straight line AB so that its acceleration is always directed towards a fixed point O in AB, and is directly proportional to its distance s from O, the motion of P is said to be *simple harmonic*.

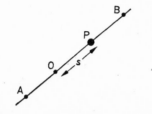

Figure 1.1. Simple harmonic motion

Particle P is ideally of infinitesimal volume but of finite mass. Practically the volume of P can usually be ignored, especially if the volume and its boundary are both invariant—a 'rigid body'—and the distance s is then conveniently measured to the centre of mass, otherwise known as the centre of gravity.

'Simple harmonic' is perhaps not very descriptive of the motion of P. The motion is 'simple' in that P oscillates about O at only one frequency, and 'harmonic' in the sense that the vibrations of bodies emitting musical sounds consist of the motions of many particles like P. Application of the term 'simple harmonic' to the kind of motion described is, however, very wide, if not universal, so the use of a more descriptive but little-used term is hardly justifiable.

Oscillatory motion of P about O is not stated in the definition of SHM but is implied. The equation of motion of P may be integrated in order to find s in terms of the time t and a sinusoidal relation is found.

The definition of SHM may be expressed symbolically by

$$\frac{d^2s}{dt^2} = \ddot{s} = -S_1 s \qquad (1.1)$$

where S_1 is a positive constant, the minus sign denoting that the acceleration always tends to decrease s.

Equation (1.1) is easily solved by using methods applicable to second-order differential equations having constant coefficients, or by writing dv/dt for d^2s/dt^2, where v is the instantaneous velocity of P and equals ds/dt. Then dv/dt may be shown to equal $v\,dv/ds$ and the resulting equation can be integrated twice. Consideration of a reference circle round which moves a particle corresponding to P is however, more instructive.

1.2. Reference Circle

Consider a particle Q moving along the circumference of a circle of radius a with *constant* angular velocity ω_0 and suppose that the instantaneous position of Q is as shown in *Figure 1.2*. Draw QP perpendicular to any diameter AB, and imagine another particle to be located at P.

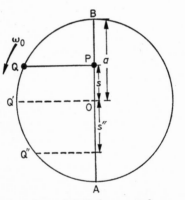

Figure 1.2. Reference circle

The acceleration of Q is $\omega_0^2 a$ along QO and hence $\omega_0^2 a \cos \theta$, which equals $\omega_0^2 s$, parallel to BA. If QP remains perpendicular to AB as Q moves, P must also have an acceleration $\omega_0^2 s$, but *along* BA directed towards O. When Q reaches Q' its acceleration parallel to AB is zero. P is then at O and its acceleration is also zero. When Q is at Q'' its acceleration parallel to AB is $\omega_0^2 s''$, so the acceleration of P is then $\omega_0^2 s''$ along AB directed towards O again. Thus as Q moves round the circle with constant angular velocity, P moves simple harmonically along AB, since its acceleration is always directed towards a fixed point (O) and is proportional to its distance from the fixed point. Further information regarding the motion of

2

P can be obtained by studying the motion of the particle Q round the reference circle.

From such a treatment a practical demonstration of SHM may be devised. A wheel on which is fitted a long straight handle H, shown in *Figure 1.3*, is rotated after being placed between a small intense source of light L and a large screen. The screen is placed parallel to the rotational axis of the wheel, and normal to a line passing through the source and the centre of the wheel. The shadow S cast by the handle on the screen executes approximate SHM.

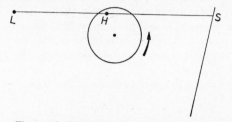

Figure 1.3. Practical demonstration of SHM

From *Figure 1.4* or the preceding analysis, the acceleration of P is d^2s/dt^2 which equals the component of the acceleration of Q parallel to AB, $\omega_0^2 a \cos \theta$. Thus

$$d^2s/dt^2 = -\omega_0^2 s. \qquad (1.2)$$

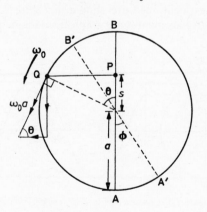

Figure 1.4. Reference circle

Comparison of *Equations (1.1)* and *(1.2)* shows that ω_0^2 is equivalent to S_1.

The velocity of $P = ds/dt = \dot{s} = v$

$$= \text{component of the velocity of Q parallel to AB}$$

$$= -\omega_0 a \sin$$

$$= -\omega_0 \sqrt{(a^2 - s^2)}$$

or $\qquad ds/dt = -\omega_0 a \sin (\omega_0 t + \phi) \qquad (1.3)$

if Q starts from B′ at time $t = 0$. The minus sign is required since P is travelling in the negative s direction. ϕ is known as the *phase angle* or *epoch*, the *phase* being conveniently taken as the time that has elapsed since the particle was at its maximum positive distance from the centre of motion. Here the phase of the motion at time t is $t + \phi/\omega_0$ since $s = a$ at time t_a given by $t_a = -\phi/\omega_0$ and the phase at time t is $t - t_a$.

The instantaneous displacement $s = a \cos \theta$ or

$$s = a \cos (\omega_0 t + \phi) \qquad (1.4)$$

a being known as the *amplitude* of the displacement. *Equations (1.3)* and *(1.4)* can also be obtained by integrating *Equation (1.2)*.

The *period T_0* of a complete vibration is the time required for the reference particle Q to travel once round the circle, so that

$$T_0 = 2\pi/\omega_0 = 2\pi/\sqrt{(S_1)}. \qquad (1.5)$$

The quantities mentioned are shown in *Figure 1.5* and the construction of a displacement–time graph from the reference circle can also be seen.

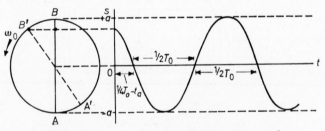

Figure 1.5. *Construction of displacement–time graph*

1.3. Examples of Simple Harmonic Motion

There is no practical system to which *Equation (1.2)* and its solutions apply rigorously, because the vibrational energy is dissipated and

4

the amplitude of the vibrations decreases, ultimately becoming zero. In some systems the energy dissipation is small and they may be idealized as shown in the following examples.

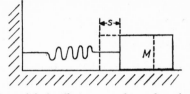

Figure 1.6. Oscillations on a frictionless plane

A mass M resting on a fixed frictionless (smooth) horizontal plane and attached to a horizontal spring having the other end fixed, as shown in *Figure 1.6.*, moves simple harmonically if the amplitude of vibration is small. Then, for a displacement s of M from the rest position, the restoring force acting on M due to the spring is Ss. For large displacements the restoring force is no longer proportional to s. S is the *stiffness* of the spring and equals $\pi n r^4/4lR^2$ for a flat helical spring, where n is the rigidity modulus of the wire composing the spring, r the radius of the wire, l the total length of the wire and R is the radius of the spring.

If M is displaced a further distance δs the work done against the spring is $Ss\delta s$ so that the work done in stretching the spring a distance s is

$$\int_0^s Ss\,\mathrm{d}s$$

which equals $\tfrac{1}{2}Ss^2$. The potential energy of the mass M is thus $\tfrac{1}{2}Ss^2$ and if its velocity is $\mathrm{d}s/\mathrm{d}t$ its kinetic energy is $\tfrac{1}{2}M(\mathrm{d}s/\mathrm{d}t)^2$.

The spring is also moving, and if its mass m is comparable with M the kinetic energy of the spring must also be considered. The end of the spring to which the mass M is fixed moves with a velocity $\mathrm{d}s/\mathrm{d}t$. The other end is fixed and a linear variation of velocity between the two ends may usually be assumed. The kinetic energy of an element δb of the wire distant b from the fixed end is

$$\frac{m\delta b}{2l}\left(\frac{b}{l}\frac{\mathrm{d}s}{\mathrm{d}t}\right)^2$$

so the total kinetic energy of the spring is

$$\int_0^l \frac{m}{2l}\left(\frac{b}{l}\frac{\mathrm{d}s}{\mathrm{d}t}\right)^2 \mathrm{d}b = \frac{m}{6}\left(\frac{\mathrm{d}s}{\mathrm{d}t}\right)^2.$$

5

The kinetic energy of the system is thus $\frac{1}{2}(M+m/3)(ds/dt)^2$ and if the total energy of the system is conserved

$$\frac{1}{2}(M+m/3)(ds/dt)^2 + \frac{1}{2}Ss^2 = \text{a constant.} \qquad (1.6)$$

Differentiating with respect to t gives, since ds/dt is not generally zero

$$(M+m/3)d^2s/dt^2 + Ss = 0 \qquad (1.7)$$

which may be compared with *Equation (1.1)*. Thus from *Equation (1.5)*

$$T_0 = 2\pi\sqrt{[(M+m/3)/S]}. \qquad (1.8)$$

$m/3$ is the *effective mass* of the spring.

No account has been taken of the mass of the surrounding fluid oscillating with M and with the spring. Such motion would effectively increase the vibrating mass, but the increase would be appreciable only at low frequencies of vibration and for dense fluids. Dense fluids usually have a large viscosity and would thus cause a large dissipation of the vibrational energy, an effect of much greater importance.

The preceding analysis holds providing that the period of vibration T_0 is not equal to or near that of one of the modes of vibration of the spring. Then the total kinetic energy of the spring cannot easily be determined, for the extension is not uniform and the coils become grouped into small bunches of turns. A similar effect occurs with the valve springs used in internal combustion engines and results in valve 'bounce' at high engine speeds. The trouble is overcome by spacing the coils forming the spring at varying distances—the spring is wound with a varying pitch—so that each spring is virtually aperiodic.

A similar analysis applies to a mass suspended from a helical spring. If s as a function of t were required in either example, *Equation (1.6)* could be integrated. The treatment thus illustrates the general principle that if s is required as a function of t an *energy equation* rather than a *force equation* should first be obtained, if there is otherwise no preference.

The vertical oscillations of a body partly immersed in a liquid are of the kind characterizing SHM if they are of small amplitude, for then the inertia and the viscosity of the liquid can be ignored.

If a volume V of liquid having a density ρ is displaced at equilibrium, the floating body has a mass ρV. A movement s above or below the equilibrium position brings into operation a restoring force $\rho g A s$, where g is the gravitational intensity and A is the cross-sectional area of the body at and near the surface of the liquid. The equation of motion is thus

$$\rho V d^2 s/dt^2 = -\rho g A s$$

if A is constant at least a distance s above and below the equilibrium position. Hence

$$d^2 s/dt^2 = -(gA/V)s$$

which is similar in form to *Equation (1.1)*. Thus, using *(1.5)*, the period of vibration T_0 is given by

$$T_0 = 2\pi\sqrt{(V/gA)} \qquad (1.9)$$

which applies to ships if the displacement amplitude is very small. If A is constant for the whole body, the mean depth of immersion h equals V/A and then *(1.9)* becomes

$$T_0 = 2\pi\sqrt{(h/g)}. \qquad (1.10)$$

A motion very similar to SHM is the rotational oscillation of a rigid body about a fixed axis. Such a motion is sometimes referred to as *angular harmonic* and the equations corresponding to *(1.1)* and *(1.5)* are

$$I d^2\theta/dt^2 = -b\theta \qquad (1.11)$$

$$T_0 = 2\pi\sqrt{(I/b)} \qquad (1.12)$$

where I is the moment of inertia of the body about the pivot 0, b the restoring torque per unit angular displacement, and θ is the angular

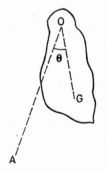

Figure 1.7. Angular motion

displacement at time t, as shown in *Figure 1.7*. G is the centre of mass of the body and OA is a fixed axis. The axis of rotation passes through

O, and is normal to the plane containing OA and OG. For *Equation (1.11)* to hold, the body must have an angular acceleration $d^2\theta/dt^2$ always directed towards the fixed axis OA and directly proportional to its angular displacement θ from OA, defined as shown.

An example of such a motion is that of a *compound pendulum*. OA is then vertical, the axis of rotation is horizontal, and the pendulum oscillates so that OG moves in a vertical plane. The restoring torque, provided by the weight of the body, equals $Mgl \sin \theta$ and is always directed towards the axis OA. Hence

$$I d^2\theta/dt^2 = -Mgl \sin \theta.$$

If r is the radius of gyration of the body about an axis through G (*Figure 1.8*) parallel to the rotational axis through O, $I = M(r^2 + l^2)$ by the parallel axis theorem and

$$d^2\theta/dt^2 = -[gl/(r^2 + l^2)] \sin \theta. \qquad (1.13)$$

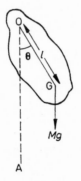

Figure 1.8. Compound pendulum

Thus for vibrations of an angular amplitude not exceeding a few degrees

$$d^2\theta/dt^2 = -[gl/(r^2 + l^2)]\theta. \qquad (1.14)$$

A comparison of *Equation (1.13)* with *(1.11)* and the use of *Equation (1.12)* gives

$$T_0 = 2\pi\sqrt{[(r^2 + l^2)/gl]}. \qquad (1.15)$$

The *simple pendulum* consists of a particle of mass M attached to an inextensible string of negligible mass and of length l. The moment of inertia I then equals Ml^2 since r is zero so that

$$T_0 = 2\pi\sqrt{(l/g)}. \qquad (1.16)$$

1.4. Damped Vibrations

The amplitudes of free vibration in practical systems always decrease in time. A force may be imagined to be acting on the system in such a way as to cause dissipation of the vibrational energy—*damping* is present. Most of the vibrational energy is converted eventually into heat, but some may be radiated as waves in the surrounding fluid or in the massive body to which the vibrating system is attached.

Usually in practical systems neither the magnitude of the damping force, nor its dependence on other factors governing the vibrations, are known accurately. The nature of damping assumed theoretically may thus be chosen to simplify the analysis, if the results do not depart seriously from experimental ones. Accordingly only four kinds of damping are examined, but an approximate method is suggested which is applicable to most kinds of damping.

(*a*) *Viscous or linear damping.*

The damping force is directly proportional to the velocity of the moving element on which the force acts, and may be due to the viscosity of the medium surrounding the vibrating system. At high velocities the force is likely to be more closely proportional to the square of the velocity. Such dependence results in a non-linear differential equation of motion, and is thus an example of non-linear damping, briefly treated in section **1.7.**

(*b*) *Coulomb damping.*

The damping force is constant in magnitude, which is roughly true when damping is provided by the friction between two dry surfaces in relative motion.

(*c*) *Hysteretic damping.*

Here the damping force is expressed in terms of velocity and a frequency. Such damping is a better approximation than viscous damping when energy dissipation is due to imperfect elasticity in the restoring element of the system.

The relevant equations of motion will now be obtained and solved.

1.5. Damping Proportional to Velocity

Here a motion similar to that considered in the beginning of section **1.3.** is examined, but the mass M is assumed to vibrate on a rough plane and the mass of the spring is ignored. The system is shown in *Figure 1.9*. The damping force is $R_m\,ds/dt$ where R_m is the mechanical resistive force per unit velocity of M, the equation of motion of which is

$$Md^2s/dt^2 = -Ss - R_m\,ds/dt$$

S being the restoring force per unit displacement as before. Thus

$$Md^2s/dt^2 + R_m\,ds/dt + Ss = 0. \qquad (1.17)$$

A similar equation is obtained for oscillations in an electrical circuit in which a resistor R, a capacitor C and an inductor L are in series.

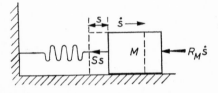

Figure 1.9. Oscillations on a lubricated rough plane

When the key K, shown in *Figure 1.10*, is placed in position 1, C is charged from the cell of constant emf E through L and R, which includes any internal resistance of the cell. If R is small i, the instantaneous current, does not decrease exponentially with time to zero but oscillates about zero.

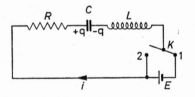

Figure 1.10. C charged through L and R

Using Kirchoff's second law

$$Ri + q/C + Ldi/dt = E$$

where q is the instantaneous charge on C. Differentiating with respect to t gives

$$Ld^2i/dt^2 + Rdi/dt + i/C = 0 \qquad (1.18)$$

since $i = dq/dt$ and $dE/dt = 0$.

10

When K is placed in position 2 after C has been charged the equation is

$$q/C - Ri - Ldi/dt = 0$$

or

$$Ld^2q/dt^2 + Rdq/dt + q/C = 0 \qquad (1.19)$$

since $i = -dq/dt$, the charge q decreasing with time.

The comparable equation for angular motion is

$$Id^2\theta/dt^2 + Bd\theta/dt + b\theta = 0 \qquad (1.20)$$

where I, θ and b have the same meaning as in *Equation (1.11)* and B is the resistive torque per unit angular velocity which, in the ballistic galvanometer, is proportional to the emf induced in the coil because of its motion in the magnetic field.

Since the *Equations (1.17)* to *(1.20)* have the same form, the solution of *(1.17)* only will be obtained. *Equation (1.17)* is rewritten in terms of the damping factor d, which equals $R_m/2\sqrt{(SM)}$, and the natural frequency of oscillation $\omega_0/2\pi$ when there is no damping, where $\omega_0^2 = S/M$. *Equation (1.17)* becomes

$$d^2s/dt^2 + 2d\omega_0 ds/dt + \omega_0^2 s = 0 \qquad (1.21)$$

or in terms of the operator D which here equals d/dt

$$(D^2 + 2d\omega_0 D + \omega_0^2)s = 0.$$

Assuming as usual for equations of this kind that $s = A \exp \alpha t$, where A and α are constants to be determined later, the auxiliary equation is

$$\alpha^2 + 2d\omega_0\alpha + \omega_0^2 = 0$$

which has roots

$$\alpha_1 = [-d + \sqrt{(d^2 - 1)}]\omega_0$$

$$\alpha_2 = [-d - \sqrt{(d^2 - 1)}]\omega_0.$$

The general solution of *(1.20)* is thus

$$s = A_1 \exp [-d + \sqrt{(d^2 - 1)}]\omega_0 t$$

$$. + A_2 \exp [-d - \sqrt{(d^2 - 1)}]\omega_0 t \qquad (1.22)$$

where A_1 and A_2 are the two required arbitrary constants, which can if necessary be written in terms of the initial displacement and velocity of the mass M.

11

The nature of the free motion depends on the value of d. Accordingly the values which characterize the possible kinds of motion will be examined.

(i) $d = 0$. *No damping.*

Here $s = A_1 \exp j\omega_0 t + A_2 \exp -j\omega_0 t$ where j equals $+\sqrt{(-1)}$. Hence

$$s = A_1(\cos \omega_0 t + j \sin \omega_0 t) + A_2(\cos \omega_0 t - j \sin \omega_0 t)$$

or

$$s = A_3 \cos \omega_0 t + A_4 \sin \omega_0 t$$

where $A_3 = A_1 + A_2$; $A_4 = j(A_1 - A_2)$. Thus s is given by

$$s = a \cos(\omega_0 t + \phi) \tag{1.4}$$

if $a = \sqrt{(A_3^2 + A_4^2)}$ and $\phi = \cos^{-1}[A_3/\sqrt{(A_3^2 + A_4^2)}]$

$$= \sin^{-1}[-A_4/\sqrt{(A_3^2 + A_4^2)}]$$

or, in terms of the original constants of the system

$$s = a \cos[t\sqrt{(S/M)} + \phi]. \tag{1.23}$$

There are three other possible solutions depending on how ϕ is defined, but the one shown is chosen since the implications of such an equation have already been studied in section **1.2**. Briefly, the equation represents SHM of displacement amplitude a and frequency $\omega_0/2\pi = \sqrt{(S/M)}/2\pi$.

(ii) $d < 1$. *Small damping.*

Here $\sqrt{(d^2 - 1)} = j\sqrt{(1 - d^2)}$ and is imaginary. From (1.22)

$$s = A_1 \exp[-d + j\sqrt{(1 - d^2)}]\omega_0 t + A_2 \exp[-d - j\sqrt{(1 - d^2)}]\omega_0 t$$

$$= [A_1 \exp j\omega_0 t\sqrt{(1 - d^2)} + A_2 \exp -j\omega_0 t\sqrt{(1 - d^2)}] \exp -d\omega_0 t$$

$$= \{A_1[\cos \omega_0 t\sqrt{(1 - d^2)} + j \sin \omega_0 t\sqrt{(1 - d^2)}]$$

$$+ A_2[\cos \omega_0 t\sqrt{(1 - d^2)} - j \sin \omega_0 t\sqrt{(1 - d^2)}]\} \exp -d\omega_0 t.$$

Thus

$$s = a(\exp -d\omega_0 t) \cos[\omega_0 t\sqrt{(1 - d^2)} + \phi] \tag{1.24}$$

where a and ϕ are defined as before, or, in terms of the original constants of the system

$$s = a(\exp -R_m t/2M) \cos[t\sqrt{(S/M - R_m^2/4M^2)} + \phi]. \tag{1.25}$$

Comparison of *Equation* (1.25) with (1.23) suggests that (1.25)

12

describes vibratory motion of decreasing displacement amplitude $a(\exp -R_m t/2M)$ and frequency of vibration

$$\omega_d/2\pi = \sqrt{(S/M - R_m^2/4M^2)}/2\pi.$$

Displacement-time graphs of *Equations* (*1.23*) and (*1.25*) are shown in *Figure 1.11*.

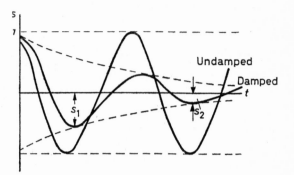

Figure 1.11. Displacement–time graphs of damped and undamped motion

We have

$$\omega_d = \sqrt{(S/M - R_m^2/4M^2)}.$$

Thus

$$\partial\omega_d/\partial M = (-S/M^2 + R_m^2/2M^3)/\sqrt{(S/M - R_m^2/4M^2)}$$

and for a maximum or minimum $\partial\omega_d/\partial M = 0$. Hence $S/M^2 = R_m^2/2M^3$ or $M = R_m^2/2S$. This corresponds to a maximum value of ω_d since $\partial^2\omega_d/\partial M^2$ is negative. Thus

$$\frac{1}{2\pi}(\omega_d)_{max} = \sqrt{[S/(R_m^2/2S) - R_m^2/(4R_m^2/4S^2)]}/2\pi = \frac{S/R_m}{2\pi}$$

which is sometimes called the *relaxation frequency* and is the maximum natural frequency obtainable in a system with a specified restoring force per unit displacement (*S*) and resistive force per unit velocity (R_m).

The frequency $\omega_d/2\pi$ of the damped motion is lower than $\omega_0/2\pi$ for the undamped motion, so that the period T_d of the damped motion is longer than T_0 for the undamped motion, as is shown in *Figure 1.11*. Also shown in this figure is the difference in phase of the two motions, even though the phase angles ϕ are the same. The phase of the undamped motion at time t is $t + \phi/\omega_0$ from section **1.2.**, while that of the damped vibration is $t + \phi/\omega_d$ and ω_d is less than ω_0.

The *decrement* of the decaying vibration is defined as the ratio s/s', where s is the displacement at time t, as before, and s' is the displacement at one whole period T_d later. For convenience s and s' may be taken as two successive maxima on the same side of zero displacement. Decrement is sometimes defined in terms of a half-period, and due allowance must then be made in any of the accompanying theory. The present definition is considered to be preferable for measurements in practical work, for example with the ballistic galvanometer, for then the displacements to be recorded are on the same side of the zero. The reading of the displacement maxima is thus facilitated and frequently the whole scale length can be used, for the deflections on the other side of the zero need not be on the scale. The decrement is given by

$$\frac{s}{s'} = \frac{a(\exp - d\omega_0 t) \cos\left[\omega_0 t \sqrt{(1 - d^2)} + \phi\right]}{a[\exp - d\omega_0 (t + T_d)] \cos\left[\omega_0 (t + T_d)\sqrt{(1 - d^2)} + \phi\right]} = \exp\, d\omega_0 T_d.$$

The *logarithmic decrement* δ is $\log_e(s/s')$. Thus δ equals $d\omega_0 T_d$ or

$$\delta = R_m T_d/2M. \tag{1.26}$$

For lightly damped systems δ would be found practically by measuring a maximum displacement, counting p maxima on the same side of the zero, and measuring the last of these, the $(p+1)$th maximum. If the two maxima are s_1 and s_{p+1} δ equals $(\log_e s_1/s_{p+1})/p$. Successive maxima s_1, s_2, s_3, . . . are in *geometrical progression* since $s_1/s_2 = s_2/s_3 = \ldots . = s_{p-1}/s_p = \exp \delta$. The *time constant* T_c is the time in which the displacement amplitude is reduced by $1/e$. The displacement amplitude at any time t, $\bar{s}$, equals $a \exp - d\omega_0 t$. After time T_c the amplitude is $\bar{s}'$ which equals $a \exp - d\omega_0(t + T_c)$ and $\bar{s}'$ equals $\bar{s}/e$. But $\bar{s}'/\bar{s} = a[\exp - d\omega_0(t + T_c)]/a \exp - d\omega_0 t$ $= \exp - d\omega_0 T_c$ and $\bar{s}'/\bar{s} = 1/e$. Thus

$$T_c = 1/d\omega_0 = 2M/R. \tag{1.27}$$

Also the logarithmic decrement is the ratio of the period of the damped oscillation to the time constant or

$$\delta = T_d/T_c. \tag{1.28}$$

14

The angular frequency ω_d, of the damped oscillation from *Equation (1.25)* is given by

$$\omega_d^2 = S/M - R_m^2/4M^2 = \omega_0^2 - R_m^2/4M^2 = \omega_0^2 - \delta^2/T_d^2.$$

Hence

$$\omega_d^2 = \omega_0^2 - \omega_d^2\delta^2/4\pi^2$$

and

$$\omega_d = \omega_0/\sqrt{(1+\delta^2/4\pi^2)} \quad \text{or} \quad T_d = T_0\sqrt{(1+\delta^2/4\pi^2)}.$$

If δ is small,

$$T_d \simeq T_0(1-\delta^2/8\pi^2). \tag{1.29}$$

For some systems, for example the movement of a ballistic galvanometer which is on open circuit or is connected across a very high resistance, δ may be very small, and then $T_d \simeq T_0$. Even if δ is sufficiently small for this approximation to be used, the first maximum displacement of the vibrating element is reduced by damping and has to be allowed for in the use of the ballistic galvanometer. The correction can be expressed in terms of δ.

The coil of the galvanometer can be assumed to be at rest at time $t = 0$, and the charge can be imagined to pass through the coil in a time which is very small in comparison with T_d or T_0. *Equation (1.25)* is thus

$$s = a(\exp - R_m t/2M) \sin \left[t\sqrt{(S/M - R_m^2/4M^2)} \right]$$

or

$$s = a(\exp - \delta t/T_d) \sin 2\pi t/T_d.$$

The first maximum occurs at $T_d/4$ and is a_1 where

$$a_1 = a \exp - \delta/4$$

or

$$a = a_1 \exp \delta/4, \text{ which is approximately}$$

$$a = a_1(1+\delta/4). \tag{1.30}$$

a_1 and δ can be obtained, and hence a, which gives a measure of the charge passing through the galvanometer, can be found.

In section **1.2.** the projection of a particle moving round a circle on to a diameter has been used to study SHM. For slightly damped harmonic motion the reference circle is replaced by a *logarithmic (or*

15

equiangular) *spiral*. The spiral can be used to obtain a displacement–time graph in a similar manner to the reference circle shown in section **1.2.** *Figure 1.5.*

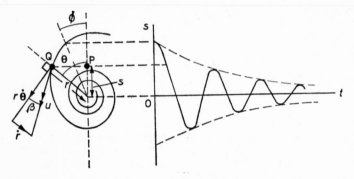

Figure 1.12. Reference spiral. Displacement–time graph

In *Figure 1.12* a similar notation has been used to that in *Figure 1.5*. The particle Q is imagined to move round the spiral at constant angular velocity ω_0 which equals $d\theta/dt$. Its instantaneous linear velocity is u which has components $rd\theta/dt$ and $-dr/dt$, directed as shown. At every point on the spiral the angle between the radius vector OQ and the tangent at Q (the direction of u) is a constant. Hence the angle β is a constant. We have $\tan \beta = -dr/dt/(rd\theta/dt)$ $= -(dr/d\theta)/r = A'$, a constant. Thus $\log_e r = -A'\theta + A''$, where A'' is an integration constant. If at $t = 0$, $\theta = \phi$ and $r = r_0$ $A'' = \log_e r_0 + A'\phi$ and $r = r_0 \exp[-A'(\theta - \phi)]$, which is an equation of a logarithmic spiral.

The velocity of $P = -ds/dt = -\dfrac{dr}{dt} \cos \theta + r\dfrac{d\theta}{dt} \sin \theta$

$$= A'r\dfrac{d\theta}{dt} \cos \theta + r\dfrac{d\theta}{dt} \sin \theta$$

since $-dr/dt = A'rd\theta/dt$. Thus

$$ds/dt = -\omega_0(A's + r \sin \theta) \qquad (1.31)$$

16

and

$$d^2s/dt^2 = -\omega_0[A'ds/dt + (\sin\theta)dr/dt + r(\cos\theta)d\theta/dt]$$

$$= \omega_0[A'ds/dt - A'r(\sin\theta)d\theta/dt + s\omega_0].$$

But $r\sin\theta = -(1/\omega_0)ds/dt - A's$ from *Equation (1.31)* so that

$$d^2s/dt^2 = -\omega_0(2A'ds/dt + A'\omega_0^2s + s\omega_0)$$

or

$$d^2s/dt^2 + 2A'\omega_0ds/dt + \omega_0^2(1+A'^2)s = 0. \qquad (1.32)$$

This equation reduces to *(1.21)* if A' is put equal to d and if d is very much smaller than unity, which is the condition for slightly damped harmonic motion.

(*iii*) $d > 1$. *Appreciable damping (Over-damping).*

Here $\sqrt{(d^2-1)}$ is real, so that *Equation (1.22)* becomes, in terms of the original constants of the system

$$s = A_1 \exp t[-R_m/2M + \sqrt{(S/M - R_m^2/4M^2)}]$$

$$+ A_2 \exp t[-R_m/2M - \sqrt{(S/M - R_m^2/4M^2)}]. \qquad (1.33)$$

The system does not vibrate about the equilibrium position, which is approached asymptotically as shown in *Figure 1.13*. Thus the term *aperiodic* is sometimes applied to over-damped motion.

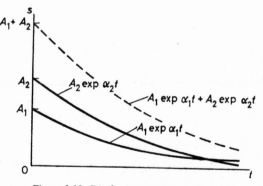

Figure 1.13. Displacement–time graph when damping is appreciable

For the purpose of *Figure 1.13*, *Equation (1.33)* has been written in terms of the roots α_1 and α_2, which are both negative

$$s = A_1 \exp \alpha_1 t + A_2 \exp \alpha_2 t. \qquad (1.34)$$

17

Hence ds/dt is always negative. The return to the equilibrium position is most rapid in the following limiting case.

(*iv*) $d = 1$. *Critical damping.*

Here the roots α_1 and α_2 are equal and the solution (*1.22*) is incomplete, since there will be only one arbitrary constant. We return to *Equation* (*1.34*)

$$s = A_1 \exp \alpha_1 t + A_2 \exp \alpha_2 t$$

and if s_0 and $\dot{s}_0$ are the values of s and ds/dt at $t = 0$

$$s_0 = A_1 + A_2$$

$$\dot{s}_0 = \alpha_1 A_1 + \alpha_2 A_2.$$

Thus

$$A_1 = (\dot{s}_0 - s_0 \alpha_2)/(\alpha_1 - \alpha_2)$$

and

$$A_2 = (s_0 \alpha_1 - \dot{s}_0)/(\alpha_1 - \alpha_2)$$

so that

$$s = \frac{(\dot{s}_0 - s_0 \alpha_2) \exp \alpha_1 t + (s_0 \alpha_1 - \dot{s}_0) \exp \alpha_2 t}{\alpha_1 - \alpha_2}.$$

The result for critical damping can now be found by letting $\alpha_1 = \alpha + \delta\alpha$ and $\alpha_2 = \alpha$, which gives

$$s = [(\dot{s}_0 - s_0 \alpha) \exp t\delta\alpha + s_0(\alpha + \delta\alpha) - \dot{s}_0](\exp \alpha t)/\delta\alpha$$

or

$$s = [(\dot{s}_0 - s_0 \alpha)(\exp t\delta\alpha - 1) + s_0 \delta\alpha](\exp \alpha t)/\delta\alpha$$

and then finding the limiting value of this as $\delta\alpha$ approaches zero. We have $\lim [(\exp t\delta\alpha - 1)/\delta\alpha] = t$ as $\delta\alpha$ approaches zero. Since in the limit $\alpha = -d$

$$s = (\exp - dt)[(\dot{s}_0 + s_0 d)t + s_0]$$

or, in terms of the original constants

$$s = [\exp - R_m t/2\sqrt{(SM)}]\{[\dot{s}_0 + s_0 R_m/2\sqrt{(SM)}]t + s_0\}. \quad (1.35)$$

Here the arbitrary constants are $(\dot{s}_0 + s_0 d)$ and s_0. The term $(\dot{s}_0 + s_0 d)t$ increases more slowly with time than $\exp - dt$ decreases. The motion is again aperiodic, but the return to the equilibrium position is quicker than for over-damped motion.

Critical damping would appear to be ideal in measuring instruments, such as voltmeters and ammeters, for then readings could be obtained more quickly than if a smaller or larger damping were used. Usually the damping is arranged to be slightly less than critical. Then one or two oscillations occur about the final position of the needle and 'stickiness' of the movement is nullified.

Equation (*1.35*) may otherwise be obtained by returning to *Equation* (*1.21*) and assuming that $s = Af(t)$ exp αt or simply $s = f(t)$ exp αt instead of $s = A$ exp αt. Another method is to approach critical damping from $d<1$ in contrast to $d>1$ as in the preceding work. Such a method has been suggested by J. Pritchett[1].

1.6. Coulomb Damping

Here the magnitude of the frictional force F is assumed to be constant, but its sense is always opposite to that of ds/dt. The equation of motion of mass M is

$$Md^2s/dt^2 \pm F + Ss = 0. \qquad (1.36)$$

The comparable equation for rotational motion is

$$Id^2\theta/dt^2 \pm \tau + b\theta = 0 \qquad (1.37)$$

where I, θ and b are as defined for *Equation* (*1.11*) and τ is the constant damping torque.

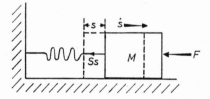

Figure 1.14. Oscillations on a rough plane—Coulomb damping

The plus sign applies when the motion of M is as shown in *Figure 1.14*, and the minus sign when M moves in the opposite sense. Writing *Equation* (*1.36*) in terms of ω_0^2, which equals S/M, gives

$$d^2s/dt^2 + \omega_0 s = \pm F/M \qquad (1.38)$$

which contains the same variables as *Equation* (*1.2*) but has in addition the constant term $\pm F/M$. Accordingly the solutions are

$$s = a_t \cos(\omega_0 t + \phi) \pm F/S \qquad (1.39)$$

since s may be replaced by $s' \pm F/\omega_0^2 M$, the *Equation* (*1.38*) solved for

19

s', and the solution then rewritten in terms of s. The frequency of vibration $\omega_0/2\pi$ is the same as that for undamped motion, but the displacement amplitude a_t decreases linearly with time and differs according to whether s and ds/dt are both positive, or both negative or differ in sign. The variation of a_t can be shown as follows.

If $s = +a_0$ and $ds/dt = 0$ at $t = 0$

$$a_0 = a_t \cos \phi + F/S$$

and

$$0 = -a_t\omega_0 \sin \phi.$$

Thus the smallest value of ϕ is zero and $a_t = a_0 - F/S$. Hence

$$s = (a_0 - F/S) \cos \omega_0 t + F/S$$

if $0 \leqslant t \leqslant \pi/\omega_0$, since the plus sign in *Equation* (*1.39*) holds for the first half-cycle. At $t = \pi/\omega_0$, $s = -a_1$, so that

$$-a_1 = -(a_0 - F/S) + F/S$$

or

$$a_1 = a_0 - 2F/S.$$

If $\pi/\omega_0 \leqslant t \leqslant 2\pi/\omega_0$, which applies to the next half-cycle, the minus sign in *Equation* (*1.39*) holds. Hence $s = a_t \cos (\omega_0 t + \phi) - F/S$. When $t = \pi/\omega_0$, $s = -a_1$ and $ds/dt = 0$ so that

$$-a_1 = a_t \cos (\pi + \phi) - F/S$$

and

$$0 = -a_t\omega_0 \sin (\pi + \phi).$$

Thus $\phi = 0$ as before, and $a_t = a_1 - F/S$. Hence if $\pi/\omega_0 \leqslant t \leqslant 2\pi/\omega_0$

$$s = (a_1 - F/S) \cos \omega_0 t - F/S.$$

At $t = 2\pi/\omega_0$, $s = a_2$ so that

$$a_2 = a_1 - 2F/S.$$

Examination of further successive half-cycles shows that their amplitudes decrease by a constant amount $2F/S$ so that $a_n = a_0 - n(2F/S)$, where a_n is the amplitude of the nth half-cycle, and $a_1, a_2, a_3, \ldots a_n$ form an arithmetical progression.

The motion ceases when $a_n \leqslant F/S$, for the restoring force Ss exerted by the spring will then be slightly less than or equal to the frictional

20

force F. If r is the number of half-cycles of oscillatory motion before cessation $a_0 - r(2F/S) \leqslant F/S$ or $r \geqslant (a_0 - F/S)2F/S$. The time variation of s is shown in *Figure 1.15*.

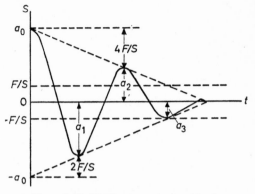

Figure 1.15. Displacement–time graph when Coulomb damping operates

1.7. Hysteretic Damping

Here a treatment which can be used also for non-linear damping will be employed. The energy dissipated per cycle when linear (viscous) damping applies is obtained, and compared with that holding for other kinds of damping. The comparison yields a damping factor, equivalent to one relating to linear damping, which may be used in linear damping analysis.

In a linear vibrating system the work done per cycle against the damping force $R_m \, ds/dt$ is

$$\int_0^{4a} R_m \frac{ds}{dt} ds$$

since the mass M moves a total distance $4a$ during one cycle. We have

$$\int_0^{4a} R_m \frac{ds}{dt} ds = \int_0^{T_d} R_m \left(\frac{ds}{dt}\right)^2 dt \qquad (1.40)$$

which equals the energy dissipated per cycle.

21

Damping in the system must be small if oscillations occur and *Equation (1.25)* can be approximated to and written

$$s = a \cos (2\pi t/T_d) \qquad (1.41)$$

if ϕ is equated to zero. Hence

$$ds/dt = -(2\pi a/T_d) \sin (2\pi t/T_d).$$

Thus the energy dissipated per cycle is

$$\frac{4\pi^2 a^2 R_m}{T_d^2} \int_0^{T_d} \sin^2(2\pi t/T_d)dt$$

$$= \frac{2\pi^2 a^2 R_m}{T_d^2}\left[t-(T_d/4\pi) \sin (4\pi t/T_d) \right]_0^{T_d}$$

or

$$E = 2\pi^2 a^2 R_m/T_d = \pi a^2 R_m \omega_d. \qquad (1.42)$$

A better approximation is obtained if required by using *Equation (1.25)* instead of *(1.41)*. Then the energy dissipated per cycle is found to be given by

$$E = \pi a^2 R_m \omega_d(1+\delta) \qquad (1.43)$$

where δ is the logarithmic decrement.

For hysteretic damping

$$E \simeq R_1 a^n \qquad (1.44)$$

where R_1 is a constant found by experiment, and n is a constant depending on the material composing the restoring element. For mild steel n ranges between 2·3 and 3·0. *Equations (1.42)* and *(1.44)* can be combined to give

$$R_m = R_1 a^{n-2}/\pi\omega_d \qquad (1.45)$$

and this value of R_m can be used in the linear analysis given in section **1.5**. *Equation (1.45)* shows that R_m is inversely proportional to frequency when the damping is hysteretic, some approximation being understood. The electrical resistance of solid conductors increases, and hence their conductance decreases, as the frequency of currents through them increases, because the proportion of current passing near the surface of the conductor becomes larger—the *skin effect*, discussed in section **8.6**. In section **2.6**. mechanical resistance is shown to be analogous to electrical conductance, so that a rough

22

electrical analogy to hysteretic damping is the skin effect. The analogy is rough because conductance is inversely proportional to the square root of the frequency of the current in thick conductors, some approximation again being required.

If the damping is directly proportional to the square of the velocity of the vibrating mass, the damping force is $R_2(ds/dt)^2$ and *Equation (1.40)* becomes here

$$E = \int_0^{T_d} R_2\left(\frac{ds}{dt}\right)^3 dt. \qquad (1.46)$$

The use of *Equation (1.41)* gives

$$E = 8a^3 R_2 \omega_d^2/3. \qquad (1.47)$$

Hence

$$R_m = 8a\omega_d R_2/3\pi \qquad (1.48)$$

which can also be used in a linear analysis.

Reference
[1] J. PRITCHETT *Math. Gaz.*, **XLIV**, 292, 1960.

FORCED VIBRATIONS

2.1. Forced Vibrations Without Damping

Vibrations are said to be *forced* if a system capable of vibrating has acting upon it an external periodically varying force. The external force is, for simplicity, taken to vary harmonically with time at a single frequency $p/2\pi$ and is given by

$$F = F_0 \cos pt \qquad (2.1)$$

where F is the instantaneous value of the force, and F_0 is its peak value. The equation of motion of the vibrating system can thus be written

$$Md^2s/dt^2 + Ss = F_0 \cos pt \qquad (2.2)$$

if no damping is present.

A similar equation can be obtained for a circuit consisting of an inductor L and a capacitor C is series with an alternator, giving an emf $E = E_0 \cos pt$, shown in *Figure 2.1*.

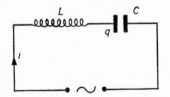

Figure 2.1. L and C in series with alternator

Using Kirchoff's second law

$$Ldi/dt + q/C = E_0 \cos pt$$

or

$$Ld^2q/dt^2 + q/C = E_0 \cos pt \qquad (2.3)$$

where i is the instantaneous current, and q is the instantaneous charge on C.

The corresponding equation for angular motion is

$$Id^2\theta/dt^2 + b\theta = \tau_0 \cos pt \qquad (2.4)$$

where I, θ and b have the same meaning as in *Equation* (*1.11*) and τ_0 is the maximum value of the applied torque.

Since the *Equations* (*2.2*), (*2.3*) and (*2.4*) have the same form, only the solution of (*2.2*) will be obtained and discussed. *Equation* (*2.2*) is rewritten

$$d^2s/dt^2 + \omega_0^2 s = f_0 \cos pt \tag{2.5}$$

where ω_0 equals S/M as before, and f_0 which equals F_0/M is the maximum impressed acceleration. The solution of this equation is composed of two parts—the *complementary function*, obtained by equating the left-hand side to zero, and the *particular integral*, which must satisfy the complete equation. The complementary function has already been found

$$s = a \cos (\omega_0 t + \phi). \tag{1.4}$$

The particular integral can be obtained by using the operator D which denotes d/dt. We have

$$(D^2 + \omega_0^2)s = f_0 \cos pt$$

or

$$s = \frac{f_0}{(D^2 + \omega_0^2)}[\cos pt].$$

Thus

$$s = -(f_0 \cos pt)/(p^2 - \omega_0^2). \tag{2.6}$$

The complete solution of *Equation* (*2.5*) is

$$s = a \cos (\omega_0 t + \phi) - (f_0 \cos pt)/(p^2 - \omega_0^2)$$

which is simplified for discussion by assuming that $s = A$ and $ds/dt = 0$ at $t = 0$. Then

$$s = [A + f_0/(p^2 - \omega_0^2)] \cos \omega_0 t - (f_0 \cos pt)/(p^2 - \omega_0^2)$$

or

$$s = A_1 \cos \omega_0 t - (f_0 \cos pt)/(p^2 - \omega_0^2) \tag{2.7}$$

where

$$A_1 = A + f_0/(p^2 - \omega_0^2).$$

Equation (*2.7*) represents periodic vibrations only in the following cases:

(*a*) $A_1 = 0$. The free oscillation does not occur.

(*b*) $p = n\omega_0$, where n is any positive integer but unity, and A_1 is not equal to zero.

(*c*) $p = \omega_0/m$, where m is any positive integer but unity, and A_1 is not equal to zero.

25

(d) $p = n\omega_0/m$, where n and m are positive integers such that n/m, or its reciprocal, does not equal an integer, and A_1 is again not equal to zero.

When A_1 is not zero, oscillations can occur at values of p other than those specified in (b), (c) and (d). The oscillations at angular frequencies ω_0 and p are superposed and form beats (see section 2.5) whose amplitude is never repeated, which happens because the frequency ratio is irrational and a particular phase angle difference between the vibrations occurs only once. In this sense the vibrations are not periodic.

In (a) there is only the particular integral which represents oscillations at the same frequency as that of the impressed force. The amplitude of these oscillations depends on p and approaches infinity as p tends towards ω_0, *resonance* being achieved when p equals ω_0. In practical systems the amplitude at resonance is limited by damping, as will be shown later, although the displacement amplitude may be sufficiently large to cause failure of the spring in the system.

In (b) the lowest vibrational frequency is contained in the complementary function and equals $\omega_0/2\pi$, corresponding to a frequency of the applied force of $n\omega_0/2\pi$ and thus being a *subharmonic of order n*.

In (c) vibrations of the lowest frequency are given by the particular integral, and equal $\omega_0/2\pi m$, the frequency of the impressed force. The motion of the system contains vibrations of m times this frequency—the *harmonic of order m*.

In (d) the particular integral represents vibrations of the lowest frequency, which is $\omega_0/2\pi m$ ($n = 1$) corresponding to a frequency $n\omega_0/2\pi m$ of the applied force. Thus the lowest frequency is again an nth subharmonic of the driving force frequency. n and m are chosen to be relatively prime, in order that no overlap occurs between (d) and (b) or (c). The results are summarized in *Table 2.1*.

Table 2.1. Possible vibrational frequencies in an undamped system

Case	Frequency of applied force	Lowest frequency	Frequency of free oscillations
a	p	p	Absent
b	$n\omega_0/2\pi$	$\omega_0/2\pi$	$\omega_0/2\pi$
c	$\omega_0/2\pi m$	$\omega_0/2\pi m$	$\omega_0/2\pi$
d	$n\omega_0/2\pi m$	$\omega_0/2\pi m$	$\omega_0/2\pi$

2.2. Forced Vibrations with Damping

All practical systems have some damping which, even if very small, suppresses the harmonics and subharmonics possible when damping is not present. For a mechanical system the equation of motion is

$$M d^2 s/dt^2 + R_m ds/dt + Ss = F_0 \cos pt \qquad (2.8)$$

if linear viscous damping is present, the force $F = F_0 \cos pt$ being applied, for example, to one end of the spring, as shown in *Figure 2.2*.

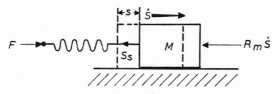

Figure 2.2. Forced oscillations on a lubricated rough plane

The corresponding electrical equation is

$$L d^2 q/dt^2 + R dq/dt + q/C = E_0 \cos pt \qquad (2.9)$$

the resistance R being placed in series with L and C shown in *Figure 2.1*.

The equation for angular motion is

$$I d^2\theta/dt^2 + B d\theta/dt + b\theta = \tau_0 \cos pt \qquad (2.10)$$

where B is again the resistive torque per unit angular velocity.

Since vibrational motion is being studied, the possible values of R_m, R or B need not be considered. All that is required is that they should be sufficiently small to allow vibrations to occur at the natural frequency of the system. Accordingly the complementary function of *Equation (2.8)*, which has already been obtained as a solution of *Equation (1.17)*, is

$$s = a(\exp - R_m t/2M) \cos [t\sqrt{(S/M - R_m^2/4M^2)} + \phi]. \qquad (1.25)$$

The particular integral can be obtained by writing *Equation (2.8)* in the form

$$d^2 s/dt^2 + 2d\omega_0 ds/dt + \omega_0^2 s = f_0 \cos pt$$

where d is $R_m/2\sqrt{(SM)}$, ω_0^2 is S/M and f_0 is F_0/M, or

$$(D^2 + 2d\omega_0 D + \omega_0^2)s = f_0 \cos pt.$$

This becomes

$$s = \frac{f_0}{D^2 + 2d\omega_0 D + \omega_0^2}\{\cos pt\}$$

or s = real part of f_0 (exp $jpt)/(-p^2 + 2jd\omega_0 p + \omega_0^2)$.
Thus

$$s = f_0[(\omega_0^2 - p^2)\cos pt + 2d\omega_0 p \sin pt]/[(\omega_0^2 - p^2)^2 + 4d^2\omega_0^2 p^2]$$

or

$$s = f_0[\cos (pt - \psi)]/\sqrt{[(\omega_0^2 - p^2)^2 - 4d^2\omega_0^2 p^2]}$$

where

$$\cos \psi = (\omega_0^2 - p^2)/\sqrt{[(\omega_0^2 - p^2)^2 + 4d^2\omega_0^2 p^2]}$$

and

$$\sin \psi = 2d\omega_0 p/\sqrt{[(\omega_0^2 - p^2)^2 + 4d^2\omega_0^2 p^2]}. \qquad (2.11)$$

In terms of the original constants

$$s = F_0 [\cos (pt - \psi)]/p\sqrt{[(S/p - Mp)^2 + R_m^2]}. \qquad (2.12)$$

The complete solution of *Equation (2.8)* is thus

$$s = a(\exp -R_m t/2M)\cos [t\sqrt{(S/M - R_m^2/4M^2)} + \phi]$$
$$+ F_0[\cos (pt - \psi)]/p\sqrt{[(S/p - Mp)^2 + R_m^2]}. \qquad (2.13)$$

The first term of *Equation (2.13)* is a *transient*, and eventually disappears from the vibrations of the system. When the steady state is reached the system vibrates at the frequency of the impressed force although in a different phase, the phase angle being ψ. The composite vibrations for the frequency of the transient greater and smaller than the forcing frequency are shown in *Figure 2.3*.

The term $\sqrt{[(S/p - Mp)^2 + R_m^2]}$, which equals $\sqrt{[R_m^2 + (pM - S/p)^2]}$, is the *mechanical impedance* Z_m of the system and can be imagined to be analogous with the electrical impedance Z, which is

$$\sqrt{[R^2 + (pL - 1/pC)^2]}$$

of the circuit to which *Equation (2.9)* applies.

2.3. Displacement and Velocity Resonance

From *Equation (2.12)* the amplitude of the term representing forced vibrations is s_0, the displacement amplitude, where

$$s_0 = F_0/p\sqrt{[(S/p - Mp)^2 + R_m^2]}$$

or

$$s_0 = F_0/M\sqrt{[(\omega_0^2 - p^2)^2 + R_m^2 p^2/M^2]}. \qquad (2.14)$$

For resonance to occur, the impressed force is imagined to be applied at constant amplitude with a gradually varying frequency $p/2\pi$. The transient, indicated in *Equation (2.13)*, can thus be ignored.

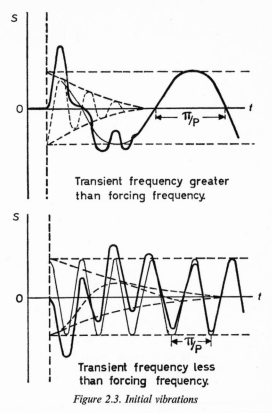

Transient frequency greater
than forcing frequency.

Transient frequency less
than forcing frequency.

Figure 2.3. Initial vibrations

In order to find the value of p at which displacement resonance occurs, *Equation (2.14)* is differentiated with respect to p and equated to zero. We have

$$4p^3 - 2p(2\omega_0^2 - R_m^2/M^2) = 0.$$

Thus $p = 0$ or

$$p_{max} = \sqrt{(\omega_0^2 - R_m^2/2M^2)}. \qquad (2.15)$$

$p = 0$ gives a minimum value of s_0 equalling $F_0/M\omega_0^2$ or F_0/S, the static displacement of mass M due to the application of a force F_0. The other value corresponds to a maximum displacement amplitude s_{max}, given by

$$s_{max} = F_0/R_m\sqrt{(S/M - R_m^2/4M^2)}. \qquad (2.16)$$

29

The period of the impressed force when displacement resonance occurs is T_{max} which equals $2\pi/p_{max}$. From *Equation (2.15)*

$$T_{max} = 2\pi/\sqrt{(\omega_0^2 - R_m^2/2M^2)} \qquad (2.17)$$

which is greater than T_0 (equals $2\pi/\omega_0$, no damping) and T_d (equals $2\pi/\sqrt{(\omega_0^2 - R_m^2/4M^2)}$, some damping present).

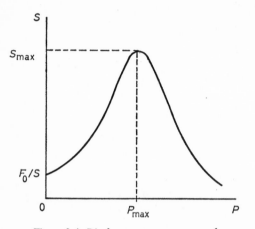

Figure 2.4. Displacement resonance graph

Figure 2.4 depicts a displacement resonance curve. The electrical equivalent of displacement resonance may be considered to be charge resonance, a phenomenon not usually observed, since measurement or detection of current or potential variations in a circuit is more convenient than that of charge. The mechanical equivalent of current resonance in a series LCR circuit is, by the same analogy, *velocity resonance*.

In order to find the frequency of the impressed force when velocity resonance occurs, *Equation (2.12)* is used. The transient can be ignored as in amplitude resonance. From *(2.12)* the velocity of the vibrating mass is

$$v = ds/dt = -F_0[\sin(pt - \psi)]/\sqrt{[(S/p - Mp)^2 + R_m^2]}$$

the velocity amplitude being v_0 given by

$$v_0 = F_0/\sqrt{[(S/p - Mp)^2 + R_m^2]} \qquad (2.18)$$

which is a maximum when $S/p - Mp = 0$ or

$$p = \sqrt{(S/M)}. \qquad (2.19)$$

30

But $\sqrt{(S/M)}$ equals ω_0, the natural angular frequency of the system when R_m is zero. Thus velocity resonance occurs when the frequency of the applied force equals the natural vibrational frequency of the undamped system. A similar statement applies to current resonance. When there is no damping present the requirements coincide for displacement and velocity resonance, and for charge and current resonance.

A velocity resonance curve is shown in *Figure 2.5*. From *Equations* *(2.18)* and *(2.19)*

$$v_{max} = F_0/R_m \qquad (2.20)$$

so the sharpness of the resonance curve depends inversely on R_m. For small values of R_m the curve is nearly symmetrical about the ordinate through ω_0 near v_{max}.

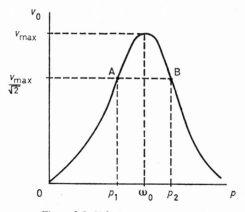

Figure 2.5. Velocity resonance graph

Consider two points A and B as shown in *Figure 2.5* for which the ordinates are both $v_{max}/\sqrt{2}$. These are known as *half-power points* since the power—the rate at which work is done—in the system is directly proportional to v_{max}^2, as is evident from the first part of section **1.3**. The distance AB can be shown to be a measure of the logarithmic decrement δ of the vibrating system as follows.

At A or B $v_0 = v_{max}/\sqrt{2} = F_0/R_m\sqrt{2}$, from *(2.20)*, or $F_0/\sqrt{[(S/p - Mp)^2 + R_m^2]} = F_0/R_m\sqrt{2}$, using *(2.18)*.

31

Thus

$$(S/p - Mp)^2 + R_m^2 = 2R_m^2$$

or

$$(S/p - Mp)^2 = R_m^2$$

which has two solutions

$$S/p_1 - Mp_1 = R_m \qquad (2.21)$$

for A and

$$S/p_2 - Mp_2 = -R_m \qquad (2.22)$$

for B. Multiplying (2.21) by p_1 and (2.22) by p_2 and subtracting the results gives

$$M(p_2^2 - p_1^2) = R_m(p_2 + p_1).$$

But since the resonance curve is nearly symmetrical if R_m is small $(p_2 + p_1)/2 \simeq \omega_0$, which $\simeq \omega_d$, the angular frequency of the damped natural vibrations. Thus

$$\omega_d R_m/M \simeq (p_2^2 - p_1^2)/2$$
$$= \omega_d^2 R_m/\omega_d M = T_d R_m \omega_d^2/2\pi M$$

From *Equation* (1.26) the logarithmic decrement δ is $T_d R_m/2M$. Thus

$$\delta \simeq \pi(p_2^2 - p_1^2)/2\omega_d^2$$

or

$$\delta \simeq \pi(p_2 - p_1)/\omega_0 \qquad (2.23)$$

since again $\omega_d \simeq \omega_0 \simeq (p_2 + p_1)/2$.

Inversely related to δ is the *quality factor* or '*magnification*' Q of a system which is defined by

$$Q_p = pM/R_m. \qquad (2.24)$$

At resonance $Q = \omega_0 M/R_m \simeq \pi/\delta$, from *Equation* (1.26). Thus, from *Equation* (2.23)

$$Q \simeq \omega_0/(p_2 - p_1) \qquad (2.25)$$

so that Q is a measure of the width of the resonance curve, a sharp resonance curve corresponding to a large Q.

If the phase angle ψ, defined by *Equations (2.11)*, is plotted against p, the shape of the curve is found to be influenced by R_m. From *(2.11)*

$$\psi = \tan^{-1}[2d\omega_0 p/(\omega_0^2 - p^2)] = \tan^{-1}[R_m p/M(\omega_0^2 - p^2)]. \quad (2.26)$$

If p is less than ω_0, ψ lies between 0 and $\pi/2$. Then the displacement of the system lags behind the applied force and ψ increases as p increases. If p equals ω_0, ψ equals $\pi/2$. If p is greater than ω_0, ψ lies between $\pi/2$ and π and the displacement is in the opposite sense to the impressed force. In *Figure 2.6* is shown the variation of ψ with p and the influence of R_m on this variation.

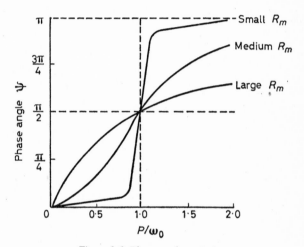

Figure 2.6. Phase angle variation

2.4. Coupled Vibrations

In the preceding sections of this chapter, the vibrations in a system have been considered to be 'forced' by an external periodically varying force acting on the system. A tacit assumption has been that the reaction of the system on the forcing agency is negligible. Frequently in practice the reaction of the system is sufficient to influence the forcing agency—'pulling' occurs, particularly if the forcing agency is a similar vibrating system to the one being forced. The vibrating systems are then said to be *coupled* and neither is able to vibrate at its natural frequency unless the coupling is very 'loose', even if the natural frequencies coincide.

33

Coupling is provided by a component which participates in the vibrations of both systems and is distributed between them. An example in mechanical systems is a mass common to both; in coupled electrical circuits there may be a capacitance or an inductance shared by both. Frequently two tuned circuits are coupled by a mutual inductance as, for example, in intermediate-frequency transformers in a superheterodyne radio or television receiver.

If damping is neglected, the equations of motion for the coupled vibrations of two masses m_1, m_2 are

$$m_1 D^2 s_1 + M D^2 s_2 + S_1 s_1 = 0$$

$$m_2 D^2 s_2 + M D^2 s_1 + S_2 s_2 = 0.$$

D here equals d/dt and M is a mass common to both systems. The combined system is said to have *two degrees of freedom* because two coordinates, s_1 and s_2, are required to specify the motion completely. In the systems previously examined only one coordinate, s or θ was needed and they thus have one degree of freedom. The second terms in both equations represent forces due to the coupling between the two systems. If ω_1 and ω_2 are the natural angular frequencies of both systems considered independently and excluding M, these equations can be written

$$D^2 s_1 + (M/m_1) D^2 s_2 + \omega_1^2 s_1 = 0 \qquad (2.27)$$

$$D^2 s_2 + (M/m_2) D^2 s_1 + \omega_2^2 s_2 = 0. \qquad (2.28)$$

Differentiating both with respect to t

$$D^4 s_1 + (M/m_1) D^4 s_2 + \omega_1^2 D^2 s_1 = 0 \qquad (2.29)$$

$$D^4 s_2 + (M/m_2) D^4 s_1 + \omega_2^2 D^2 s_2 = 0. \qquad (2.30)$$

From *Equation (2.27)* $D^2 s_2 = -m_1(D^2 s_1 + \omega_1^2 s_1)/M$ so that *Equation (2.30)* becomes

$$D^4 s_2 = -(M/m_2) D^4 s_1 + \omega_2^2 m_1(D^2 s_1 + \omega_1^2 s_1)/M$$

and substituting for $D^4 s_2$ in (2.29) gives

$$D^4 s_1 - (M^2/m_1 m_2) D^4 s_1 + \omega_2^2 D^2 s_1 + \omega_1^2 \omega_2^2 s_1 + \omega_1^2 D^2 s_1 = 0$$

or

$$(1 - k^2) D^4 s_1 + (\omega_1^2 + \omega_2^2) D^2 s_1 - \omega_1^2 \omega_2^2 s_1 = 0 \qquad (2.31)$$

where k, the coefficient of coupling, equals $\sqrt{(M^2/m_1 m_2)}$.

Suppose vibrations of angular frequency Ω occur in the coupled system. Then, since damping is neglected

$$D^2 s_1 + \Omega^2 s_1 = 0 \qquad (2.32)$$

in terms of displacement s_1. A similar equation for s_2 could also be written. Differentiating (2.32) twice with respect to t and removing $D^2 s_1$ by using (2.32) again gives

$$D^4 s_1 - \Omega^4 s_1 = 0. \qquad (2.33)$$

Substituting in *Equation* (2.31) for $D^2 s_1$ and $D^4 s_1$ from (2.32) and (2.33) yields

$$(1 - k^2)\Omega^4 - (\omega_1^2 + \omega_2^2)\Omega^2 + \omega_1^2 \omega_2^2 = 0$$

from which

$$\Omega^2 = \{(\omega_1^2 + \omega_2^2) \pm \sqrt{[(\omega_1^2 - \omega_2^2)^2 + 4\omega_1^2 \omega_2^2 k^2]}\}/2(1 - k^2).$$

If $\omega_1 = \omega_2 = \omega_0$, $\Omega^2 = \omega_0^2 (1 \pm k)/(1 - k^2)$ or

$$\Omega_1 = \omega_0/\sqrt{(1 - k)} \qquad \Omega_2 = \omega_0/\sqrt{(1 + k)} \qquad (2.34)$$

where $\Omega_2 < \omega_0 < \Omega_1$.

Because of the coupling between the two systems, both masses vibrate in *compound harmonic motion*. There are superposed vibrations of frequencies $\Omega_1/2\pi$ and $\Omega_2/2\pi$, the resultant displacement being s which equals $s_1 + s_2$ where $s_1 = a \cos \Omega_1 t$, $s_2 = a \cos \Omega_2 t$, if equal amplitudes and phases are assumed for the two vibrations. Thus

$$s = \{2a \cos [t(\Omega_1 - \Omega_2)/2]\} \cos [t(\Omega_1 + \Omega_2)/2] \qquad (2.35)$$

which indicates a vibration at the mean frequency $(\Omega_1 + \Omega_2)/4\pi$, the amplitude varying at a much lower frequency $(\Omega_1 - \Omega_2)/4\pi$ and is examined in more detail in the next section.

Such vibrations are illustrated, for example, by a pair of simple pendulums having the same natural frequency and being suspended from the same horizontal string under slight tension. If the vibrations of one pendulum are started, the other begins almost immediately to vibrate with gradually increasing amplitude, while that of the first decreases at the same rate. Eventually the first pendulum comes to rest and the other is then vibrating at its maximum amplitude. Interchange of energy then occurs in the opposite sense, until the first pendulum is again vibrating at maximum amplitude and the other one is at rest. The process continues until all the vibrational energy is dissipated.

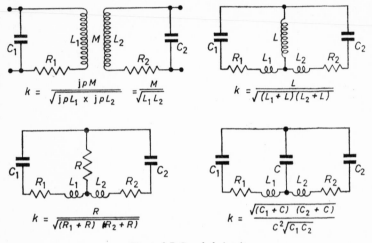

Figure 2.7 Coupled circuits

The coupling coefficient k has been defined as $\sqrt{(M^2/m_1 m_2)}$ for the purposes of *Equation (2.31)*. Generally k is given by the ratio of the common impedance to the square root of the product of the separate impedances, of the same kind as the common impedance in electrical circuits, and a similar definition can be formulated for mechanical systems. Some coupled circuits with the relevant values of k are shown in *Figure 2.7*. The response of tuned circuits is considerably altered when they are closely coupled. The system resonates at the two frequencies $\Omega_1/2\pi$ and $\Omega_2/2\pi$ given by *Equation (2.34)* if the natural frequencies of the circuits taken separately are both $\omega_0/2\pi$. The form of the resonance curve is shown in *Figure 2.8*, which also shows curves corresponding to smaller coupling coefficients ($k_1 < k_2 < k_3$). k_2 is a critical value of the coupling coefficient for which a curve having a flattened peak is produced, and equals $1/Q$ for circuits coupled by a mutual inductance. Such a response curve is useful in radio and television reception, where a band-pass response is usually required in order to deal with the wide range of frequencies associated with a wave of particular carrier frequency. The ideal rectangular response curve is, of course, unattainable, although a close approach

36

is possible with suitable filters. For smaller values than k_2 the ordinary resonance curve is obtained, the maximum being decreased as the coupling is reduced, since energy transfer is thereby reduced.

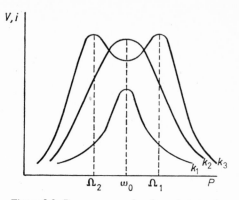

Figure 2.8. Resonance graphs of coupled circuits

2.5. Compound Harmonic Motion

In the previous section the superposition of two collinear simple harmonic motions of different frequencies has been mentioned. The motions were given by

$$s_1 = a \cos \Omega_1 t \quad \text{and} \quad s_2 = a \cos \Omega_2 t$$

the resultant displacement being $s_1 + s_2$ or s where

$$s = \{2a \cos [t(\Omega_1 - \Omega_2)/2]\} \cos [t(\Omega_1 + \Omega_2)/2]. \qquad (2.35)$$

Figure 2.9 shows the graphs of s_1, s_2 and s against time t if the two frequencies are not very different. The amplitude of s slowly fluctuates between zero and $\pm 2a$ at a frequency $(\Omega_1 - \Omega_2)/4\pi$ but the frequency of successive maximum values is double this, $(\Omega_1 - \Omega_2)/2\pi$, which is the *beat frequency*. Such frequency doubling is similar to that which occurs when both halves of a sinusoidal alternating current are rectified, as in most mains-derived zero-frequency power supplies, and is independent of any detecting device.

The various aspects of the audible detection of beats are very complex because of non-linear and subjective factors, and will not be discussed in detail. Briefly, the *beat note* can be heard by sounding simultaneously two pure equal amplitude tones of any audio frequencies differing by not more than about 30 c/s. A tone of the mean frequency, $(\Omega_1 + \Omega_2)/4\pi$, is heard whose amplitude pulsates—'beats'

37

—at the difference in frequency between the two components, which can usually be distinguished at lower beat frequencies than 30 c/s. The beat note can still be heard if the amplitudes of the tones are different but is not so prominent, for then cancellation is not complete and the components are more easily distinguished. Above about 30 c/s the beat frequency corresponds to that of tones, and the ampli-

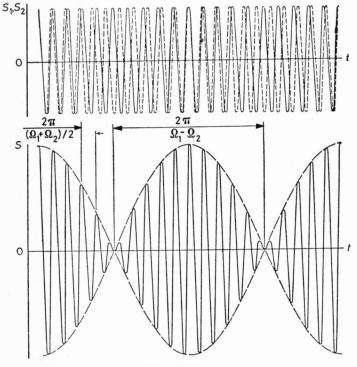

Figure 2.9 Beats

tude pulsations become merged with the composite sound. If the frequency ratio Ω_1/Ω_2 exceeds about 3/2 the superposition becomes simpler, in that the high frequency vibration occurs about a datum which alters with time at the lower frequency, and beats are no longer formed. For smaller ratios beats may be shown on an oscilloscope.

A constant phase angle difference between the two components has the effect of only altering the times at which all the maxima and minima occur in the resultant wave—the time origin is altered. Here the distinction between *phase angle difference* and *phase difference* is well demonstrated. A constant phase difference cannot be properly referred to in this instance, as the phase difference is altering all the time because of the different frequencies.

Beats can also be obtained by fitting a simple pendulum with a heavy bob, to which is attached another simple pendulum with a much lighter bob. The motion of the lighter bob is similar to that indicated by the graph of *s* in *Figure 2.9* if the pendulums vibrate in the same plane at nearly the same frequency, but the minima are not generally zero.

Sometimes oscillations in electrical circuits are said to 'beat' together when a number of resultant oscillations of sum and difference frequencies are produced. These are *combination tones*, discussed in section **3.7.**, and some kind of non-linearity in the circuit is necessary for their production. The term 'beat' is thus an unfortunate choice because no non-linearity is required for the production of beats, which are merely the amplitude fluctuation of an oscillation having the mean frequency of the two components.

If the superposed simple harmonic motions are at right-angles, the resultant motion depends on the frequencies and phase angle difference of the components. For two vibrations of equal frequency $p/2\pi$ and phase angle difference ϕ, the displacements x and y are

$$x = a \cos pt$$

$$y = b \cos (pt+\phi)$$

where a and b are the amplitudes. We have

$$y/b = (\cos pt) \cos \phi - \sqrt{(1-\cos^2 pt)} \sin \phi$$

$$= (x \cos \phi)/a - \sqrt{(1-x^2/a^2)} \sin \phi$$

Thus

$$[y/b - (x \cos \phi)/a]^2 = (1-x^2/a^2) \sin^2\phi.$$

or

$$x^2/a^2 - 2xy(\cos \phi)/ab + y^2/b^2 = \sin^2\phi. \tag{2.36}$$

This is an equation of an ellipse in the xy plane, the shape depending on the amplitudes a and b, and on the phase angle ϕ.
(*i*) $\phi = \pi/2$ or $3\pi/2$. The curve is given by

$$x^2/a^2 + y^2/b^2 = 1.$$

Thus the locus of a particle subjected to the specified component

D   39

motions is an ellipse having axes $2a$ and $2b$ coincident with the x and y axes respectively. If a equals b the locus is a circle.

(ii) Imagine ϕ to be made gradually smaller than $\pi/2$. The ellipse becomes thinner, and the axes rotate away from the x and y axes until, at ϕ equals zero, the ellipse becomes two coincident straight lines of length $2\sqrt{(a^2+b^2)}$ passing through the origin and being inclined to the x axis at an angle $\tan^{-1} b/a$. This locus may be imagined to be followed by a particle moving simple harmonically and, since the locus is obtained by composing two motions, the converse also holds—one SHM may be resolved into two component motions at right-angles. Further decrease in ϕ causes the ellipse to increase in thickness until $3\pi/2$ is reached, after which the ellipse again becomes narrower and, at ϕ equals π, the ellipse has become two coincident straight lines of the same length as before but now inclined to the x axis at an angle $\tan^{-1} -b/a$. The ellipse then thickens until ϕ equals $\pi/2$ when the same sequence of changes will be repeated if ϕ is still decreased. Such changes would be observed if the frequency of vibration in the x direction were slightly larger than that in the y direction, for then ϕ would become slowly reduced.

If the frequency ratio is 1:2 the resultant locus has two loops. The analysis is laborious unless particular values of ϕ are taken. We assume that

$$x = a \cos pt$$

$$y = b \cos (2pt+n\pi/2)$$

where n equals 0, 1, 2 or 3. Hence

$$y/b = (\cos 2pt) \cos n\pi/2 - (\sin 2pt) \sin n\pi/2. \qquad (2.37)$$

If $n = 0$ or 2, from *Equation* (2.37)

$$y/b = \pm \cos 2pt = \pm(2 \cos^2 pt - 1)$$

$$= \pm(2x^2/a^2 - 1)$$

which gives

$$x^2 = a^2(b \pm y)/2b \qquad (2.38)$$

where the plus sign refers to n equals zero, and the minus sign to n equals 2. Both equations represent parabolas.

If $n = 1$ or 3, from *Equation* (*2.37*)

$$y/b = \pm \sin 2pt$$

or

$$y^2/b^2 = \sin^2 2pt = 4(\sin^2 pt)\cos^2 pt$$
$$= 4x^2(1 - x^2/a^2)/a^2$$

which gives

$$4x^2(x^2/a^2 - 1)/a^2 + y^2/b^2 = 0. \qquad (2.39)$$

This equation represents a symmetrical figure of eight in which there are clearly two loops, as suggested. That there are two loops in the parabolic locus is not evident until one frequency is made slightly different from the other. Then the locus is seen to vary from a parabola to a distorted figure of eight, a symmetrical one and a dis-

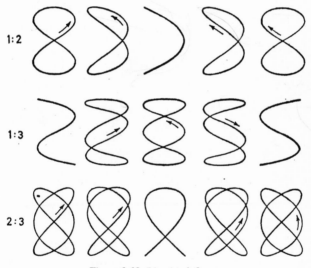

Figure 2.10. Lissajous' figures

torted one to an inverted parabola, and so on back to the original parabola, which is thus seen to consist of two coincident parabolas traced in opposite senses. The vertex is not a loop; the loops are the 'ends' of the parabola.

These loci are known as *Lissajous' figures* after the French mathematician who studied the phenomenon. *Figure 2.10*, taken from Rayleigh's 'Theory of Sound', shows some loci for various frequency ratios and phase angles. In each the x displacement (horizontal) frequency is higher than that of the y displacement. The frequency ratio can be found by counting the number of loops in the x and y directions, and is the inverse ratio of the number of loops. This can be done for figures traced on the screen of an oscilloscope tube for any rational frequency ratio up to about 1:10 or 10:1. In practice one frequency is sometimes altered slightly if possible, for then the figure rotates slowly and the number of loops can be found unambiguously. If the frequency ratio is irrational a locus is obtained which varies continuously and is not retraced periodically.

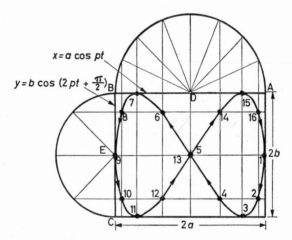

Figure 2.11. Construction of Lissajous' figures

Lissajous' figures can be constructed as shown in *Figure 2.11*. The component motions are assumed to start at A and E. The first point plotted is thus 1, the second 2, and so on. A graph of *Equation (2.39)* is finally obtained.

Some experimental methods of obtaining Lissajous' figures are indicated in *Figure 2.12*. In Blackburn's pendulum (*a*) (so called, but probably discovered first by Dean) there are two effective lengths of string, l_1 and l_2 for vibrations perpendicular to, and in the plane of, the diagram respectively. Thus if motion of the bob is started in some random direction, two simple harmonic motions are simultaneously combined to give the motion of the bob. The bob may be a heavy container of fine dry sand which, falling through a narrow outlet on to a stationary horizontal tray, marks the locus of the bob.

With a heavy container the change in the effective lengths l_1 and l_2 due to the alteration in position of the centre of mass of the bob would be negligible.

Wheatstone's kaleidophone (b) consists of two springy steel strips of different lengths fixed end to end with their widths at right-angles. A bright metal bead is attached to the free end of one strip, while the second strip is clamped at its other end. The strips are easily bent in the direction of their smaller cross-sections but are nearly rigid across their widths. Thus the bead is simultaneously subjected to two perpendicular oscillations of frequencies dependent on l_1 and l_2, and with strong illumination the motion of the bead can be projected on a screen in order to demonstrate the various loci.

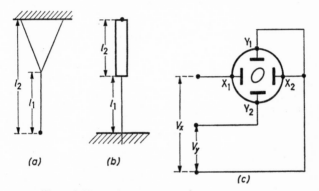

Figure 2.12. Methods of observing Lissajous' figures

Figure 2.12 (c) represents the x and y plates of an oscilloscope cathode ray tube connected to two alternating potentials V_x and V_y. If the phase angles and frequencies of these are varied, Lissajous' figures can be obtained on the tube screen. The potentials may be the amplified outputs of signal generators, one of which can be calibrated from the other as indicated previously.

2.6. Electrical Analogies

The following equations have been previously obtained

$$M\mathrm{d}^2s/\mathrm{d}t^2 + R_m\mathrm{d}s/\mathrm{d}t + Ss = 0 \qquad (1.17)$$

$$L\mathrm{d}^2q/\mathrm{d}t^2 + R\mathrm{d}q/\mathrm{d}t + q/C = 0 \qquad (1.19)$$

$$M\mathrm{d}^2s/\mathrm{d}t^2 + R_m\mathrm{d}s/\mathrm{d}t + Ss = F_0 \cos \omega t \qquad (2.8)$$

$$L\mathrm{d}^2q/\mathrm{d}t^2 + R\mathrm{d}q/\mathrm{d}t + q/C = E_0 \cos \omega t \qquad (2.9)$$

the angular frequency ω replacing p in the original equations.

From the similarity of these equations there would appear to be a strong case for taking mass M as equivalent to inductance L, mechanical resistance R_m to electrical resistance R, the reciprocal of stiffness S (compliance C_m) to capacitance C, force F_0 to emf E_0 and displacement s as equivalent to charge q. These equivalences form the basis of a system of analogues which is used extensively to obtain results for mechanical systems from previously known or easily obtained results for electrical circuits, or to enable the behaviour of a system of one kind to be simulated and thus investigated.

An obvious analogy is not necessarily the best, and there is usually some difficulty with the analogy based on the preceding equations in composing an equivalent electrical diagram from one representing a particular configuration of mechanical components. The difficulty arises because 'through' in one system must be interpreted as 'across' in the other. For example, a force through must be represented as an emf across. Hence there are various inconsistencies including

(a) Mechanical components in series must be represented by electrical components in parallel, and mechanical components in parallel by electrical ones in series.

(b) The equivalent impedance of a number of mechanical impedances in series is the reciprocal of the sum of reciprocals of the individual impedances, instead of the sum as would be expected.

(c) There is no exact mechanical analogue of Kirchoff's laws.

An analogy proposed by Firestone[1] is free from these inconsistencies and is simpler to apply. It is based on the similarity of the equations

$$v = FY_m \qquad\qquad (2.40a)$$

$$E = IZ \qquad\qquad (2.40b)$$

where v is the velocity difference across, F is the force through and Y_m is the mechanical admittance of a mechanical component; E is the potential difference across, I the current through and Z the impedance of an electrical component. The corresponding equations consistent with the analogues following from *Equations (2.8)* and *(2.9)* are

$$F = vZ_m \qquad\qquad (2.41a)$$

$$E = IZ \qquad\qquad (2.41b)$$

Equations (2.40b) and *(2.41b)* being identical. Z_m is the mechanical impedance, the reciprocal of Y_m. Firestone, instead of using Y_m, employs $\bar{z}$ which he calls 'bar impedance' in the hope that it will ultimately supersede the present well-known and widely used Z_m as defined in *Equation* (*2.41a*) and then 'bar impedance' can be shortened to 'impedance'. The present writer is not so optimistic, for there is no evidence that the usual conception of mechanical impedance has become less popular since 1933 and cannot agree the 'admittance' spoils the analogy or causes confusion as suggested in Firestone's paper. Illogicality which has become established through usage cannot easily be removed, as is seen in the concept of 'resistance' of a conductor. The use of the idea of 'conductance' to a much greater extent than it is used at present would be more logical, but efforts to discard the well-established concept of resistance would be of no avail.

Just as *Equations* (*2.41a*) and (*2.41b*) are consistent with the differential equations (*2.8*) and (*2.9*), there are differential equations in accord with (*2.40a*) and (*2.40b*). They are

$$C_m \mathrm{d}^2 p/\mathrm{d}t^2 + G_m \mathrm{d}p/\mathrm{d}t + p/M = v_0 \cos \omega t \qquad (2.42)$$

$$L \mathrm{d}^2 q/\mathrm{d}t^2 + R \mathrm{d}q/\mathrm{d}t + q/C = E_0 \cos \omega t \qquad (2.9)$$

where p is the impulse $\int F \mathrm{d}t$ and G_m is the mechanical conductance. *Equation* (*2.42*) refers to C_m, G_m and M in series. v, which equals $v_0 \cos \omega t$, is the velocity across the system—the velocity of M relative to a fixed frame of reference, the other end of the compliance C_m also being fixed. F is the force through C_m, G_m and M. *Equation* (*2.9*) would be expected to reappear because the electrical equations (*2.40b*) and (*2.41b*) are the same.

A list of the corresponding quantities in Firestone's analogy is given in *Table 2.2* and includes those in acoustical systems, although these arguments supporting a new analogy in preference to the conventional one are very much less cogent. On balance there seems to be little to choose between the two analogies. Firestone's one is included in the table for a reason given later, and for uniformity since the basic analogies are electro-mechanical and electro-acoustical and if these are similar their use is facilitated. Otherwise differences have to be carefully remembered in their applications. Furthermore a simple mechanical–acoustical analogy is obtained.

An explanation of some of the acoustical quantities is apposite here. In acoustical systems, since the motion of volumes of gas occurs, *volume displacement* s_a is used instead of a linear displacement s. s_a equals As, where A is the area of the tube in which the fluid is moving, s being normal to A. The first derivative of s_a with respect

45

to time is the *volume velocity* v_a, called volume current in the conventional analogy because it corresponds to electrical current. The reason for the use of *inertance* M_a instead of mass may not be

Table 2.2. *Electrical, mechanical and acoustical analogues*

Electrical	Mechanical	Acoustical
Potential E	Velocity $v = \dot{s}$	Volume velocity $v_a = Av$
Current $I = \dot{q}$	Force $F = \dot{p}$	Pressure $P = \dot{p} = F/A$
Charge $q = \int I dt$	Impulse $p = \int F dt$	Pressure impulse $p_a = \int P dt$
Potential impulse $e = \int E dt$	Displacement s	Volume displacement $s_a = As$
Capacitance C	Mass M	Inertance $M_a = M/A^2$
Inductance L	Compliance C_m	Capacitance C_a
Reactance X	Susceptance B_m	Susceptance B_a
Susceptance B	Reactance X_m	Reactance X_a
Resistance R	Conductance G_m	Conductance G_a
Conductance G	Resistance R_m	Resistance R_a
Impedance Z	Admittance Y_m	Admittance Y_a
Admittance Y	Impedance Z_m	Impedance Z_a
$\Sigma I = 0$ at a junction	$\Sigma F = 0$	$\Sigma P = 0$
$\Sigma E = 0$ round a mesh	$\Sigma v = 0$	$\Sigma v_a = 0$
Power $= IE$	Power $= Fv$	Power $= Pv_a$
Capacitative energy $\frac{1}{2}CE^2$	Kinetic energy $\frac{1}{2}Mv^2$	Kinetic energy $\frac{1}{2}M_a v_a^2$
Inductive energy $\frac{1}{2}LI^2$	Elastic energy $\frac{1}{2}C_m F^2$	Volume energy $\frac{1}{2}C_a P^2$

apparent, since the motion of masses of gas occurs in acoustical systems as well as in mechanical ones. Consider a mass M of gas all moving at velocity v. The kinetic energy of this mass is $\frac{1}{2}Mv^2$ which equals

$$\frac{1}{2}\frac{M}{A^2}(Av)^2 \text{ or } \frac{1}{2}M_a v_a^2.$$

Thus M and M_a are directly analogous in the two systems. Just as a mass M may be said to have inertia, that is, to resist changes of velocity, so may inertance M_a be said to resist changes in volume velocity.

The restoring force of a spring compressed or extended a length s from its equilibrium position is Ss. In moving a further distance δs the work done by the spring against an applied force F, which equals Ss if equilibrium was again established when the spring was strained, is $Ss\delta s$. Thus the work W done in compression or extension is

$$\int_0^s Ss ds = \frac{1}{2}Ss^2$$

46

which is the elastic energy stored by the spring or by an elastic compressible material. Further

$$W = \tfrac{1}{2}Ss^2 = (Ss)^2/2S = \tfrac{1}{2}C_mF^2$$

since the compliance C_m is $1/S$ and Ss equals F. In an acoustical system, pressures P are analogous to forces F, and W may then be written

$$W = \tfrac{1}{2}C_mA^2P^2 = \tfrac{1}{2}C_aP^2$$

where A is the area over which P is applied normally. The acoustical capacitance C_a equals C_mA^2, which is in accord with the alternative definition

$$C_a = s_a/P \qquad (2.43)$$

s_a being the volume displacement corresponding to an applied pressure P. The corresponding equation for an inductance L is

$$L = \frac{1}{I}\int E\mathrm{d}t \qquad (2.44)$$

for which the time derivative is the well-known equation

$$E = L\mathrm{d}I/\mathrm{d}t$$

so that C_a is clearly analogous with L. L is assumed to be constant in electrical circuit theory, as are the other quantities C, R and so on, even though there may be some variation in them with frequency, for example. Furthermore, they are usually taken as 'lumped' or else, as in transmission line analysis, as uniformly distributed. In mechanical and particularly in acoustical systems there is frequently a much greater variation, not always of the same kind as in corresponding electrical quantities, and the location of, for example, an inertance may be indefinite. Thus in analogies precise quantitative correlation cannot be expected.

Figure 2.13 shows symbols representing various quantities in electrical, mechanical, and acoustical systems. Acoustical resistance R_a is represented by a number of fine lines, corresponding to fine tubes, drawn in the main tube, since the acoustical resistance of a tube increases with reduction in cross-sectional area. Acoustical capacitance is denoted by an enclosed volume of medium which tends to oppose any change in pressure. Inertance refers to a particular mass and cross-section of medium, so that the mass in a tube having an associated inertance is distinguished by thickened lines drawn on the wall of the tube.

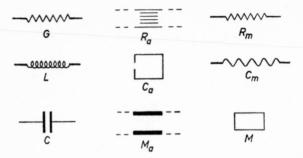

Figure 2.13. Symbols in electrical, acoustical and mechanical systems

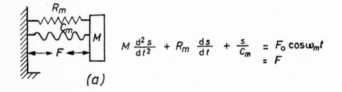

$$M \frac{d^2 s}{dt^2} + R_m \frac{ds}{dt} + \frac{s}{C_m} = F_0 \cos\omega_m t$$
$$= F$$

(a)

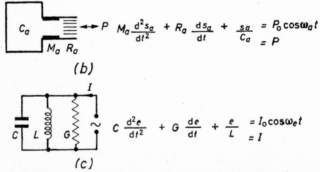

$$M_a \frac{d^2 s_a}{dt^2} + R_a \frac{ds_a}{dt} + \frac{s_a}{C_a} = P_0 \cos\omega_a t$$
$$= P$$

(b)

$$C \frac{d^2 e}{dt^2} + G \frac{de}{dt} + \frac{e}{L} = I_0 \cos\omega_e t$$
$$= I$$

(c)

Figure 2.14. Electrical equivalent of mechanical and acoustical systems

The electrical equivalent of simple mechanical and acoustical systems is shown in *Figure 2.14*, the Firestone analogy having been used. *Figure 2.14(a)* is a more diagrammatic representation than *Figure 2.2* of the forced vibration of a mass M on a lubricated rough plane. In the mechanical and acoustical systems the displacements, and hence the velocities across, are the same for the various members. Force and pressure components can be written in terms of these displacements and their sums equal the applied force or pressure. In the analogous electrical circuit the potential difference is the same across G, L and C so that the sum of the currents through them, written in terms of the potential impulse e, give the current I obtained from a generator.

The difficulty of drawing an acoustical equivalent system is seen in *Figure 2.14(b)*, for the components appear to be in series. The decision regarding whether the acoustical components are in series or parallel depends on whether the pressures through, or the volume velocities across them are equal, as previously suggested, and not on the appearance of the diagram. The diagram actually represents a Helmholtz resonator and, since R_a is usually very small in such systems, the resonant frequency is $1/2\pi\sqrt{(M_aC_a)}$, which can be written in terms of the dimensions of the resonator and the speed of sound in the contained fluid, usually air.

If l is the length of the neck and a is its radius, the inertance M_a is $\pi a^2 l \rho_0/\pi^2 a^4$ which equals $\rho_0 l/\pi a^2$, where ρ_0 is the density of the fluid in the resonator. From section **4.2.** the speed c of small amplitude waves in the fluid is $\sqrt{(\kappa/\rho_0)}$, where κ, the bulk modulus of the fluid, is $P/(s_a/V)$. P is the pressure change producing a volume displacement s_a of the total volume V of the fluid in the resonator, so that s_a/V is the volume strain. But $s_a/P = C_a$ so that $\kappa = V/C_a$ and $C_a = V/\rho_0 c^2$. Thus the resonant frequency is

$$1/2\pi\sqrt{(M_aC_a)} = 1/2\pi\sqrt{(\rho_0 lV/\pi a^2 \rho_0 c^2)} = (c/2\pi)\sqrt{(\pi a^2/lV)}.$$

This is the fundamental frequency. There are other frequencies at which resonance will occur corresponding to particular modes of vibration, but no account can be taken of these in the preceding analysis.

R_a has been neglected but can be found as follows, since it can reasonably be assumed to be located in the whole of the neck and to be negligible elsewhere in the resonator. The volume of fluid flowing per unit time, that is the volume velocity v_a, in a tube of radius a and length l is $\pi a^4 P/8\eta l$, where P is the pressure difference between the ends and η is the coefficient of viscosity of the fluid. But $R_a = P/v_a$ by analogy with the electrical equation $G = I/E$ so that

$$R_a = 8\eta l/\pi a^4 = (8\eta/a^2)(l/\pi a^2) = \beta_a(l/\pi a^2)$$

where β_a, which equals $8\eta/a^2$, is the *acoustical resistivity*.

Firestone's electro-acoustical analogy is more logically applied than the conventional one to acoustic waves in the fluid contained by a tube. Equations can be derived which are analogous to those for electrical transmission lines. An open end of the tube corresponds to insulated ends of the line, while a closed end of the tube is analogous to short-circuited line ends. Similar remarks apply to waves on strings[2]. A converse relation holds between end conditions when the conventional analogy is used.

In order that two systems may be completely analogous, the various quantities in the systems must be grouped non-dimensionally and such groupings of one system must have the same values as their counterparts in the other system. As an example, consider the systems represented by *Figures 2.14(a)* and *(c)*. The dimensions of the various quantities in the mechanical system are

$$M \quad \text{M} \qquad\qquad s \quad \text{L}$$
$$R_m \quad \text{MT}^{-1} \qquad\qquad F_0 \quad \text{MLT}^{-2}$$
$$C_m \quad \text{M}^{-1}\text{T}^2 \qquad\qquad \omega_m \quad \text{T}^{-1}$$

Omitted from this list are the natural frequency of the system and the velocity and acceleration of the mass M. The natural frequency is allowed for because M and C_m are included, while velocity and acceleration depend on ω_m, the forcing angular frequency, and s, the instantaneous displacement, both of which have been included.

According to *Buckingham's π theorem*, if there are a quantities specifying a system and b fundamental dimensions, the number of independent dimensionless groups π_1, π_2, π_3, . . that can be formed is a—b. Here there are six quantities and three fundamental dimensions, so there will be three independent non-dimensional groups. In order to find these groups we choose three quantities raised to different powers to use repeatedly in conjunction with the remaining quantities. The general number of quantities to be chosen is easily seen from Buckingham's theorem to equal b, the number of fundamental dimensions, for then there will be a—b π groups. The only restriction on the choice is that all the fundamental dimensions should be included, but, for economy in writing, the quantities with the least numbers of dimensions should be selected in preference to the others. Accordingly M, s and ω_m are chosen. A different choice leads to different non-dimensional groups, but they can be shown to be equivalent to the first groups by substitution. We have

$$\pi_1 = M^a s^b \omega_m^c R_m \qquad \text{M}^a\text{L}^b\text{T}^{-c}\text{MT}^{-1}$$
$$\pi_2 = M^a s^b \omega_m^c C_m \qquad \text{M}^a\text{L}^b\text{T}^{-c}\text{M}^{-1}\text{T}^2$$
$$\pi_3 = M^a s^b \omega_m^c F_0 \qquad \text{M}^a\text{L}^b\text{T}^{-c}\text{MLT}^{-2}$$

In a dimensionless grouping the algebraic sum of the exponents of each fundamental dimension must equal zero, so that there are three simultaneous equations in a, b and c for each π group

π_1:
$$a+1 = 0 \; ; a = -1$$
$$b = 0 \; ; b = 0$$
$$-c-1 = 0 \; ; c = -1$$

Thus $\pi_1 = M^{-1}\omega_m^{-1}R_m$.

π_2:
$$a-1 = 0 \; ; a = 1$$
$$b = 0 \; ; b = 0$$
$$-c+2 = 0 \; ; c = 2$$

Thus $\pi_2 = M\omega_m^2 C_m$.

π_3:
$$a+1 = 0 \; ; a = -1$$
$$b+1 = 0 \; ; b = -1$$
$$-c-2 = 0 \; ; c = -2$$

Thus $\pi_3 = M^{-1}s^{-1}\omega_m^{-2}F_0$.

The non-dimensional groups for the equivalent electrical system can be obtained by the substitution of the appropriate analogues

$$\pi_1 = R_m/M\omega_m = G/C\omega_e \qquad (2.45a)$$

$$\pi_2 = M\omega_m^2 C_m = C\omega_e^2 L \qquad (2.45b)$$

$$\pi_3 = F_0/Ms\omega_m^2 = I_0/Ce\omega_e^2. \qquad (2.45c)$$

As a check, the groupings of the electrical quantities can be shown to be dimensionless. For example, $G/C\omega_a$ has, in the MKSC system, the dimensions

$$(M^{-1}L^{-2}T^2Q^2)^{-1}(ML^2T^{-1}Q^{-2})^{-1}(T)$$

that is, zero. For the electrical quantities there would appear to be only two π groups because there are apparently the four fundamental dimensions M, L, T and Q. Although four simultaneous equations in a, b, c and d are found, two of these are the same for both π groups so that a, b, c and d cannot be completely determined. Thus only three dimensions can be treated as fundamental and three π groups are thereby found.

e, which equals $\int Edt$, is not easily measured and the displacement s can usually be found by simpler methods than the analogous circuit. Hence from practical considerations (2.45c) is better written in terms of E and v. We have, by inverting *Equation* (*2.45c*) and finding the time derivative of both sides

$$Mf_m^2 v/F_0 = Cf_e^2 E/I_0 \qquad (2.45d)$$

where frequency f replaces ω since the factor 2π cancels, as it does in the other two equations.

The resistances in the systems may be found to be such that free oscillations are possible in one system but not in the other. This is of no significance in the preceding analogy because forced vibrations are being studied and resonance occurs irrespective of the resistance present, which affects only the amplitude of displacement, velocity and acceleration. In an analogy drawn between systems vibrating freely, numerical values would have to be found that allowed free vibrations to occur in both systems.

When the electrical components are selected to give the same numerical values of the π groups as the mechanical ones, the two systems are completely equivalent. Thus the behaviour of the mechanical system could be predicted from measurements made in the electrical one providing that the frequency variation, if any, in both systems was limited so as to avoid changes in any of the quantities L, C, C_m, M and so on. Analogies have been of considerable use in the design of the 'sound box' on early gramophones, acoustic filters including 'silencers' for the exhaust and inlet of internal combustion engines, vibration isolators of machines and sensitive apparatus, and in many other applications.

References

[1] F. A. FIRESTONE *J. Acoust. Soc. Amer.* **4**, 249, 1933.
[2] R. V. SHARMAN *J. Electronics & Control*, **XI**, 233, 1961.

3

NON-LINEAR VIBRATIONS

3.1. Large Amplitude Motion of a Pendulum

For a compound pendulum swinging freely the following equation of motion has been obtained

$$d^2\theta/dt^2 = -[gl/(r^2+l^2)] \sin \theta \qquad (1.13)$$

where θ is the instantaneous angular displacement, l the distance between the centre of mass and the axis of rotation, and r the radius of gyration of the pendulum about an axis through the centre of mass, parallel to the axis about which rotation occurs. The solution of (1.13) has been given for small values of θ, and the period of vibration was found to be

$$T_0 = 2\pi\sqrt{[(r^2+l^2)/gl]}. \qquad (1.15)$$

Equation (1.13) can thus be written

$$d^2\theta/dt^2 = -(4\pi^2/T_0^2) \sin \theta. \qquad (3.1)$$

The same equation applies to a simple pendulum, and is non-linear in the sense that $\sin \theta$ appears instead of θ.

Multiplying *Equation* (3.1) by $2\ d\theta/dt$ and integrating with respect to t gives

$$(d\theta/dt)^2 = (8\pi^2/T_0^2) \cos \theta + A$$

where A is constant. If $d\theta/dt$ is zero when θ equals θ_0

$$A = -(8\pi^2/T_0^2) \cos \theta_0.$$

Thus

$$d\theta/dt = (2\pi/T_0)\sqrt{[2(\cos \theta - \cos \theta_0)]}$$

and

$$\frac{2\pi t}{T_0} = \int \frac{d\theta}{\sqrt{[2(\cos \theta - \cos \theta_0)]}}$$

which is an elliptic integral of the first kind. Writing the integral in terms of half-angles and supposing that $\theta = 0$ at $t = 0$ and $\theta = \theta_0$ at $t = T/4$ we have

$$\frac{2\pi}{T_0}\left(\frac{T}{4}\right) = \int_0^{\theta_0} \frac{d\theta}{2\sqrt{(\sin^2 \frac{1}{2}\theta_0 - \sin^2 \frac{1}{2}\theta)}}.$$

Now let $\sin \frac{1}{2}\theta = (\sin \frac{1}{2}\theta_0) \sin \phi$

so $\frac{1}{2}(\cos \frac{1}{2}\theta)\delta\theta = (\sin \frac{1}{2}\theta_0)(\cos \phi)\delta\phi$

and

$$\frac{\pi T}{2T_0} = \int_0^{\pi/2} \frac{d\phi}{\sqrt{[1 - (\sin^2\frac{1}{2}\theta_0) \sin^2\phi]}}$$

$$= \int_0^{\pi/2} (1 + \frac{1}{2}(\sin^2\frac{1}{2}\theta_0) \sin^2\phi + \frac{3}{8}(\sin^4\frac{1}{2}\theta) \sin^4\phi + ..)d\phi$$

$$= (\pi/2)[1 + (\frac{1}{2}\sin^2\frac{1}{2}\theta_0)\frac{1}{2} + (\frac{3}{8}\sin^4\frac{1}{2}\theta_0)\frac{3}{4}\cdot\frac{1}{2} + ..]$$

or

$$T = T_0(1 + \frac{1}{4}\sin^2\frac{1}{2}\theta_0 + \frac{9}{64}\sin^4\frac{1}{2}\theta_0 + ...) \qquad (3.2)$$

or approximately

$$T = T_0(1 + \frac{1}{4}\sin^2\frac{1}{2}\theta_0). \qquad (3.3)$$

T is larger than T_0 by less than 2 per cent for an angular amplitude not exceeding 30°, and at θ_0 equals 90° the error is only 18 per cent. Thus 'linearizing'—writing θ in place of $\sin \theta$—equations of the kind of (1.13) is usually justifiable.

3.2. Forced Oscillations—Non-linear Restoring Force

Equation (3.1) applies to a particular example of free oscillations of an undamped non-linear system. Forced undamped oscillations are represented generally by a Duffing equation

$$M d^2s/dt^2 + f(s) = F_0 \cos pt$$

or

$$d^2s/dt^2 + (1/M)f(s) = f_0 \cos pt \qquad (3.4)$$

f(s) being a non-linear function of s which must be specified before *Equation (3.4)* can be solved and which can often be written as a polynomial in s. In practical systems f(s) is frequently $S_1s + S_2s^3$, the cubed term ensuring that the restoring force has the same magnitude whether s is positive or negative. The vibrations are then symmetrical about the rest position. If both S_1 and S_2 are positive the

54

restoring force is greater for a particular displacement than it would be in a linear system, in which S_2 is zero, for the same displacement. Since the restoring force is often supplied by a spring, the spring is then described as *hard*. A *soft* spring occurs if S_2 is negative and is not usually found in practical systems unless, for example, the elastic limit of the spring material is exceeded. Then the restoring force is smaller than that in a linear system for the same displacement. Large amplitude vibrations of a pendulum could be regarded as being controlled by a soft spring because sin θ in *Equation (3.1)* could be equated with fair accuracy to $\theta - \theta^3/6$. The variation of the restoring force with displacement for different kinds of spring is shown in *Figure 3.1*.

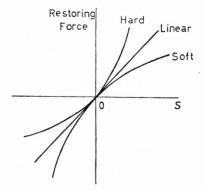

Figures 3.1. Variation of restoring force with displacement

Writing *Equation (3.4)* in terms of S' and S'', which equal S_1/M and S_2/M respectively, we have

$$d^2s/dt^2 + (S's + S''s^3) = f_0 \cos pt. \qquad (3.5)$$

The sign of S'' can be reconsidered after this equation is solved, for the method of getting the solution is unaffected by the sign of S''. Putting $pt = \phi$ in (3.5) gives

$$p^2 d^2s/d\phi^2 + (S's + S''s^3) = f_0 \cos \phi. \qquad (3.6)$$

A solution of *Equation (3.6)* is assumed to be

$$s = \sum_{n-1}^{\infty} (a_{n/3} \cos n\phi/3 + b_{n/3} \sin n\phi/3)$$

and S'' is assumed to be small in comparison with S'. Further examination of the assumed solution shows that all the sine terms,

E   55

and all the cosine terms having n even, are zero, so the solution is written

$$s = a_{1/3} \cos \phi/3 + a_1 \cos \phi + \ldots \qquad (3.7)$$

The amplitudes $a_{1/3}$ and a_1 are determined while the other harmonics are ignored.

Substitution of (3.7) in (3.6) and the use of formulae reducing multiples of cosine and sine terms to multiples of ϕ, such as

$$\cos^3 \phi/3 = \tfrac{3}{4} \cos \phi/3 + \tfrac{1}{4} \cos \phi$$

gives the relations

$$(S' - p^2/9)a_{1/3} + \tfrac{3}{4}S''(a_{1/3}^3 + a_{1/3}^2 a_1 + 2a_{1/3}a_1^2) = 0 \qquad (3.8)$$

$$(S' - p^2)a_1 + \tfrac{1}{4}S''(a_{1/3}^3 + 6a_{1/3}^2 a_1 + 3a_1^3) = f_0. \qquad (3.9)$$

If the linear system, in which S'' is zero, is now considered $a_{1/3}$ is zero unless p equals $3\sqrt{(S')}$, according to *Equation (3.8)*. If p is $3\sqrt{(S')}$, $a_{1/3}$ can be given an arbitrary value while a_1, which equals $-f_0/8S'$, is determined from (3.9) for a given value of f_0 when S'' is zero. Thus the term $a_{1/3} \cos \phi/3$ represents an oscillation of arbitrary amplitude which may be superposed on the forced vibration—$(f_0/8S') \cos \phi$. *Equations (3.8)* and *(3.9)* can now be rewritten

$$p^2 = 9S' + (a_{1/3}^2 + a_{1/3}a_1 + 2a_1^2)27S''/4 \qquad (3.10)$$

$$-8S'a_1 = f_0 - \tfrac{1}{4}S''(a_{1/3}^3 + 6a_{1/3}^2 a_1 + 3a_1^3) + a_1(p^2 - 9S') \qquad (3.11)$$

which give

$$-8S'a_1 = f_0 - \tfrac{1}{4}S''(a_{1/3}^3 - 21a_{1/3}^2 a_1 - 27a_{1/3}a_1^2 - 51a_1^3). \qquad (3.12)$$

If *Equation (3.6)* is made linear by putting S'' equal to zero a solution would be, according to *Equation (2.6)*

$$s = a \cos \phi$$

where $a = -f_0/8S' = a_1$. Thus *Equations (3.10)* and *(3.12)* become

$$p^2 = 9S' + (a_{1/3}^2 + a_{1/3}a + 2a^2)27S''/4 \qquad (3.13)$$

$$a_1 = a + (a_{1/3}^3 - 21a_{1/3}^2 a - 27a_{1/3}a^2 - 51a^3)S''/32S' \qquad (3.14)$$

which are the next approximation. Thus an approximate solution of *Equation (3.5)* is

$$s = a_{1/3} \cos pt/3 + a_1 \cos pt \qquad (3.15)$$

where $a_{1/3}$ is arbitrary and a_1 can be found from (*3.14*). From *Equation* (*3.13*)

$$\partial p^2/\partial a_{1/3} = (2a_{1/3}+a)27S''/4$$

which equals zero for a maximum or minimum value of p^2. The maximum value of p^2 occurs when S'' is less than zero, and the minimum is when S'' is greater than zero if $a_{1/3}$ equals $-a/2$. p^2 is then $9(S'+21S''a^2/16)$. Thus the subharmonic vibration occurs only for

$$p \lessgtr 3\sqrt{(S'+21S''a^2/16)} \text{ when } \begin{matrix} S'' \leqq 0 \\ S'' > 0 \end{matrix}. \tag{3.16}$$

If S'' is not zero, p does not equal $3\sqrt{(S')}$, $\sqrt{(S')}/2\pi$ being the natural frequency of vibration of the linear system. Thus the subharmonic vibration with exactly the same frequency as that of natural vibration of the linear system does not occur. Furthermore, if the system is excited by a force having a frequency n times the natural frequency of the corresponding linear system, no actual subharmonic is generated, although the lower frequency may differ very little from a subharmonic if S' and S'' are both small. Although this conclusion has been shown to apply to *Equation* (*3.5*) the same conclusion is very likely applicable to other Duffing equations in which f(s) can be represented by a polynomial in s.

The same conclusion is certainly reached if f(s) equals $S_1 s + S_2 s^2$, which often applies to oscillations asymmetrical about the rest position. A solution of the form $s = a_{1/2} \cos \frac{1}{2}\phi + a_1 \cos \phi$ is assumed and is found to yield.

$$p = 2\sqrt{S'}$$

$$a = -f_0/3S'$$

and in the next approximation

$$p = 2\sqrt{(S'-aS'')}$$

so again no subharmonic of the exciting force is generated, if the exciting force has a frequency n times that of the natural vibrations of the corresponding linear system.

Although a non-linear system without damping does not occur practically, the preceding treatment is not substantially modified if damping is taken into account. The subharmonic is found not to be present if the damping coefficient per unit mass is appreciably greater numerically than S''. A method of treating non-linear damping has been suggested in section **1.7**.

The preceding analysis illustrates the method of *iteration* for solving non-linear differential equations. The method is applicable generally, and consists of putting an assumed solution taking the form of a Fourier expansion in the basic simplified differential equation (for example (*3.7*) in (*3.6*)). The Fourier coefficients are then evaluated in terms of the constants of the original differential equation (for example (*3.8*) and (*3.9*)) which is then 'linearized'— the corresponding linear equation is written down—to give simplified relations for these coefficients ((*3.10*), (*3.11*), (*3.12*), (*3.13*) and (*3.14*)). Iteration forms the basis of many methods of solution, although

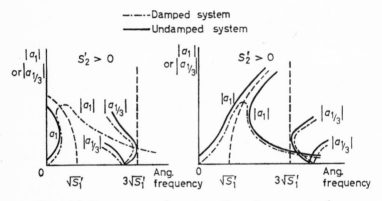

Figure 3.2. Response curves for system with non-linear restoring force

nowadays a computer could be used to give numerical solutions to any degree of accuracy required.

In *Figure 3.2* response curves are shown for a system in which the restoring force is given by $S_1s + S_2s^3$ for positive and negative values of S_2 and with and without damping. These curves indicate an effect which is not found in linear systems, and which occurs because there are two possible values of amplitude at particular frequencies. Referring to *Figure 3.3*, suppose the frequency of the impressed force is gradually increasing. The portion OEA is followed, but at A the displacement amplitude suddenly drops to the value corresponding to B, the rest of the curve being followed as usual.

If the frequency is gradually reduced from a high value, the portion CBD is followed, but at D a jump will be made to E, and if the frequency is still reduced the rest of the curve back to 0 will be followed. There is, in addition to the change in amplitude, an alteration in the phase difference between the impressed force and the moving component of the system, similar to that shown in section **2.3,** *Figure 2.6*. Thus if a response curve for such a non-linear system as that described is obtained experimentally, the result will be like

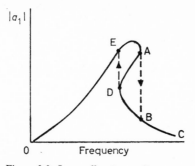

Figure 3.3. Jump effect in non-linear system

Figure 3.3 less the portion AD. Olsen[1] had obtained such a result for a direct-radiator moving-coil loudspeaker.

3.3. Triode Oscillator. Van Der Pol's Equation

Figure 3.4 is the circuit diagram of a simple triode oscillator. Instantaneous currents and potentials are shown, and the grid

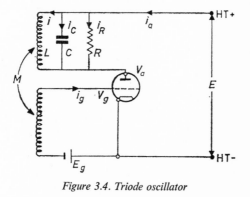

Figure 3.4. Triode oscillator

current i_g is assumed to be zero. Applying Kirchoff's laws we have

$$Ldi/dt = Ri_R = \frac{1}{C}\int i_C dt$$

$$i_a = i + i_R + i_C$$

$$v_g = Mdi/dt - E_g$$

$$v_a = E - Ldi/dt.$$

For a triode, i_a is a function of v_a and v_g

$$i_a = f(v_a + \mu v_g)$$

where μ is the amplification factor. Thus

$$[LCD^2 + (L/R)D + 1]i = f[E - \mu E_g + (\mu M - L)Di] \quad (3.17)$$

where $D = d/dt$, $D^2 = d^2/dt^2$. The triode characteristic curve is shown in *Figure 3.5*. P is assumed to be the operating point given by $x_1 = E - \mu E_g$, about which the grid potential varies and is a point of

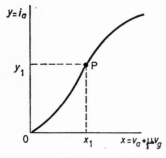

Figure 3.5. Triode characteristic

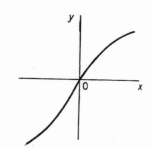

Figure 3.6. Graph of $y = mx - nx^3$

inflexion. *Figure 3.6* is a graph of $y = mx - nx^3$ where both m and n are positive, the point of inflexion being at the origin. This graph is similar to the triode characteristic, which is thus written in terms of a similar cubic, P being transferred to the origin

$$f(x) - y_1 = m(x - x_1) - n(x - x_1)^3.$$

60

Thus

$$f[x_1+(\mu M-L)Di] = y_1+m(\mu M-L)Di-n(\mu M-L)^3(Di)^3$$
$$= y_1+aDi-b(Di)^3$$

where $a = m(\mu M-L)$ and $b = n(\mu M-L)^3$. Thus (3.17) is

$$LCD^2i+(L/R-a)Di+b(Di)^3+i = y_1 \qquad (3.18)$$

or

$$LCD^2I+(L/R-a)DI+b(DI)^3+I = 0 \qquad (3.19)$$

where $I = i-y_1$. A solution of *Equation (3.18)* is $i = y_1$ so that y_1 is the current through L when there are no oscillations. y_1 is thus the static anode current, since L is assumed to have a negligible resistance and statically i is very much larger than i_R, i_C being zero when there are no oscillations. Hence I may be taken to be the oscillatory component of i. On making the substitutions

$$L/R-a = -A \qquad\qquad t = T\sqrt{(LC)}$$
$$I = U\sqrt{(LCA/3b)} \qquad e = A/\sqrt{(LC)}$$

we have from *Equation (3.19)*

$$d^2U/dT^2-e[dU/dT-(dU/dT)^3/3]+U = 0$$

and differentiating this equation with respect to T gives

$$d^3U/dT^3-e[1-(dU/dT)^2]d^2U/dT^2+dU/dT = 0$$

or

$$d^2s/dT^2-e(1-s^2)ds/dT+s = 0$$

where s is dU/dT. This is a form of van der Pol's equation which is usually written

$$d^2s/dt^2-\varepsilon(1-s^2)ds/dt+s = 0 \qquad (3.20)$$

the damping force being negative for small displacements s but becoming positive for large ones. This accounts for the oscillations ultimately reaching a constant amplitude of about twice the value at which the damping is zero, in the preceding example.

The negative damping is derived from a contribution of energy to the vibrating system. Hence the method described in section **1.7.** for finding a linear damping force equivalent to a non-linear one, from the consideration of the energy dissipated per cycle, cannot here be applied. *Equation (3.20)* can be solved approximately by iterative or other approximate methods but these, while instructive, are too long to be shown here. Instead an examination of (*3.20*) will be deferred and some features important in the general treatment of non-linear motion will be investigated.

3.4. Phase Plane

The phase plane is defined by the rectangular axes s and v, where v is ds/dt, and is so called because each point on the plane shows the phase of a moving particle or an analogous particle in a vibrating system. s and v are both functions of time t so that curves—*trajectories*—in the s,v plane may be regarded as being defined in parametric form, with t as the parameter. Closed curves in the phase plane, each corresponding to a different total energy level, are particularly important since they represent periodic motion. After one circuit of the contour the initial conditions will be repeated. The period of vibration is given by the line integral $\oint \dfrac{ds}{v}$ taken along the closed trajectory in the direction of increasing time. Successive curves which are almost coincident—for example those for harmonic motion with small damping—and some continuous curves are also of interest.

The phase plane trajectories, otherwise known as *energy curves*, can be used to deduce the nature of motions described by second order differential equations whose solutions are difficult. Generally we have

$$f(d^2s/dt^2, ds/dt, s) = 0. \qquad (3.21)$$

But $ds/dt = v$ and $d^2s/dt^2 = v\,dv/ds$ so (*3.21*) becomes

$$f(vv', v, s) = 0 \qquad (3.22)$$

which is a first order equation, where $v' = dv/ds$. If this equation can be solved for v' we arrive at

$$v' = g(v, s). \qquad (3.23)$$

The solution of (*3.23*) is determinable if the initial conditions are known; if not they are often more easily found than the solution of equation (*3.21*). From the solution of (*3.23*) energy (integral) curves can be plotted, from which the nature of the vibrations may be deduced.

As an example consider *Equation (1.2)*

$$d^2s/dt^2 + \omega_0^2 s = 0$$

which represents SHM of frequency $\omega_0/2\pi$. This equation corresponds to (3.21); the equation corresponding to (3.22) is

$$vv' + \omega_0^2 s = 0 \tag{3.24}$$

which integrates to give

$$\omega_0^2 s^2 + v^2 = \omega_0^2 a^2 \tag{3.25}$$

if $s = a$ when $v = 0$. *Equation (3.25)* defines in the phase plane a family of ellipses, semi-axes a and $a\omega_0$, having various values of a and centres at the origin of the s and v axes. They are traced in a

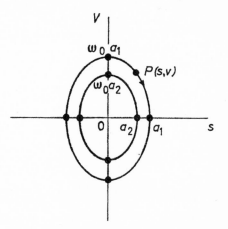

Figure 3.7. Phase plane trajectories for SHM

clockwise sense as shown in *Figure 3.7*. At the point P the gradient is negative, because v decreases as s becomes larger. From *Equation (3.25)*

$$v = \omega_0\sqrt{(a^2 - s^2)}.$$

The period of oscillation T_0 is given by

$$T_0 = \oint \frac{ds}{v} = \frac{1}{\omega_0} \oint \frac{ds}{\sqrt{(a^2 - s^2)}} = \frac{4}{\omega_0}\left[\sin^{-1} s/a\right]_0^a.$$

Thus T_0 equals $2\pi/\omega_0$, as previously noted in *Equation (1.5)*.

3.5. Method of Isoclinals

Equation (3.23) may not be integrable in terms of known functions. The method of isoclinals may then sometimes be used to get the phase plane curves. Consider all points in the phase plane whose coordinates (s,v) satisfy

$$g(s, v) = C \qquad (3.26)$$

where C is a constant. From *Equation (3.23)*

$$dv/ds = g(s, v)$$

so that at such points the slope of the trajectory dv/ds equals C. These points all lie on a curve which can be plotted from *Equation (3.26)* and is known as an *isoclinal*. By giving C a range of values, a family of isoclinals can be obtained and hence trajectories may be plotted.

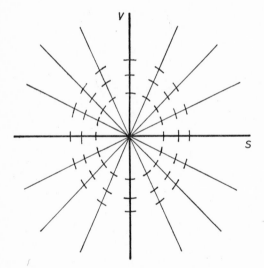

Figure 3.8. Isoclinals for SHM

Returning to the preceding example, from *(3.24)* we have $v' = -\omega_o^2 s/v$ so that the isoclinals have equations $-\omega_o^2 s/v = C$ and are thus straight lines passing through the origin of the s and v axes. A few have been drawn in *Figure 3.8*, the appropriate gradient being shown by short lines drawn on each one. The trajectories are thus indicated to be ellipses, as shown before.

The solution of van der Pol's equation can now be considered in the light of the foregoing remarks. The equation is

$$d^2s/dt^2 - \varepsilon(1-s^2)ds/dt + s = 0 \qquad (3.20)$$

and writing it in terms of v gives

$$v' = \varepsilon(1-s^2) - s/v \qquad (3.27)$$

which is not integrable in terms of known functions.
The isoclinals are given by

$$\varepsilon(1-s^2) - s/v = C$$

or

$$v = s/[\varepsilon(1-s^2) - C] \qquad (3.28)$$

and can be plotted for a particular value of ε. *Figure 3.9* shows the isoclinals plotted for ε equals unity, and three energy curves a, b and c. These, and any others, tend towards a closed trajectory d and ultimately coincide independently of initial conditions. Curve d is known as a *limit cycle*, so called by Poincaré, and represents the steady state of self-excited vibrations, periodic but not generally sinusoidal.

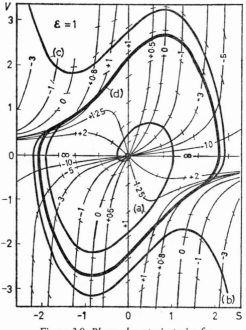

*Figure 3.9. Phase plane trajectories for
van der Pol's equation*

65

In the oscillations defined by van der Pol's equation, the shape and size of the limit cycle depends on ε. If ε is small the limit cycle will be small and circular and the motion will be nearly simple harmonic. As ε increases the limit cycle increases in size and distortion and the motion departs from simple harmonic. *Figure 3.10* shows v as a function of t for various values of ε, the disturbance at $t = 0$ being very small. These graphs have to be obtained from *Equation (3.20)* by approximate integration or from experiments and cannot be derived from the limit cycles.

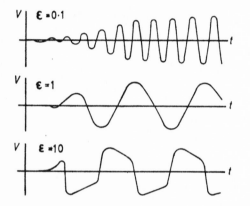

Figure 3.10. Change in form of oscillations

For ε greater than about ten the vibrations are very jerky and are known as *relaxation oscillations*. Such oscillations could occur by making M large or L, R or C small in the circuit illustrated by *Figure 3.4*. Other sources of relaxation oscillations will be discussed in the next section. The van der Pol equation with large ε is probably the most general mathematical description of relaxation oscillations known at present.

3.6. Relaxation Oscillations

Relaxation oscillations are characterized by a physical quantity, such as displacement, velocity, current, potential and so on, fluctuating between two values and remaining at or near either level alternately for times which are long compared with the times during which transition occurs. The changes between the levels are due to a loss of internal equilibrium. Examples are the change in potential across a capacitor discharging through a gaseous conductor such as a neon lamp or thyratron, the output of multivibrators and the circuit described by *Figure 3.4* if ε is large, the vibrations produced by the 'slip-stick' action of brakes, and many others.

Impulse-excited oscillations are superficially similar, but the energy stored in the system changes abruptly during the alteration of the physical quantity because of the action of external impulsive agents. Examples of impulse-excited systems are the balance-wheel or pendulum mechanism in clocks, quenched-spark oscillators, a triode

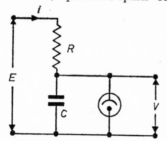

Figure 3.11. *Capacitor discharging through a gaseous conductor*

oscillator with a circuit similar to the one indicated by *Figure 3.4* but with *L* in the grid circuit and *M* large, a ball striking parallel walls with elastic or inelastic impacts, and so on.

Often both kinds of oscillations are collectively called relaxation oscillations, but the distinction is necessary because the analytical treatment for both kinds differs substantially.

Figure 3.11 shows a circuit diagram of a relaxation oscillation generator, the output being an approximate 'saw-tooth'. *E* is a constant zero-frequency potential, *i* the instantaneous current and *V* is the potential across the capacitor *C* and the gas-filled discharge tube. *V* varies with time *t* as shown in *Figure 3.12* if *E* is sufficiently large.

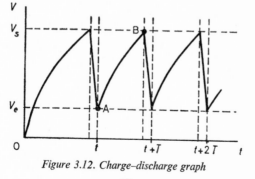

Figure 3.12. *Charge–discharge graph*

67

At $t = 0$ $V = 0$ if C is uncharged. V then rises exponentially to V_s, the striking potential of the discharge tube, and suddenly falls to V_e, the potential at which extinction of the glow in the tube occurs. The sudden drop to V_e takes place because the resistance between the electrodes is very small when the glow is present, for the gas has become ionized and thus highly conducting. The charge–discharge cycle then repeats as shown.

For a capacitor C charging through a resistor R

$$i = i_0 \exp(-t/CR) \qquad (3.29)$$

where $i = i_0$ when $t = 0$. Hence

$$V = E - Ri_0 \exp(-t/CR).$$

The charging of C begins at point A in *Figure 3.12* when $V = V_e$, the first cycle being ignored because it is not part of the steady state. Thus

$$V_e = E - Ri_0 \exp(-t/CR). \qquad (3.30)$$

The discharge of C commences at B when $V = V_s$ given by

$$V_s = E - Ri_0 \exp[-(t+T)/CR] \qquad (3.31)$$

since B corresponds to time $t+T$ nearly, the discharge being very rapid. T is the period of oscillation. Subtracting (3.30) from (3.31) gives

$$V_s - V_e = Ri_0\{\exp(-t/CR) - \exp[-(t+T)/CR]\}$$

$$= Ri_0[\exp(-t/CR)][1 - \exp(-T/CR)]$$

or

$$1 - \exp(-T/CR) = (V_s - V_e)/(E - V_e)$$

using *Equation (3.31)*. Thus

$$\exp(-T/CR) = (E - V_s)/(E - V_e)$$

or

$$T = CR \log_e[(E - V_e)/(E - V_s)]. \qquad (3.32)$$

Hence the period of oscillation is directly proportional to the time constant CR. E must be greater than V_s otherwise T is imaginary.

A device which illustrates the action of such a circuit is shown in *Figure 3.13*. The container C which is originally empty is gradually filled with water. The filling causes the centre of mass of the volume of water to move away from the axis of rotation passing through A. As the moment of the weight of water becomes larger, the platform P leaves the stop S and becomes horizontal or nearly so. When the moment of the weight of water exceeds the moment of weight W about A, the platform suddenly swings over to the stop S' and the

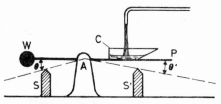

Figure 3.13. Mechanical simulation of capacitor discharging through gaseous conductor

water is emptied rapidly. The platform then swings back quickly to the other stop and the process is repeated. The initial position, at which θ is zero, corresponds to V_e while V_s is related to $\theta + \theta'$ measured clockwise from the initial position.

3.7. Combination Tones

If a force applied to a non-linear vibrating system contains two or more components of different frequencies, *combination tones* are produced in the form of oscillations at many frequencies besides the original two. The phenomenon was first studied by Helmholtz[2] in connection with the theory of physiological acoustics. He found that the inner ear receives sounds which are not contained in the incident acoustic wave, and showed how the slightly funnel-shaped form of the tympanic membrane might account for asymmetrical vibrations represented by

$$d^2s/dt^2 + (S's + S''s^2) = F(t) \qquad (3.33)$$

where $F(t)$ is the exciting force due to the periodically varying pressure of the incident sound wave. If the sound wave contains two frequencies $p_1/2\pi$ and $p_2/2\pi$, $F(t)$ is given by

$$F(t) = a \cos p_1 t + b \cos p_2 t. \qquad (3.34)$$

69

With this substitution in (3.33) Helmholtz found an approximate solution by a perturbation method, instead of the iteration method previously described. The solution contained terms representing vibrations of angular frequencies p_1, p_2, $p_1 - p_2$ and $p_1 + p_2$. The effect is sometimes called *cross modulation* and also occurs in circuits containing non-linear electronic devices.

Suppose a non-linear conductor of electricity has a characteristic equation

$$i = f(v) \qquad (3.35)$$

where i is the current through the device and v is the potential across it. Often f(v) is given by

$$f(v) = A_1 v + A_2 v^2 + A_3 v^3 + \ldots \qquad (3.36)$$

the coefficients A decreasing with sufficient rapidity to justify the retention of only a few terms. We assume the impressed potential to be

$$v = k(\cos p_1 t + \cos p_2 t) \qquad (3.37)$$

and substituting for v from *Equation (3.37)* in (3.35) and (3.36) combined we have, taking only the first three terms of *Equation (3.36)*

$$i = A_1 k(\cos p_1 t + \cos p_2 t) + A_2 k^2 (\cos p_1 t + \cos p_2 t)^2$$
$$+ A_3 k^3 (\cos p_1 t + \cos p_2 t)^3. \qquad (3.38)$$

The first term of *Equation (3.38)* gives the angular frequencies p_1 and p_2; the second $2p_1$, $2p_2$, $p_1 + p_2$ and $p_1 - p_2$; the third p_1, $3p_1$, p_2, $3p_2$, $2p_1 + p_2$, $2p_1 - p_2$, $2p_2 + p_1$ and $2p_2 - p_1$. The current i thus contains components of all these angular frequencies, together with a zero frequency term which arises from the trigonometrical transformations, and is a feature of an asymmetrical characteristic containing terms of even powers. If the frequencies $p_1/2\pi$ and $p_2/2\pi$ are assumed to be 120 and 100 c/s the frequency spectrum of i will comprise: 0, 20, 80, **100, 120**, 140, 200, 220, 240, 300, 320, 340, 360.

The presence of these combination frequencies can be demonstrated by an experiment in which the sinusoidal outputs of two audio-frequency oscillators are fed, for example, to the grid of an electron valve such as a triode. The preceding angular frequencies will be found in the anode current by the use of a harmonic analyser or a calibrated band-pass filter and valve voltmeter, providing that the valve is being operated so that *Equation (3.36)* holds. If a linear part of the characteristic is used only p_1 and p_2 are found, showing that the combination frequencies are due to non-linearity. Beats, mentioned in section **2.5.**, occur if p_1 and p_2 have suitable values. If the input frequencies are changed, the whole frequency spectrum alters but the same frequency combinations are found. An experiment of this nature is described by Reich[3].

In a radio transmitter the frequency $p_1/2\pi$ is that of radio waves. This carrier wave is usually *amplitude modulated* by a much lower audio-frequency component $p_2/2\pi$ in a non-linear device, usually a valve, which is followed by amplifiers passing a narrow band of frequencies centred about $p_1/2\pi$. The transmitter output is thus $p_1 \pm p_2$ and p_1, the sidebands and the carrier wave.

In a superheterodyne radio receiver, a local oscillator of variable frequency supplies a signal usually having a frequency equal to that of the carrier wave plus the intermediate frequency. This signal and the incoming one are both passed into a non-linear device or 'mixer', often a multi-electrode valve which also forms part of the local oscillator circuit. From the mixer output is selected the difference frequency, which is the modulated intermediate frequency, and is amplified and 'demodulated', the radio frequency component being filtered out. Thus only the audio component remains and after amplification is fed to the loudspeaker. Combination tones can therefore be seen to have an important practical use.

An unmodulated vibration may be represented by

$$s = a \cos (p_1 t + \phi)$$

where s may be a displacement, potential, current or other suitable quantity varying sinusoidally with time, a being the amplitude of this quantity, p_1 the angular frequency and ϕ a phase angle. If such an oscillation is amplitude modulated by another one of angular frequency p_2 we have

$$s = (a + b \cos p_2 t) \cos (p_1 t + \phi)$$

where b is the modulating amplitude and the ratio b/a is known as the *modulation factor*, often expressed as a percentage. Thus

$$s = a \cos (p_1 t + \phi) + \tfrac{1}{2}b \cos [(p_1 + p_2)t + \phi]$$

$$+ \tfrac{1}{2}b \cos [(p_1 - p_2)t + \phi]. \quad (3.39)$$

Hence the composite oscillation contains the frequencies $(p_1 \pm p_2)/2\pi$ and $p_1/2\pi$. In order to get an amplitude modulated resultant the components have to be passed through a non-linear device, or have to occur in a non-linear system, for amplitude modulation is not obtained simply by superposing the two components. The other combination tones are suppressed or eliminated by the use of selective amplifiers or filters.

Many radio signals are nowadays *frequency modulated*. This kind of modulation is discussed in the next section and is again produced by what are essentially non-linear systems or circuits.

3.8. Frequency and Phase Modulation

In the preceding section two combination tones have been shown to be produced by amplitude modulation. Both *frequency* and *phase modulation* result in a large number of combination tones.

If the vibration $s = a \cos (pt + \phi)$ were frequency modulated, p would at first sight appear to vary as $\cos p_2 t$, $p_2/2\pi$ being the modulation frequency, but then the frequency of the resultant vibration would vary with time t. Thus at various times a different resultant vibration would be obtained with the same components. An associated wave sent out from a transmitter would be very difficult to receive and interpret.

Let $s = a \cos \theta$, where $\theta = pt + \phi$. Then

$$p = d\theta/dt \text{ or } \theta = \int p dt$$

ϕ being the constant of integration. p can be imagined to be an instantaneous frequency, the complete argument θ of the cosine function being given by its time integral. Thus

$$s = a \cos (pt + \phi) = a \cos(\int p dt).$$

Suppose that $p = p_1(1 + m_f \cos p_2 t)$, where m_f is a frequency modulation factor and p_2 is less than p. The vibration $s = a \cos (\int p dt)$ is then frequency modulated. We have

$$s = a \cos (\int p dt) = a \cos [p_1 t + (p_1 m_f/p_2) \sin (p_2 t) + \phi] \qquad (3.40)$$

$p_1 m_f/2\pi$ being the *frequency deviation*. Hence

$$s = a \cos (b \sin p_2 t) \cos (p_1 t + \phi)$$

$$-a \sin (b \sin p_2 t) \sin (p_1 t + \phi) \qquad (3.41)$$

where $b = p_1 m_f/p_2$.

The expansions of cos $(b \sin p_2 t)$ and sin $(b \sin p_2 t)$ are

$$\tfrac{1}{2}\cos (b \sin p_2 t) = \tfrac{1}{2}J_0(b) + J_2(b) \cos 2p_2 t + J_4(b) \cos 4p_2 t + \ldots$$

$$\tfrac{1}{2}\sin (b \sin p_2 t) = J_1(b) \sin p_2 t + J_3(b) \sin p_2 t + \ldots$$

where $J_n(b)$ is a Bessel function of the first kind and nth order and is given by

$$J_n(b) = \sum_{q=0}^{\infty} \frac{(-1)^q}{q!(q+n)!}\left(\frac{b}{2}\right)^{n+2q} \qquad (3.42)$$

q being zero or a positive integer. The values of $J_n(b)$ have been tabulated for various values of n and b.

Hence *Equation (3.41)* becomes

$$s/a = J_0(b) \cos (p_1 t + \phi)$$

$$+ J_1(b)\{\cos [(p_1 + p_2)t + \phi] - \cos [(p_1 - p_2)t + \phi]\}$$

$$+ J_2(b)\{\cos [(p_1 + 2p_2)t + \phi] + \cos [(p_1 - 2p_2)t + \phi]\}$$

$$+ \ldots \qquad (3.43)$$

and in the resultant vibration there are thus components of angular frequencies p_1, $p_1 \pm p_2$, $p_1 \pm 2p_2$, $\ldots$ $p_1 \pm np_2$, n being zero or a positive integer. The same is true for a frequency modulated wave. Both the transmitter and the receiver would appear to require amplifiers having a very wide response, but $J_n(b)$, the amplitude factor of the term containing angular frequencies $p_1 \pm np_2$, becomes very small as n increases beyond b. Thus a response bandwidth of a few hundred kilocycles per second is sufficient even for high-quality signals. Nevertheless this is very much larger than the bandwidth required for amplitude modulated signals (about 10 kc/s) so the carrier frequency $p_1/2\pi$ is usually at least 50 Mc/s for frequency modulated waves.

In a phase modulated vibration the phase angle varies at the frequency of modulation p_2 so now

$$s = a \cos [p_1 t + (\phi + m_p \sin p_2 t)] \qquad (3.44)$$

where ϕ is a constant phase angle and m_p is a phase modulation factor. The comparison of *Equation (3.44)* with *(3.40)* shows that phase and frequency modulations differ only in the coefficient of the modulating term, there being m_p instead of $p_1 m_f/p_2$, so that further

73

analysis is not required. The similarity occurs because the time derivative of a sinusoidal wave is still sinusoidal in form. There is a considerable difference between phase and frequency modulation when the modulating signal is complex. The distinction is made very apparent by examining the effect on a sinusoidal carrier of phase and frequency modulation produced by square waves. The modulated signals have appreciably different forms for the same modulating waveforms.

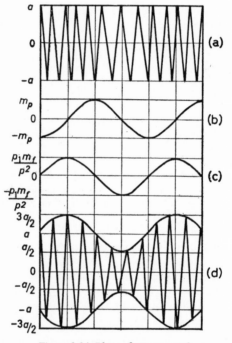

Figure 3.14. Phase, frequency and amplitude modulation

The approximate form of a phase or frequency modulated carrier is shown in *Figure 3.14(a)*. The phase and frequency modulating signals, not to the same scale as in (a), are shown by (b) and (c), while (d) is a wave of the same frequency and amplitude as the carrier in (a), amplitude modulated by a signal of the same form as in (c),

74

the modulation factor being 50 per cent. *Figure 3.15* shows the frequency spectrum of a sinusoidal carrier of frequency C, phase or frequency modulated by another sinusoid of frequency 10 kc/s. The amplitudes are plotted on a logarithmic scale, those of the carrier and sidebands of an amplitude modulated wave being denoted by a_a. The amplitude modulation factor $b/a = m_p/\phi = m_f p_1/p_2 \phi$. The spectrum bandwidth is 140 kc/s, the amplitudes of components outside being negligible. Phase and amplitude modulation are used in some wave velocity measurements described in chapter 9.

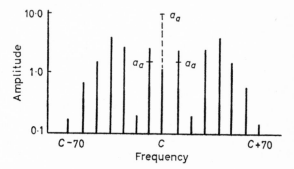

Figure 3.15. Frequency spectrum of phase or frequency and amplitude modulated waves

References

[1] H. F. OLSEN '*Acoustical Engineering*': Van Nostrand, p. 167, 1948 and *J. Acoust. Soc. Amer.*, **16**, 1, 1944.

[2] H. HELMHOLTZ 'Sensations of Tone': Dover, Appendix xii, 1954. (Reprint).

[3] H. J. REICH '*Theory and Application of Electron Tubes*': McGraw-Hill, p. 79, 1944.

4

GENERAL WAVE EQUATION

4.1. Transverse Waves on a String

Imagine a rope, initially taut and horizontal, fixed at one end and held in the hand at the other. If the hand is moved up and down regularly, the rope near the hand assumes a sinuous form which appears to travel along the rope. *Transverse waves* are thus set up and vibrational energy is transmitted along the rope, the particles of which move up and down and do not travel with the wave. In *longitudinal waves* the particles oscillate in the same direction as that in which the wave advances, but are again not transmitted with the wave. A wave is thus the continuous transfer of variables such as particle displacement and velocity, pressure, temperature, electric and magnetic intensities and so on from one place to another without the transmission of a medium, the result being a flow of energy.

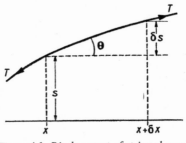

*Figure 4.1. Displacement of string element
at time* t

Consider an element of a string as shown in *Figure 4.1*. The string is assumed to be perfectly elastic and flexible, uniform in density and cross-section, and to have a tension T in it, the stress being constant across a section normal to the length. The effect of gravity is ignored. Each particle of the string vibrates about the x axis which corresponds to the undisplaced position of the string, the phase of each vibration varying continuously along the string. For small transverse

76

displacements s from the x axis, T is constant throughout the string. The restoring force acting at time t on the element shown is

$$T(\sin \theta)_{x+\delta x} - T(\sin \theta)_x$$

$$\simeq T(\tan \theta)_{x+\delta x} - T(\tan \theta)_x$$

since θ is small for small transverse displacements

$$\simeq T(\delta s/\delta x)_{x+\delta x} - T(\delta s/\delta x)_x$$

$$\simeq T\frac{\delta s}{\delta x} + T\frac{\partial}{\partial x}\left(\frac{\delta s}{\delta x}\right)\delta x - T\frac{\delta s}{\delta x}$$

$$\simeq T(\partial^2 s/\partial x^2)\delta x$$

$$= \sigma(\partial^2 s/\partial t^2)\delta x$$

where σ is the mass per unit length of the string. Thus

$$\partial^2 s/\partial t^2 \simeq (T/\sigma)\partial^2 s/\partial x^2. \qquad (4.1)$$

T/σ has the dimensions of the square of a velocity. Although there is no justification for saying that the wave velocity c thus equals $\sqrt{(T/\sigma)}$, this will be assumed for the present. Later the multiplier of $\partial^2 s/\partial x^2$ in equations such as (4.1) will be identified with the square of the wave velocity.

A similar result holds for transverse waves on a membrane or very thin plate. *Figure 4.1* can then be taken to represent a cross-section of waves travelling in the x direction. T is the tension per unit length, assumed constant in all directions, and σ is the surface density or mass per unit area of the membrane, also assumed constant. The other necessary assumptions are the same as those for the string.

4.2. Plane Longitudinal Waves

Figure 4.2 shows an element of length δx, area of cross-section A, of a solid or fluid. AA' and BB' represent planes in which particles of

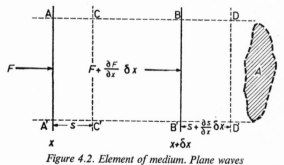

Figure 4.2. Element of medium. Plane waves

77

the medium lie before being disturbed. During the passage of a plane wave, the particles in a plane normal to the direction of the wave all vibrate in SHM of the same amplitude and phase. CC' and DD' are planes instantaneously containing the displaced particles. F is the force in the medium at x. The resultant force acting on the element in the sense of x increasing is

$$F - [F + (\partial F/\partial x)\delta x]$$

$$= -(\partial F/\partial x)\delta x$$

$$= \rho_0 A\delta x \ \partial^2 s/\partial t^2$$

or

$$A\rho_0 \ \partial^2 s/\partial t^2 = -\partial F/\partial x \qquad (4.2a)$$

ρ_0 being the density of the medium, which is assumed to be homogeneous. The stress acting on the element is F/A and the strain of the element is $-(\partial s/\partial x)\delta x/\delta x$ which equals $-\partial s/\partial x$, the minus sign arising since the element is compressed and its length is thus reduced. The elastic modulus κ for the material is hence $-F/A\partial s/\partial x$ or F equals $-A\kappa\partial s/\partial x$. Thus

$$\partial^2 s/\partial t^2 = (\kappa/\rho_0)\partial^2 s/\partial x^2 \qquad (4.2)$$

and the wave velocity c is $\sqrt{(\kappa/\rho_0)}$.

For longitudinal waves in a rod, κ equals Young's modulus E. If the rod is clamped rigidly along its sides, or otherwise forms part of an infinite medium, $\kappa = K + 4n/3$ where K is the bulk modulus of the solid and n is the rigidity modulus. Longitudinal waves in the earth are called variously *primary, irrotational, condensational* or *push* waves.

For normal fluids n is zero, and the appropriate bulk modulus is the adiabatic one which equals γK, where γ is the ratio of the specific heat at constant pressure to that at constant volume—the principal specific heats. K is the isothermal bulk modulus, the one usually obtained by compressibility measurement with long time intervals between successive values. The adiabatic modulus is required because, in sound waves, compressions follow rarefactions very rapidly. The local temperatures in normal fluids hence vary over a certain range, although there may be some doubt regarding whether the range is always a maximum. Stokes showed from simple reasoning on a thermodynamical basis that either adiabatic or isothermal conditions are required, for otherwise the wave is highly attenuated. Since the attenuation of sound waves is usually small, the conclusion is that adiabatic conditions generally hold, but Herzfeld and Rice[1] disagree.

For many liquids γ is close to unity but for gases γ is appreciably larger; in addition K equals P_0, the static gas pressure, for small amplitude waves. If V is a volume of gas, PV is nearly a constant if the gas temperature is fixed and the departure from normal pressures is small, as it is for small amplitude waves. Assuming that PV equals a constant, $P\delta V + V\delta P$ is zero, δV being the change in volume corresponding to a change in pressure δP. Thus

$$P = -V\delta P/\delta V = -\delta P/(\delta V/V) = P_0.$$

But $K = -\delta P/(\delta V/V)$, the minus sign being required since an increase in pressure gives a decrease in volume. Thus

$$K = P_0. \qquad (4.3)$$

4.3. Torsional Waves

When a rod is twisted, the torque at a cross-section distance x from one end is $B\partial\phi/\partial x$ where B is the torsional constant (equals $\pi n r^4/2$ for circular rods of radius r) and ϕ is the angular rotation at x. The resultant torque on an element δx in rotational vibration is thus $B(\partial^2\phi/\partial x^2)\delta x$, which equals the product of the moment of inertia of the element about the axis of the rod and the angular acceleration. Thus

$$B(\partial^2\phi/\partial x^2)\delta x = (\rho_0 A\delta x)k^2\partial^2\phi/\partial t^2$$

where k is the radius of gyration about the axis of the rod. Hence

$$\partial^2\phi/\partial t^2 = (B/\rho_0 Ak^2)\partial^2\phi/\partial x^2. \qquad (4.4)$$

For a circular rod $B = \pi n r^4/2$, $A = \pi r^2$ and $k^2 = r^2/2$. Thus *Equation (4.4)* becomes

$$\partial^2\phi/\partial t^2 = (n/\rho_0)\partial^2\phi/\partial x^2 \qquad (4.5)$$

the wave velocity c being $\sqrt{(n/\rho_0)}$. *Equation (4.5)* also applies to transverse waves in an infinite solid, those in the earth being called *secondary, equivoluminal, distortional* or *shake* waves in addition to transverse.

Other waves that travel through the earth are *Rayleigh* and *Love* waves, so called from the names of their discoverers. Rayleigh waves travel in a thin layer close to the surface of the earth along a great circle from the *epicentre*, which is the point on the surface nearest to the source of the waves. The particle displacement is in a vertical plane containing the direction of propagation, and can be resolved into a vertical component and a horizontal component in the direction of propagation. Such a wave travels much greater distances than other kinds of wave because the attenuation is small.

In Love waves the particle displacement is horizontal and transverse to the wave velocity, which is smaller at the surface of the earth than below. Because of the inhomogeneity of the earth, these waves have a speed dependent on frequency—*dispersion* occurs, as with primary, secondary and Rayleigh waves.

4.4. General Wave Equation

Equations (4.1), (4.2), (4.3), (4.4) and *(4.5)* all have the form

$$\partial^2 s/\partial t^2 = c^2 \partial^2 s/\partial x^2 \tag{4.6}$$

which is a one-dimensional general wave equation—one-dimensional in the sense that waves obeying it are travelling parallel to the x axis, and only this dimension of space appears in the equation. Because *(4.6)* is a second order partial differential equation, its solution must contain two arbitrary functions so we write

$$s = f_1(ct - x) + f_2(ct + x) \tag{4.7}$$

which yields

$$\partial f_1/\partial t = cf_1'(ct - x)$$

$$\partial^2 f_1/\partial t^2 = c^2 f_1''(ct - x)$$

$$\partial^2 f_1/\partial x^2 = f_1''(ct - x)$$

where f_1' and f_1'' are the first and second partial derivatives of f_1 with respect to x or t. The substitution of these last two results in *Equation (4.6)* shows that $f_1(ct - x)$ is a solution. In a similar manner $f_2(ct + x)$ may be shown to be a solution, so the sum of these two functions is a possible complete solution.

The functions are different from those previously examined in that both x and t appear in the same function. For a particular value of t the functions give the instantaneous displacements of particles at $x_1, x_2, \ldots$ while the displacement–time variations are given for all the particles individually by putting in their appropriate values of x.

The functions both represent travelling disturbances. *Figure 4.3* indicates the form a graph of $s' = f_1(ct - x)$ might take at $t = 0 (s_0' = f_1(-x))$ and at unit time later $(s_1' = f_1(c - x))$. Although s is here drawn at right-angles to x, as in transverse wave motion, s

could also be in the same direction as x as in longitudinal waves. The graphical representation of longitudinal variations by transverse ones is very convenient and is often used. The second graph differs

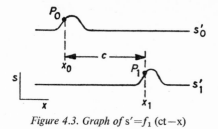

Figure 4.3. Graph of $s' = f_1 (ct-x)$

from the first in that each specific value of the displacement s_1' occurs at $x+c$ instead of at x. The displacement at P_0, for example, equals that at P_1 if

$$f_1(-x_0) = f_1(c-x_1). \qquad (4.8)$$

The simplest solution of this equation is

$$-x_0 = c-x_1 \text{ or } x_1 = x_0+c. \qquad (4.9)$$

Thus the entire curve has moved a distance c in the *positive* x direction in unit time, so that c is the velocity with which the disturbance travels.

For the function f_2 the equation corresponding to (4.8) is

$$f_2(x_0) = f_2(c+x_1)$$

so that

$$x_1 = x_0-c \qquad (4.10)$$

and the entire curve thus moves a distance c in the *negative* x direction in unit time.

The *shape* of the disturbance remains the same as it travels, since f_1 and f_2 are not altered in the preceding analysis. Practically, the amplitude of the disturbance decreases because of the dissipation of energy, while the functions may change considerably near the source of the disturbance if the initial amplitude is large as, for example, in sound waves produced by big explosions. Large amplitude sound waves progress with a speed dependent on amplitude, as shown in chapter 7, so that c can no longer be regarded as a constant and the wave motion is not described by *Equation (4.6)*.

81

4.5. Equation of Continuity

For some wave motions an approach leading directly to an equation like (*4.6*) is not possible without making too many simplifying assumptions. An almost universal basis for alternative treatments is an *equation of continuity*. *Figure 4.4* shows a point Q at the centre of

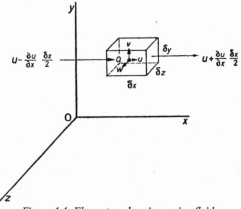

Figure 4.4. Elementary box in moving fluid

an elementary rectangular parallelepiped having sides δx, δy and δz in a fluid. u, v, w and ρ are the instantaneous components of the stream velocity and density at Q at time t. The stream velocities at the centres of the yz faces of the volume are also shown.

The time rate of increase of mass of fluid in the x direction is

$$\{[\rho u - (\partial(\rho u)/\partial x)(\delta x/2)] - [(\rho u + (\partial(\rho u)/\partial x)(\delta x/2)]\}\delta y \delta z$$
$$= -[\partial(\rho u)/\partial x]\delta x \delta y \delta z$$

and is measured, for example, in kg sec^{-1}. There are similar expressions for the rates in the other two directions, so the total rate of increase is

$$-[\partial(\rho u)/\partial x + \partial(\rho v)/\partial y + \partial(\rho w)/\partial z]\delta x \delta y \delta z$$

which equals $(\partial \rho/\partial t)\delta x \delta y \delta z$. Thus

$$\left.\begin{array}{c} \partial\rho/\partial t + \partial(\rho u)/\partial x + \partial(\rho v)/\partial y + \partial(\rho w)/\partial z = 0 \\[2mm] \partial\rho/\partial t + \text{div } \rho\mathbf{V} = 0 \end{array}\right\} \quad (4.11)$$

or

where $\rho\mathbf{V} = \hat{i}\rho u + \hat{j}\rho v + \hat{k}\rho w$, $\hat{i}$, $\hat{j}$ and $\hat{k}$ being unit vectors in the x, y and z positive directions.

(4.11) is an *equation of continuity* and was originally formulated by *Euler*. Equations expressing a similar concept but tracing the movement of individual particles were obtained by *Lagrange*, and are usually referred to as Lagrangian, although Euler appears to have used them previously[2]. Such equations are cumbersome but are very useful for a few special problems.

If the fluid is incompressible, or if ρ is independent of the instantaneous pressure in the fluid, which is true for sound waves of very small amplitudes, $\partial\rho/\partial t$ is zero and *Equation* (4.11) becomes

$$\operatorname{div} \rho \mathbf{V} = 0. \qquad (4.12)$$

If the fluid is homogeneous at all times, ρ is constant so that $\partial\rho/\partial t$ is zero and

$$\operatorname{div} \mathbf{V} = 0 \qquad (4.13)$$

If the fluid motion is *irrotational* curl $\mathbf{V}$ is zero or

$$\partial v/\partial z = \partial w/\partial y; \ \partial w/\partial x = \partial u/\partial z; \ \partial u/\partial y = \partial v/\partial x$$

and the component velocities may then be expressed in terms of a single function ϕ, the *velocity potential*, where

$$\left.\begin{array}{c} \mathbf{V} = -\operatorname{grad} \phi \\[4pt] \mathbf{u} = -\hat{i}\partial\phi/\partial x; \ \mathbf{v} = -\hat{j}\partial\phi/\partial y; \ \mathbf{w} = -\hat{k}\partial\phi/\partial z. \end{array}\right\} \qquad (4.14)$$

or

The minus sign is used in order to emphasize the mathematical similarity between velocity potential and others such as electric and magnetic potentials. *Equation* (4.13) becomes, if the fluid motion is irrotational

$$\left.\begin{array}{c} \operatorname{div} \operatorname{grad} \phi = 0 \\[4pt] \partial^2\phi/\partial x^2 + \partial^2\phi/\partial y^2 + \partial^2\phi/\partial z^2 = 0. \end{array}\right\} \qquad (4.15)$$

or

That the motion is irrotational is a necessary and sufficient condition for the existence of a velocity potential.

A quantity which can be associated with velocity potential is the *stream function* ψ. Two points A and P lie in an *xy* plane, as in

Figure 4.5, and there is a steady flow of fluid parallel to this plane. The volume of fluid flowing in unit time is $\int q_n dl$, where δl is the arc length of a curve between A and P of unit thickness normal to the xy plane and q_n is the normal component of fluid velocity given by

$$q_n = v \cos \alpha - u \sin \alpha$$

α being the gradient of the tangent to δl. But $\sin \alpha \simeq \delta y/\delta l$ and $\cos \alpha \simeq \delta x/\delta l$ so the volume flowing in unit time, the flux, is $\int (v dx - u dy)$. If a closed curve containing no sources or sinks is drawn through A and P, there is no total outward or inward flux

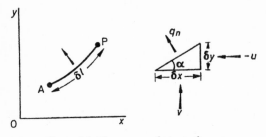

Figure 4.5. Flux across element of curve

over the closed curve. This implies that the flow *into* the enclosed region over the portion of curve from A to P equals the flow *out of* the region over the portion of curve from P to A. Because these two portions are any curves, the flow across any path from A to P is independent of the path. Thus the flux integral

$$\int (v dx - u dy) = \psi \qquad (4.16)$$

is independent of the path of integration, and depends only on the points A and P.

Suppose A is fixed and P moves so as to keep ψ constant. For this to occur P must move so that no more fluid crosses AP than was originally crossing—the locus of P has to be a stream line. Thus the curves represented by $\psi =$ a constant are stream lines, and ψ is called a *stream function*, a term first employed in this sense by Earnshaw. If the fluid flow is not steady, the locus of P would give the instantaneous directions of the particle velocities at successive instants.

If P moves a distance δx in the positive x direction, the corresponding increment in ψ is $\delta \psi$ which equals $+v \delta x$ if the anticlockwise flow shown in *Figure 4.5* is taken as positive, since then right-hand screw conformity is achieved with a z axis out of the plane of the diagram. Thus

$$\mathbf{v} = \hat{\mathbf{j}}\partial\psi/\partial x. \tag{4.17}$$

Again, if P moves a distance δy in the positive y direction we have $\delta\psi$ equals $-u\delta y$ or

$$\mathbf{u} = -\hat{\mathbf{i}}\partial\psi/\partial y. \tag{4.18}$$

If the fluid motion is irrotational, *Equations* (*4.17*) and (*4.18*) become, on using (*4.14*)

$$\partial\phi/\partial x = +\partial\psi/\partial y; \; \partial\phi/\partial y = -\partial\psi/\partial x \tag{4.19}$$

which are satisfied by

$$\phi + \mathbf{j}\psi = \mathbf{f}(x+\mathbf{j}y) \tag{4.20}$$

where $\mathbf{j} = +\sqrt{(-1)}$. Furthermore

$$\delta\psi = (\partial\psi/\partial x)\delta x + (\partial\psi/\partial y)\delta y$$

$$= 0 \text{ for a stream line, since then } \psi \text{ is constant.}$$

Thus

$$(\mathrm{d}y/\mathrm{d}x)_{\psi \, const} = -(\partial\psi/\partial x)(\partial\psi/\partial y)$$

$$= (\partial\phi/\partial y)(\partial\phi/\partial x) = -(\mathrm{d}x/\mathrm{d}y)_{\phi \, const}$$

since

$$\delta\phi = (\partial\phi/\partial x)\delta x + (\partial\phi/\partial y)\delta y$$

$$= 0 \text{ along equipotential lines, where } \phi \text{ is a constant.}$$

Hence equi-velocity potential lines are perpendicular to stream lines. This would be expected because ϕ and ψ are conjugate functions. They can be very useful in fluid flow analysis, but their immediate application here is to an examination of waves on liquids.

4.6. Waves on Liquid Surfaces

The presence of waves on liquids implies varying amounts of curvature over the liquid surfaces. There is a pressure difference δp between the opposite sides of the surface because of the surface tension T according to

$$\rightarrow \delta p = T(1/R_1 + 1/R_2) \tag{4.21}$$

where R_1 and R_2 are the principal radii of curvature of the surface measured on the same side, the pressure being greater on the concave side. For simplicity, plane waves travelling parallel to the x axis are considered, so that a two-dimensional xy graph represents a cross-section of the waves for any value of z; the liquid surface would have a similar appearance to a sheet of corrugated iron. Then only one radius is required and is

$$- [1 + (\partial s/\partial x)^2]^{3/2} \Big/ \frac{\partial^2 s}{\partial x^2}$$

which equals $-1/\partial^2 s/\partial x^2$ for small amplitude waves, s being the instantaneous displacement perpendicular to the x axis of any particle on the surface.

Waves travelling only in one direction without a change of form can be brought to rest by impressing on the whole mass of liquid a velocity equal and opposite to that of the waves[3]. The forces acting on any particle are the same as before the system of waves was brought to rest, and a simple form of Bernoulli's theorem may be applied to the surface, which is a stream line.

The fluid motion can be assumed to be irrotational. Any vortices formed in the liquid near the boundaries imposed by the walls of a container necessarily remain near the boundaries instead of being carried elsewhere in the liquid, because the stream velocity is periodically reversed. The vortices may each oscillate over a small distance, which probably accounts for the corrugations seen on sandy beaches.

Equation (4.20) here takes the form

$$\phi + j\psi = -c(x+jy) - jP \exp[jk(x+jy)] + jQ \exp[-jk(x+jy)]$$

c being the wave velocity as before, P and Q constants, and k the wave constant $2\pi/\lambda$; where λ is the wavelength. Thus

$$\phi = -cx + [Q \exp(ky) + P \exp(-ky)] \sin kx \qquad (4.22)$$

$$\psi = -cy + [Q \exp(ky) - P \exp(-ky)] \cos kx. \qquad (4.23)$$

Suppose $y = 0$ at the undisturbed level of the free surface. ky then never exceeds ka, where a is the displacement amplitude of the waves. If ka is assumed to be very much smaller than unity, ψ is zero for the surface. From *Equation (4.23)*

$$y = (1/c)(Q-P) \cos kx \qquad (4.24)$$

since $\exp(ky) \simeq \exp(-ky) \simeq 1$ at the free surface, and

$$a = (Q-P)/c$$

We also assume that the bottom of the liquid, where y is $-h$, is a stream line so that there ψ is a constant and $\partial\psi/\partial x$ is zero. From *Equation (4.23)*

$$\partial\psi/\partial x = -k[Q \exp{(ky)} - P \exp{(-ky)}] \sin{kx}$$

which is zero at the bottom and since $\sin kx$ is not generally zero

$$Q \exp{(kh)} - P \exp{(-kh)} = 0. \qquad (4.25)$$

Bernoulli's theorem may be written

$$\delta p/\rho + gy + \tfrac{1}{2}V^2 = \text{a constant} \qquad (4.26)$$

and here $\mathbf{V} = \mathbf{u} + \mathbf{v} = -\hat{\mathbf{i}}\partial\phi/\partial x - \hat{\mathbf{j}}\partial\phi/\partial y$, from *Equation (4.14)*. Thus

$$\mathbf{V}^2 = (\hat{\mathbf{i}}\partial\phi/\partial x + \hat{\mathbf{j}}\partial\phi/\partial y)\cdot(\hat{\mathbf{i}}\partial\phi/\partial x + \hat{\mathbf{j}}\partial\phi/\partial y)$$
$$= (\partial\phi/\partial x)^2 + (\partial\phi/\partial y)^2$$

since $\hat{\mathbf{i}}.\hat{\mathbf{i}} = \hat{\mathbf{j}}.\hat{\mathbf{j}} = 1$ and $\hat{\mathbf{i}}.\hat{\mathbf{j}} = \hat{\mathbf{j}}.\hat{\mathbf{i}} = 0$. Alternatively $\mathbf{V}$ is the resultant of two perpendicular velocities so that

$$V^2 = u^2 + v^2 = (\partial\phi/\partial x)^2 + (\partial\phi/\partial y)^2.$$

From *Equation (4.21)* and the comments following

$$\delta p = -T\partial^2 s/\partial x^2.$$

From *Equation (4.24)*

$$y = (1/c)(Q - P) \cos kx = s$$

because *Equation (4.24)* refers to the surface. Hence

$$\partial^2 s/\partial x^2 = -(k^2/c)(Q - P) \cos kx$$

and *Equation (4.26)* becomes

$$(Tk^2/\rho c)(Q - P) \cos kx + (g/c)(Q - P) \cos kx$$

$$+ \tfrac{1}{2}\{[c + k(Q + P) \cos kx]^2 + k^2(Q - P)^2 \sin^2 kx\} = \text{a constant}$$

because

$$\partial\phi/\partial x = -c + k(Q + P) \cos kx$$

and

$$\partial\phi/\partial y = k(Q - P) \sin kx$$

from *Equation (4.22)*, at the free surface since again exp (ky) $\simeq$ exp $(-ky) \simeq 1$. Thus we now have

$(Tk^2/\rho c)(Q-P) \cos kx + (g/c)(Q-P) \cos kx$

$$+ \tfrac{1}{2}c^2 + ck(Q+P) \cos kx = \text{a constant}$$

since terms of the order of k^2P^2 or k^2Q^2 may be neglected in comparison with ckP or ckQ. The ratio of such terms is, according to *Equation (4.24)*, of the order of ka which is assumed to be very small. Equating the coefficients of cos kx gives

$$Tk/\rho + g/k = -c^2(Q+P)/(Q-P)$$

and from *Equation (4.25)* $Q = P$ exp $(-2kh)$. Hence

$(Q+P)/(Q-P) = P[\exp(-2kh)+1]/P[\exp(-2kh)-1]$

$$= [\exp(-kh)+\exp(kh)]/[\exp(-kh)-\exp(kh)] = -\coth kh.$$

Thus

$$c^2 = (Tk/\rho + g/k) \tanh kh. \tag{4.27}$$

If h is large compared with λ, kh is very much greater than unity and tanh kh is nearly unity. Then

$$c^2 = Tk/\rho + g/k$$

or

$$c^2 = 2\pi T/\lambda\rho + g\lambda/2\pi \tag{4.28}$$

which has a minimum value if $k_{min}^2 = \rho g/T$ or $\lambda_{min}^2 = 4\pi^2 T/\rho g$. For water λ_{min} is about 1·7 cm and c_{min} is 27 cm sec^{-1}. Kelvin suggested that waves of length less than λ_{min} should be called *ripples*. For such waves, surface tension T is largely the controlling force and a measurement of λ may be used to find T experimentally since

$$c^2 \simeq 2\pi T/\lambda\rho \tag{4.29}$$

if λ is small. These waves are appreciably damped because of the viscosity of the liquid, which cannot easily be allowed for in the preceding analysis.

For wavelengths greater than λ_{min}, but still small compared with the depth of the liquid, the gravitational intensity g preponderates and

$$c^2 = g\lambda/2\pi. \tag{4.30}$$

The length of such *gravity waves* ranges from a few centimetres, when a stone is dropped into water, to hundreds of metres—ocean rollers and 'swell' at sea. Viscosity usually has a very small effect on these waves. The orbits of the liquid particles are roughly circles which become smaller as the bottom is approached.

If the depth of the liquid is small compared with the wavelength, tanh kh is nearly kh and *Equation (4.27)* becomes

$$c^2 = Tk^2h/\rho + gh$$

or

$$c^2 = 4\pi^2Th/\lambda^2\rho + gh. \qquad (4.31)$$

The first term is usually negligible, as the curvature of the free surface is generally sufficiently small to eliminate the effect of surface tension. Thus the wave velocity is almost independent of wavelength and is determined by the depth of the liquid, as in tidal waves, when the effective wavelength may be thousands of miles, and in waves in canals, straits and estuaries if these are shallow. The orbits of the liquid particles are ellipses which become increasingly flattened vertically as the bottom is approached.

The liquid particles move with the wave at crests, and in the opposite sense at troughs[4]. Thus if a wave is moving in a positive x direction, the orbits are traced clockwise. If circular orbits are assumed to be followed, a simple analysis can be devised which leads to *Equation (4.28)*.

Figure 4.6 represents a section of the liquid at the surface in a vertical plane parallel to the direction of the wave velocity c. The

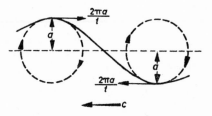

Figure 4.6. Section of waves on liquid

circles shown, of radii a, are traced by the liquid particles in clockwise senses in time t. We assume that t is also the time required for the wave to move through a distance λ, the wavelength. The wave system is brought to rest by imposing on it a velocity c, shown in

Figure 4.6, in the opposite sense to the wave velocity. Then at a crest, the instantaneous horizontal particle velocity v_1 is given by

$$v_1 = c - 2\pi a/t \qquad (4.32)$$

while at a trough

$$v_2 = c + 2\pi a/t. \qquad (4.33)$$

The particle motion can be thought to be similar to that of a mass sliding on a vertical ring, frictional forces being negligible. Accordingly the change in particle velocity may be imagined to be due to the particle dropping through a distance $2a$ under the action of gravity. Thus

$$v_2^2 = v_1^2 + 4ga$$

or

$$4ga = v_2^2 - v_1^2.$$

An application of Bernoulli's theorem leads to the same equation. From *Equations (4.32)* and *(4.33)*

$$v_2^2 - v_1^2 = 8\pi ac/t$$

and

$$t = \lambda/c.$$

Thus

$$c^2 = g\lambda/2\pi$$

which agrees with *Equation (4.30)*.

The effect of surface tension is easily incorporated. For sinusoidal surface waves

$$y = s = a \sin (2\pi x/\lambda)$$

and as before the curvature is approximately $-\partial^2 s/\partial x^2$ which thus equals $4\pi^2 s/\lambda^2$. Hence the surface pressure excess is $4\pi^2 Ts/\lambda^2$ and the difference of pressure from crest ($s = +a$) to trough ($s = -a$) is $8\pi^2 Ta/\lambda^2$. Bernoulli's equation is then

$$2a + 8\pi^2 Ta/g\lambda^2\rho = (1/2g)(v_2^2 - v_1^2) = 4\pi ac^2/\lambda g$$

which gives

$$c^2 = 2\pi T/\lambda\rho + g\lambda/2\pi$$

in accordance with *Equation (4.28)*.

4.7. Spherical Waves

In section **4.4.** a solution of the general one-dimensional wave equation *(4.6)* has been examined. Spherical waves can also be expressed in terms of a one-dimensional equation because symmetry can be assumed, although the motion is essentially three-dimensional.

S, shown in *Figure 4.7* is a source of spherical waves, for example a pulsating sphere. AA' and BB' are portions of two concentric spheres, radii r and $r+\delta r$, defined by a cone having its vertex at S. The areas of these portions are in the ratio $(r+\delta r)^2/r^2$ which is nearly $(1+2\delta r/r)$ so that the areas are almost equal if δr is small in comparison with r, and the lines BS and B'S can be supposed to be nearly

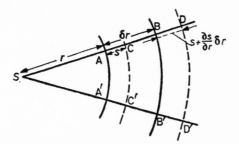

Figures 4.7. Element of medium. Spherical waves

parallel. *Figure 4.7* is then effectively the same as *Figure 4.2* even though the spherical portions AA', BB', .. replace the planes AA', BB', .. The curvature has no effect for resultant forces equivalent to F and $F+(\partial F/\partial x)\delta x$ acting on AA' and BB' can be found.

Accordingly a treatment may be developed as in section **4.2.** which leads to a form of *Equation (4.2a)*

$$\rho_0 \partial^2 s/\partial t^2 = -\partial P/\partial r \qquad (4.34)$$

where r replaces x and P, which is F/A, is the pressure at the surface of radius r. The analysis differs when P is written in terms of the elastic modulus of the medium, because allowance must be made for the curvature of the surfaces.

The undisplaced total volume of medium contained between the two spheres is $4\pi r^2 \delta r$ and the displaced total volume is nearly

$$4\pi(r+s)^2[\delta r+(\partial s/\partial r)\delta r].$$

Hence the change in volume is

$$4\pi r^2 \delta r(\partial s/\partial r+2s/r)$$

and is negative for a pressure increase. The volume strain is thus

$$-4\pi r^2 \delta r(\partial s/\partial r+2s/r)/4\pi r^2 \delta r$$

91

so that the modulus κ is given by

$$\kappa = -P/(\partial s/\partial r + 2s/r)$$

or

$$P = -\kappa(\partial s)\partial r + 2s/r).$$

Hence, substituting for P in *Equation (4.34)*

$$\rho_0 \partial^2 s/\partial t^2 = \kappa \frac{\partial}{\partial r}(\partial s/\partial r + 2s/r)$$

or

$$\partial^2 s/\partial t^2 = c^2[\partial^2 s/\partial r^2 + (2/r)\partial s/\partial r - 2s/r^2] \qquad (4.35)$$

where $c^2 = \kappa/\rho_0$. Both s and r must be differentiated in the preceding equation, because s varies with r. A solution of *Equation (4.35)* is

$$s = (1/r^2)f_1(ct-r) + (1/r)f_1'(ct-r) + (1/r^2)f_2(ct+r)$$
$$+ (1/r)f_2'(ct+r) \qquad (4.36)$$

where f_1' and f_2' are the first derivatives of f_1 and f_2 with respect to t or r, f_1 and f_2 being the two required arbitrary functions. The first pair of terms in *(4.36)* represent a wave diverging from the source and the second pair a wave converging on the source, both travelling with velocity c. Neither wave extends to the source, where r is zero, for the preceding analysis is clearly not then valid. The size of the source becomes important for waves near the source and cannot be allowed for in the simple analysis.

Equation (4.35) is, in terms of velocity potential ϕ

$$\partial^2 \phi/\partial t^2 = c^2[\partial^2 \phi/\partial r^2 + (2/r)\partial \phi/\partial r]$$

or

$$\partial^2 (r\phi)/\partial t^2 = c^2 \partial^2 (r\phi)/\partial r^2 \qquad (4.37)$$

which can be shown to give the same result for s if its solution is written as

$$r\phi = cf_1'(ct-r) + cf_2'(ct+r) \qquad (4.38)$$

since $\partial s/\partial t = u = -\partial \phi/\partial r$ from *Equation (4.14)* and

$$u = (c/r^2)f_1'(ct-r) + (c/r)f_1''(ct-r)$$
$$+ (c/r^2)f_2'(ct+r) + (c/r)f_2''(ct+r). \qquad (4.39)$$

If r is large

$$u \simeq (c/r)[f_1''(ct-r) + f_2''(ct+r)].$$

Thus u is inversely proportional to r, and the kinetic energy of the wave, which is directly proportional to the square of u, follows an inverse square law variation as it is transmitted. Nearer the source both $1/r$ and $1/r^2$ become appreciably different from zero, and an inverse square law variation of kinetic energy would appear not to be followed. The terms having $1/r^2$ as a coefficient do not, however, correspond to energy transfer because they effectively differ by $\pi/2$ in phase angle from the instantaneous pressure P, which equals $\rho_0 \partial \phi / \partial t$, and is thus directly proportional to $f_1''\ (ct-r) + f_2''(ct+r)$ from *Equation (4.38)*. Such a component of the kinetic energy could be imagined to be analogous with the reactive power in an electrical circuit.

Although the amplitudes of spherical waves alter as they travel because of the coefficients containing r, that is because the waves are diverging or converging, the wave shape is not changed. This is a property of waves which move in an odd number of dimensions, in contrast with cylindrical waves which change form as they progress in two dimensions.

References

[1] W. F. HERZFELD and F. O. RICE *Phys. Rev.* **31**, 691, 1928.

[2] G. TEMPLE *'An Introduction to Fluid Dynamics'*: Oxford University Press, p. 10, 1958.

[3] RAYLEIGH *Phil. Mag.* Series 5, **1**, 257, 1876.

[4] L. M. MILNE-THOMSON *'Theoretical Hydrodynamics'*: Macmillan, p. 356, 1949.

MODES OF VIBRATION

5.1. Stationary Waves. Modes of Vibration

In section **4.4.** a solution of the equation

$$\partial^2 s/\partial t^2 = c^2 \partial^2 s/\partial x^2 \tag{4.6}$$

in terms of two functions has been suggested and examined. The two functions were shown to represent disturbances travelling in opposite senses with the same speed c. Particular forms of these functions are now considered.

By substitution, the following may be shown to be a solution of *Equation (4.6)*

$$s = a_1 \sin\left[2\pi(t/T - x/\lambda)\right] + a_2 \sin\left[2\pi(t/T + x/\lambda)\right]$$
$$+ b_1 \cos\left[2\pi(t/T - x/\lambda)\right] + b_2 \cos\left[2\pi(t/T + x/\lambda)\right]$$

where a_1, a_2, b_1 and b_2 are arbitrary constants. Each of the terms represents a *harmonic wave* travelling in the positive or negative x direction, depending on whether the sign is negative or positive. The period T of the wave is the time taken for one complete wave to pass any point on the x axis. During this time the wave travels a distance λ, the wavelength. Hence the wave velocity c is λ/T. The frequency f is the number of waves passing a fixed point in unit time, so that f equals $1/T$ and c is $f\lambda$. The variables are arranged in the same way as in the functions f_1 and f_2 occurring in section **4.4.** because

$$2\pi(t/T - x/\lambda) = (2\pi/\lambda)(ct - x)$$

and

$$2\pi(t/T + x/\lambda) = (2\pi/\lambda)(ct + x)$$

$2\pi/\lambda$ being a constant usually called the *wave constant*. $1/\lambda$ is the *wave number*, the number of waves in unit length.

Another convenient form of solution of *(4.6)* is the exponential

$$s = A \exp\left[2\pi j(t/T - x/\lambda)\right] + B \exp\left[2\pi j(t/T + x/\lambda)\right]$$

or

$$s = A \exp\left[2\pi j(ct - x)/\lambda\right] + B \exp\left[2\pi j(ct + x)/\lambda\right]$$

where A and B are constants and j is $+\sqrt{(-1)}$. Both the terms can be expanded to give sine and cosine terms, the choice depending on whether s is required to be real or imaginary. Usually the real part is required and an analysis can often be facilitated by using the exponential form from which the real part is obtained at the end, instead of using a sine or cosine function throughout.

The exponential function can be expanded to give a product of a sinusoidal function of t and a similar one of x. For example, if
$s = A \exp [2\pi j(ct-x)/\lambda]$

$$s = A[\exp (2\pi jct/\lambda)] \exp (-2\pi jx/\lambda).$$

The wave equation (4.6) can then be easily written solely in terms of x or t. The equation in terms of x is very useful, in that it can be used to find the space part of the displacement and is frequently used in determining modes of vibration. In terms of t the equation represents a displacement variation with time at any particular point along the x axis, so that it is then effectively a vibration equation akin to (1.1) and similar equations.

If the nature of s is not known from a previous result or examination, the most general assumption is that s is complex. Then s is usually written in the exponential form, as with Schrödinger's wave function ψ. The advantage is that ψ is then composed of two independent quantities p and q which define the state of the wave at any point, as in light and sound waves when the quantities are the electric and magnetic vectors and particle displacement and velocity, for example. We have, if ψ is complex, $\psi = p+jq$ and $\psi^* = p-jq$ so that

$$|\psi|^2 = \psi\psi^* = p^2+q^2$$

where ψ^* is the conjugate of ψ. Another advantage is that $|\psi|^2$ can then be given a physical meaning, because it can then be made independent of time t. For example, it can be equated to the number of particles per unit volume or to the probability of finding a particle at the point where the value of ψ is known. If ψ is complex we might have

$$\psi = A \exp [2\pi j(ct-x)/\lambda]$$

or

$$\psi = A \cos [2\pi(ct-x)/\lambda]+jA \sin [2\pi(ct-x)/\lambda]$$

so that

$$p = A \cos [2\pi(ct-x)/\lambda]$$

$$q = A \sin [2\pi(ct-x)/\lambda]$$

and

$$|\psi|^2 = p^2+q^2 = A^2.$$

If ψ were not complex we might put

$$\psi = A \sin \left[2\pi(ct-x)/\lambda\right]$$

so that

$$\psi^2 = A^2 \sin^2 \left[2\pi(ct-x)/\lambda\right].$$

Then ψ^2 varies from zero to A^2 with time and cannot be given a physical interpretation which is of use in wave mechanics.

The sine and cosine form of solution of *Equation (4.6)* is

$$s = a_1 \sin \left[2\pi(t/T-x/\lambda)\right] + a_2 \sin \left[2\pi(t/T+x/\lambda)\right]$$
$$+ b_1 \cos \left[2\pi(t/T-x/\lambda)\right] + b_2 \cos \left[2\pi(t/T+x/\lambda)\right]$$

and if there is no displacement at $x = 0$ we get

$$0 = (a_1+a_2) \sin 2\pi t/T + (b_1+b_2) \cos 2\pi t/T$$

which gives, if there is never any displacement

$$a_1+a_2 = 0 \text{ and } b_1+b_2 = 0$$

or

$$a_2 = -a_1 \text{ and } b_2 = -b_1.$$

Thus for there to be no resultant displacement at $x = 0$ at any time, the similar wave components travelling in opposite senses must be completely out of phase and we now have

$$s = a_1\{\sin \left[2\pi(t/T-x/\lambda)\right] - \sin \left[2\pi(t/T+x/\lambda)\right]\}$$
$$+ b_1\{\cos \left[2\pi(t/T-x/\lambda)\right] - \cos \left[2\pi(t/T+x/\lambda)\right]\}$$

or

$$s = 2(b_1 \sin 2\pi t/T - a_1 \cos 2\pi t/T) \sin 2\pi x/\lambda.$$

If there is also no displacement at $x = L$ at all times

$$\sin 2\pi L/\lambda = 0$$

or

$$2\pi L/\lambda_n = n\pi$$

where n is a positive integer, which gives

$$L = n\lambda_n/2. \qquad (5.1)$$

Thus for the prescribed conditions at $x = 0$ and $x = L$ only particular vibrational frequencies are possible. They are given by

$$f_n = nc/2L \qquad (5.2)$$

since

$$f = c/\lambda.$$

The *modes of vibration* are thus defined and, in the absence of any further restrictions, all the frequencies specified by *Equation (5.2)* will be present in the composite vibration. The frequencies bear an integral ratio to the lowest one, and are thus *harmonics*.

The total instantaneous displacement is

$$s = \sum_{n=1}^{\infty} [(A_n \cos 2\pi t/T_n + B_n \sin 2\pi t/T_n) \sin 2\pi x/\lambda_n] \qquad (5.3)$$

where $A_n = -2a_n$ and $B_n = 2b_n$. The vibration corresponding to the nth harmonic is given by

$$s_n = (A_n \cos 2\pi t/T_n + B_n \sin 2\pi t/T_n) \sin 2\pi x/\lambda_n$$

and s_n is zero at all times for values of x such that

$$\sin 2\pi x/\lambda_n = 0$$

or

$$2\pi x/\lambda_n = m\pi$$

where $m = 0, 1, 2, \ldots . n$. Thus

$$nx/L = m \qquad (5.4)$$

since $\lambda_n = 2L/n$ from *Equation (5.1)*. $m = 0$ and $m = n$ correspond to the conditions that $s = 0$ at $x = 0$ and at $x = L$. These, and the $(n-1)$ points in between are called *nodes*. At them, waves travelling in one direction are completely cancelled by waves travelling in the opposite sense. Because they are fixed points the composite wave is called *standing* or *stationary*. The distance between nodes for the nth mode of vibration is L/n which equals $\lambda_n/2$. Thus a measurement of the nodal separation gives λ_n and if the wave frequency is known the wave velocity may be found as in, for example, Melde's experiment, Kundt's tube, experiments with Lecher wires and so on. Midway between the nodes are points at which maximum displacement occurs periodically. These are called *antinodes* or *loops*. That points are nodes for a particular physical quantity does not imply that they are nodes or even antinodes for any other quantity. For example, a particle displacement node in a resonance tube usually corresponds to a pressure antinode, while a current node on transmission lines may correspond to a potential antinode.

5.2. Initial Conditions

Equation (5.3) is

$$s = \sum_{n=1}^{\infty} [(A_n \cos 2\pi t/T_n + B_n \sin 2\pi t/T_n) \sin 2\pi x/\lambda_n]$$

97

where s is the total instantaneous displacement. A_n and B_n can be determined from a knowledge of particle displacements and velocities between $x = 0$ and $x = L$ at $t = 0$. Hence the amplitude a_n of the nth mode of vibration can be found since

$$a_n = \sqrt{(A_n^2 + B_n^2)}$$

Equation (5.3) gives the displacement at all times. In particular, at $t = 0$

$$s_0 = \sum_{n=1}^{\infty} (A_n \sin 2\pi x/\lambda_n) \qquad (5.5)$$

and

$$\dot{s}_0 = \sum_{n=1}^{\infty} [B_n(2\pi/T_n) \sin 2\pi x/\lambda_n] \qquad (5.6)$$

where $\dot{s}_0$ is the value of ds/dt at $t = 0$. s_0 and $\dot{s}_0$ can both be expressed as parts of Fourier series which are infinite and convergent, and integrals giving A_n and B_n can be found.

For simplicity there is assumed to be no motion at $x = 0$ and at $x = \pi$ at any time, and no motion anywhere at $t = 0$, but particles may be displaced. B_n is thus zero, and *Equation (5.3)* becomes

$$s = \sum_{n=1}^{\infty} [A_n(\sin 2\pi x/\lambda_n) \cos 2\pi t/T_n]. \qquad (5.7)$$

From *Equation (5.1)* $\lambda_n = 2L/n$ and here L is replaced by π, so that $\lambda_n = 2\pi/n$. From *Equation (5.2)* $f_n = nc/2L = 1/T_n$. Thus $T_n = 2\pi/nc$ and *Equation (5.7)* becomes

$$s = \sum_{n=1}^{\infty} [A_n(\sin nx) \cos nct] \qquad (5.8)$$

n having the dimension $\mathbf{L}^{-1}$.

Let s_0 be the value of s at $t = 0$. Then, from *Equation (5.8)*

$$s_0 = A_1 \sin x + A_2 \sin 2x + A_3 \sin 3x + \dots$$

Multiplying both sides by $\sin nx$ and integrating between the limits 0 and π gives

$$\int_0^\pi s_0 \sin nx \, dx = A_1 \int_0^\pi (\sin x) \sin nx \, dx + A_2 \int_0^\pi (\sin 2x) \sin nx \, dx +$$

The term containing A_n is

$$A_n \int_0^\pi \sin^2 nx \; dx$$

which equals

$$\tfrac{1}{2}A_n \int_0^\pi (1-\cos 2nx)dx = \tfrac{1}{2}A_n\left[x-(1/2n)\sin 2nx\right]_0^\pi = \tfrac{1}{2}\pi A_n.$$

The term involving any other coefficient A_r is

$$\tfrac{1}{2}A_r \int_0^\pi (\sin rx) \sin nxdx = \tfrac{1}{2}A_r \int_0^\pi [\cos (n-r)x - \cos (n+r)x]dx$$

$$= \tfrac{1}{2}A_r\left\{[1/(n-r)] \sin (n-r)x - [1/(n+r)] \sin (n+r)x\right\}_0^\pi = 0.$$

Thus all the terms vanish except the one containing A_n so that

$$\int_0^\pi s_0 \sin nx \; dx = \tfrac{1}{2}\pi A_n$$

or

$$A_n = (2/\pi)\int_0^\pi s_0 \sin nx \; dx \qquad (5.9)$$

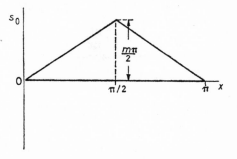

Figure 5.1. Initial displacement of a string

5.3. Static Linear Initial Displacement

The initial particle displacement is assumed to be as shown in *Figure 5.1*. The displacement is static in that all the particles are at rest at

$t = 0$ and linear because s_0 is given by linear functions of x which are

$$s_0 = mx \text{ for } 0 \leqslant x \leqslant \pi/2$$

and

$$s_0 = m(\pi - x) \text{ for } \pi/2 \leqslant x \leqslant \pi.$$

The gradient m determines the amplitude of the initial vibrations. Using *Equation* (5.9) we get

$$\tfrac{1}{2}A_n\pi = \int_0^{\pi/2} mx \sin nx \, dx + \int_{\pi/2}^{\pi} m(\pi - x) \sin nx \, dx$$

$$= (m/n^2)\Big(\sin nx - nx \cos nx\Big)_0^{\pi/2}$$

$$- (m/n)\Big[\pi \cos nx + (\sin nx - nx \cos nx)/n\Big]_{\pi/2}^{\pi}$$

$$= (2 \sin \tfrac{1}{2}n\pi - \sin n\pi)m/n^2.$$

Thus

$$A_n = (2m/\pi n^2)(2 \sin \tfrac{1}{2}n\pi - \sin n\pi).$$

n may be odd or even.

n odd

$$A_n = (2m/\pi n^2)[2(\pm 1) - 0] = \pm 4m/\pi n^2.$$

The plus sign applies when $n = 4r - 3$ while the minus sign holds when $n = 4r - 1$, r being any positive integer.

n even

$$A_n = 0. \text{ Thus } A_2 = A_4 = A_6 = \ldots = 0.$$

Hence, from *Equation* (5.8)

$$s = (4m/\pi)[\sin x \cos ct - (1/9) \sin 3x \cos 3ct$$

$$+ (1/25) \sin 5x \cos 5ct - \ldots]$$

or

$$s = (4m/\pi) \sum_{q=1}^{\infty} [(-1)^{\frac{1}{2}(q-1)}(1/q^2) \sin qx \cos qct] \qquad (5.10)$$

where q is an odd integer. For a length L instead of π, q becomes $q\pi/L$ while $4m/\pi$ is changed to $4m/L$ so that

$$s = (4mL/\pi^2) \sum_{q=1}^{\infty} [(-1)^{\frac{1}{2}(q-1)}(1/q^2) \sin (q\pi x/L) \cos (q\pi ct/L)]. \quad (5.11)$$

Thus for the initial displacement shown in *Figure 5.1* only the odd harmonics appear in the composite vibration. The even harmonics all have a node at the centre where there is initially an antinode, so the preceding example illustrates Young's law: overtones which have a node where there is initially an antinode are missing from the resultant vibration. The law holds when vibrations on a string are generated by other means such as bowing or striking. In a pianoforte the strings are struck at close approximations to points lying between one seventh and one ninth the length of each string from one end, their positions being determined empirically. The explanation usually given is that objectionable harmonics are then missing from the composite vibrations in accordance with Young's law. The seventh, ninth or other high frequency harmonics could hardly be said to be objectionable over the whole of the frequency range of a pianoforte, and in any event their amplitudes would be very small in comparison with those of their fundamentals. George and Beckett[1] and later Kock[2] have shown that when the striking point is located as mentioned, the energy transfer from the hammer to the string is greatest. This, and not the omission of harmonics, is of paramount importance.

The preceding analysis applies to the transverse vibration of a string fixed at both ends, longitudinal vibrations in a bar or column of fluid having rigid or free ends, electro-magnetic oscillations on transmission lines having open or connected ends, and any other system where an equation like (*4.6*) holds. Because of the high harmonic content, the composite vibration is far from sinusoidal. *Figures 5.2* and *5.3* are displacement–time graphs of points on plucked strings and show clearly the non-sinusoidal vibrations which, because of energy loss, gradually approach sinusoidal form. The amplitudes of the high frequency harmonics become negligible in comparison with those of the low frequency components after a sufficient time has elapsed.

The analysis illustrates the application of a Fourier series to the determination of the amplitudes of harmonics. s_0, from *Equation* (*5.8*), is given by a Fourier sine series which is valid over the interval 0 to π if s_0, which is a function of x, is not infinite, is single valued and contains a finite number of discontinuities, maxima and minima. These, the *Dirichlet conditions*, are necessarily obeyed because of the limitations imposed by the medium on, or in, which the vibrations occur. The half range 0 to π is in the preceding analysis more convenient than the widely used full range 0 to 2π.

B_n has been assumed to be zero, but is not if there is an initial particle velocity distribution. It can be found independently of A_n and is given by

$$B_n = (2/nc\pi)\int_0^\pi \dot{s}_0 \sin nx \, dx \qquad (5.12)$$

or, writing A_n and B_n in terms of L:

$$A_n = (2/L)\int_0^L s_0 \sin (n\pi x/L) \, dx \qquad (5.13)$$

$$B_n = (2/nc\pi)\int_0^L \dot{s}_0 \sin (n\pi x/L) \, dx \qquad (5.14)$$

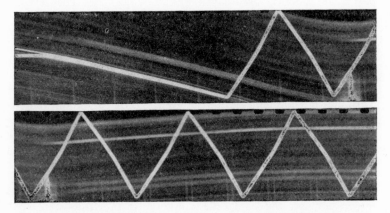

Figure 5.2. Plucked string. Plucking and observation points at L/2

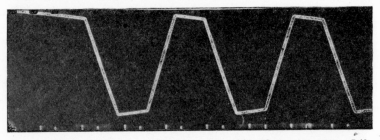

Figure 5.3. Plucked string. Plucking point at L/4. Observation point at L/2

5.4. Vibrational Modes of Strings, Fluid Column and Rods

The modes of vibration (eigentones) of a finite portion of medium can be determined as shown in section 5.1. from a knowledge of end

102

conditions, which generally approximate to nodes or antinodes. The amplitudes of the various modal vibrations depend on the initial conditions and can be found as shown in the two preceding sections. While there is no simple method of determining amplitudes, the possible modes can be found diagrammatically.

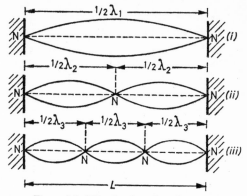

Figure 5.4. Vibrational modes of a string

Figure 5.4 shows the first few modes of vibration of a string fixed at both ends. (*i*) is the first mode, for which $L = \lambda_1/2$. For the second mode (*ii*) $L = \lambda_2$ and for the third (*iii*) $L = 3\lambda_2/2$. Generally $L = n\lambda_n/2$, which agrees with *Equation (5.1)*.

The modes of vibration for longitudinal waves in rods or columns of fluid can be similarly depicted. Although the instantaneous particle displacement *s* has then to be measured along the *x* axis, for graphical purposes *s* may be plotted perpendicularly to the *x* axis by taking the

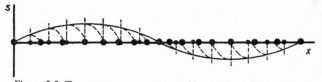

Figure 5.5. Transverse representation of longitudinal displacements

equilibrium positions of the particles as centres, the displacements as radii, and drawing arcs to cut the perpendiculars passing through the equilibrium positions. Such a construction is shown in *Figure 5.5*. Thus *Figure 5.4* also applies to vibrations in bars or fluid columns rigid at both ends. If they are free at both ends *Figure 5.4* still applies, because then the nodes N become replaced by antinodes A.

For a rod or fluid column rigidly fixed at one end and free at the other, the first few modes are indicated in *Figure 5.6*. For the first mode (*i*) $L = \lambda_1/4$. For the second mode (*ii*) $L = 3\lambda_2/4$ and for the third mode (*iii*) $L = 5\lambda_3/4$. Generally, for the nth mode

$$L = (2n-1)\lambda_n/4. \tag{5.15}$$

In all the preceding work L is the *effective length* of the string, bar or fluid column, because practically nodes or antinodes are not located precisely at the ends of the primary vibrating medium. They are usually slightly beyond the ends. Thus for gas columns an anti-

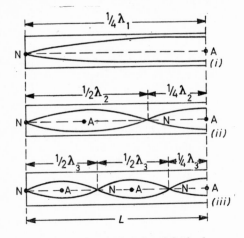

Figure 5.6. Vibrational modes of fluid column with one free end

node is roughly $0 \cdot 6R$ beyond the end of the tube, R being its radius, providing that λ_n is large compared with R. This *end correction* depends on λ, so that the overtones are only approximate harmonics. The correction is not accurately calculable for the open end of an ordinary tube, but has been found for one joining an infinite flange and for bell-shaped mouths. For one of hyperbolic form, the radius of the wider end being $R\sqrt(2)$, the end correction is zero according to Helmholtz.

There is also a correction at a fixed or closed end, because of the lack of complete rigidity of the plug, clamp or bridge. For a steel wire 336 cm long, 0·036 cm in diameter and loaded with nearly 16kg the total effective increase in length due to yielding clamps was found to be 1·65 per cent. The upper clamp was of mass 194 g and was bolted to a steel joist supporting the floor in a room above, so the inertia was very small but the stiffness was large. The lower clamp was bolted to a large lead block of mass about 50 kg which was fixed to a brick and concrete pillar keyed to the wall of the room. This clamp was hence very massive and rigid but, together with the upper clamp, still produced a significant increase in effective length. The yielding bridges in stringed musical instruments have an appreciable effect on the vibrations, especially as one of them is attached to a sound-board or to one side of a resonating chamber.

5.5. Vibrational Modes of Membranes

Figure 5.7 indicates a homogeneous rectangular membrane or very thin plate clamped at the edges, which are of length X and Y. The velocity of transverse waves is constant over all the membrane and is $\sqrt{(T/\sigma)}$ according to the reasoning in section **4.1**. T is the tension per unit length in the membrane, assumed constant, and σ is the mass per unit area.

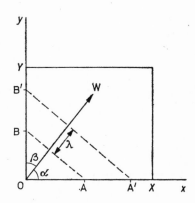

Figure 5.7. Waves on a rectangular membrane

Suppose a wave is travelling along OW. AB and A'B' are two adjacent positions of the wave in the same phase, for example a crest or a trough, so that the distance between them along OW is λ. For a standing wave in the Ox direction AA' is the effective wavelength, hence, from *Equation (5.1)*

$$X = \tfrac{1}{2}p\mathrm{AA}'$$

or

$$p = 2X/\mathrm{AA}'$$

where p is a positive integer. Similarly for a stationary wave in the Oy direction

$$q = 2Y/BB'$$

where q is another positive integer. These two equations apply simultaneously for standing waves on the membrane. From *Figure 5.7* $AA' = \lambda/\cos \alpha$ and $BB' = \lambda/\cos \beta$ where

$$\cos^2\alpha + \cos^2\beta = 1$$

Thus

$$p^2\lambda^2/4X^2 + q^2\lambda^2/4Y^2 = 1$$

or

$$2/\lambda = \sqrt{(p^2/X^2 + q^2/Y^2)}$$

$$= 2f_{pq}/c.$$

Hence

$$\omega_{pq} = \pi c\sqrt{(p^2/X^2 + q^2/Y^2)}. \tag{5.16}$$

ω_{pp}, which equals $2\pi f_{pq}$, is the angular frequency at which the membrane vibrates in the p, q mode. ω_{11} is the lowest angular frequency, ω_{22} equals $2\omega_{11}$, ω_{33} is $3\omega_{11}$, . . and there are two overtones between successive harmonics. For example, between ω_{11} and ω_{22} are ω_{12} and ω_{21}. When X equals Y, ω_{pq} equals ω_{qp}, which typifies *degeneracy* if p is not equal to q. Then there are fewer possible frequencies of vibrational components in the resultant vibration. Degeneracy also occurs if X and Y are relatively rational.

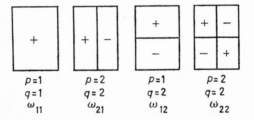

$$
\begin{array}{cccc}
p=1 & p=2 & p=1 & p=2 \\
q=1 & q=2 & q=2 & q=2 \\
\omega_{11} & \omega_{21} & \omega_{12} & \omega_{22}
\end{array}
$$

Figure 5.8. Nodal lines on a rectangular membrane

On the vibrating membrane are *nodal lines* corresponding to the various modes of vibration. Some are shown in *Figure 5.8*. In the p, q mode there are $p-1$ nodal lines in the x direction and $q-1$ in the y direction, excluding the boundaries. The plus and minus signs in *Figure 5.8* indicate the portions of the membrane that are moving in or out of phase. The parts marked $+$ could be imagined to be raised above the plane of the diagram, while those marked − would be below, the nodal lines and the edges of the membrane lying in the plane of the diagram.

A formal method of arriving at *Equation (5.16)* is to take a two-dimensional form of *Equation (4.6)*

$$\partial^2 s/\partial t^2 = c^2(\partial^2 s/\partial x^2 + \partial^2 s/\partial y^2) \qquad (5.17)$$

and to assume that s is a function of x, y and t

$$s = F(x)[G(y)] \exp -j\omega t.$$

F and G here denote different functions of x and of y. We then find

$$\partial^2 s/\partial x^2 = G(y) \exp(-j\omega t)\partial^2 F/\partial x^2$$

$$\partial^2 s/\partial y^2 = F(x) \exp(-j\omega t)\partial^2 G/\partial x^2$$

$$\partial^2 s/\partial t^2 = -\omega^2 F(x) G(y) \exp(-j\omega t).$$

The functions $F(x)$ and $G(y)$ have been abbreviated to F and G in the derivatives. Substitution in *Equation (5.17)* gives

$$G\partial^2 F/\partial x^2 + F\partial^2 G/\partial y^2 = -FG\omega^2/c^2$$

or

$$(1/F)\partial^2 F/\partial x^2 = -(1/G)(\omega^2 G/c^2 + \partial^2 G/\partial y^2)$$

abbreviations being used as before. This equation holds only if both sides are independent of x and y, that is, constant. Let them both equal $-\Omega^2/c^2$. Then

$$\partial^2 F/\partial x^2 = -(\Omega^2/c^2)F$$

and

$$\partial^2 G/\partial y^2 = -(\omega^2 - \Omega^2)G/c^2.$$

A solution of these is

$$s = A \cos(\Omega x/c - \beta_x) \cos(\tau y/c - \beta_y) \cos(\omega t - \beta)$$

where $\tau^2 = \omega^2 - \Omega^2$ and β_x, β_y and β are phase angles. If the boundary is rigidly fixed $s = 0$ at $x = 0$ and X and at $y = 0$ and Y at all times. Thus

$$\beta_x = \beta_y = \pi/2$$

$$\Omega_p X/c = p\pi \text{ or } \Omega_p = p\pi c/X$$

and

$$\tau_q Y/c = q\pi \text{ or } \tau_q = q\pi c/Y$$

where p and q are integers. Hence

$$s = A\psi_{pq} \cos (\omega_{pq}t - \beta). \tag{5.18}$$

ψ_{pq} is the *characteristic function* and is $\sin (\pi px/X) \sin (\pi qy/Y)$. We have

$$\omega_{pq}^2 = \Omega_p^2 + \tau_q^2$$

so that

$$\omega_{pq} = \pi c \sqrt{(p^2/X^2 + q^2/Y^2)}$$

which is *Equation (5.16)*.

For a circular membrane circular waves are necessarily considered, as there is no equivalent of the preceding simple analysis giving the vibrational modes of a rectangular membrane. The two-dimensional wave equation is here written in polar form

$$\frac{\partial^2 s}{\partial t^2} = c^2 \left[\left(\frac{1}{r}\right)\frac{\partial}{\partial r}\left(\frac{r\partial s}{\partial r}\right) + \left(\frac{1}{r^2}\right)\frac{\partial^2 s}{\partial \phi^2} \right] \tag{5.19}$$

and s is assumed to be given by

$$s = R(r)\Phi(\phi) \exp -j\omega t.$$

s must be a single-valued function of position, that is s as a point (r,ϕ) must equal s at $(r,\phi + 2n\pi)$. Thus s is a periodic function of ϕ. Accordingly we let $\Phi(\phi)$ equal $\cos n\phi$ or $\sin n\phi$ and $R(r)$ becomes $R_n(r)$ where n is an integer or zero. We have

$$\partial s/\partial r = \Phi (\exp -j\omega t)\partial R_n/\partial r$$

$$\partial^2 s/\partial r^2 = \Phi (\exp -j\omega t)\partial^2 R_n/\partial r^2$$

$$\partial^2 s/\partial \phi^2 = -n^2\Phi (\exp -j\omega t)R_n$$

$$\partial^2 s/\partial t^2 = -\omega^2\Phi (\exp -j\omega t)R_n$$

where Φ denotes $\cos n\phi$ or $\sin n\phi$. Substitution in *Equation (5.19)* gives

$$\partial^2 R_n/\partial r^2 + (1/r)\partial R_n/\partial r + (\omega^2/c^2 - n^2/r^2)R_n = 0.$$

A solution is

$$R_n(r) = J_n(kr)$$

where $J_n(kr)$ is a Bessel function of the first kind, mentioned in section **3.8.**, and k is the wave constant $2\pi/\lambda$ which equals ω/c. The second solution becomes very large as r approaches zero and is inadmissable here, but is applicable to forced vibrations of the membrane. Hence s is given by

$$s = AJ_n(kr) \cos n\phi \cos (\omega t + \beta)$$

or

$$s = BJ_n(kr) \sin n\phi \cos (\omega t + \beta)$$

A, B and β are constants. The first equation applies to *even* modes of vibration, the second to *odd* modes, so for any possible value of k these equations are combined in arbitrary proportions to yield

$$s = CJ_n(kr) \cos (\phi + \alpha) \cos (\omega t + \beta) \tag{5.20}$$

C and α being constants.

If the membrane is fixed at the circumference, s is zero when r equals a, the radius. Thus $J_n(ka) = 0$, which determines the allowed values of k, and hence defines the natural frequencies of vibration of the membrane. The complete solution of *Equation (5.19)* is then found by summing s for all values of n and k. For motion symmetrical about the centre, the lowest value of n is zero. The roots of $J_0(ka) = 0$ are thus required. These are

$$ka = 0 \cdot 7666\pi, \ 1 \cdot 757\pi, \ 2 \cdot 755\pi, \ \ldots$$

the corresponding angular frequencies being

$$\omega_{01} = 0 \cdot 7666\pi c/a; \ \omega_{02} = 1 \cdot 757\pi c/a; \ \omega_{03} = 2 \cdot 755\pi c/a; \ . .$$

There is a sequence of frequencies for each value of n. They are $\omega_{01}, \omega_{02}, \omega_{03}, \ldots$ corresponding to solutions of $J_0(ka) = 0$, ω_{11}, $\omega_{12}, \omega_{13}, \ldots$ corresponding to solutions of $J_1(ka) = 0$ and so on. If m is large

$$\omega_{nm} = (m + \tfrac{1}{2}n - \tfrac{1}{4})\pi c/a.$$

An examination of *Equation (5.20)* shows that there are on the vibrating membrane nodal lines where no motion occurs. These are of two kinds, concentric *nodal circles* with radii given by $J_n(kr) = 0$, of which there are theoretically a large number, and *nodal diameters* given by

$$\phi + \alpha = (2p + 1)\pi/2n$$

where p is an integer. There are n of these diameters arranged uniformly about the centre, the angle included between adjacent diameters being π/n but otherwise their positions are arbitrary. Some arrangements of nodal lines are indicated in *Figure 5.9*. Degeneracy occurs since there are two characteristic functions for each frequency

$$\text{Even} \quad \psi_{enm} = J_n(kr) \cos n\phi$$

$$\text{Odd} \quad \psi_{onm} = J_n(kr) \sin n\phi.$$

There are many overtones with no harmonic relations, although some are very nearly harmonics. In the first three octaves above the fundamental there are 44 overtones.

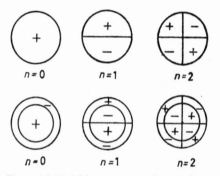

Figure 5.9 Nodal lines on a circular membrane

Vibration patterns on membranes and plates, including those shown in *Figure 5.8* and *Figure 5.9*, are called *Chladni figures* after the experimenter who originally studied them by bowing plates at suitable points after sprinkling fine sand on them. The sand collected along the nodal lines, which for plates are much more complex than they are for membranes. Such patterns have also been obtained by Robinson and Stephens on soap films, and by Waller on rectangular and circular plates, whose method of exciting the vibrations is of interest. In her method solid carbon dioxide of sufficiently high density is held in contact with the metal plate. The carbon dioxide sublimes at $-80°C$ so that, on touching the warmer metal, gas is rapidly formed at a high local pressure which sets the plate into vibration. Vibrations are maintained by the repeated contacts of the plate with the solid material. The method is effective with all good thermal conductors as far as can be ascertained. For other materials there are several electrical methods.

For vibrations in the fundamental mode, the membrane can be shown to be equivalent to a piston which produces the same sound field. In transducers, such as hydrophones and loudspeakers, the ideal vibrating element is a perfectly rigid piston. Then resonances corresponding to the large number of overtones for a circular disc will not occur. Selective reproduction of sound and the generation of spurious tones at these frequencies will be avoided, and the shape of the sound field can be predicted from a few measurements. A limit is set to the rigidity obtainable by the smallness of the vibrating mass that is usually required, but is increased by forming ribs or pleats on the diaphragm. These help further by causing the diaphragm to vibrate in a few well-defined modes whose frequencies can be made considerably different, thus spreading resonances or removing them to an unimportant part of the frequency range.

5.6. Modes of Vibrations in a Rectangular Enclosure

The sides of a rectangular enclosure, of lengths X, Y and Z, are imagined to lie along x, y and z axes, the origin being at one corner of the enclosure. A three-dimensional wave equation is now required

$$\partial^2 s/\partial t^2 = c^2 \nabla^2 s \qquad (5.21)$$

which is of the form mentioned in section **8.2.** Here c is $\sqrt{(\gamma P/\rho_0)}$ from section **4.2.**, and

$$\nabla^2 = \partial^2/\partial x^2 + \partial^2/\partial y^2 + \partial^2/\partial z^2.$$

A solution of (5.21) is

$$s = f_1(lx + my + nz - ct) + f_2(lx + my + nz + ct) \qquad (5.22)$$

where l, m and n are direction cosines. For a wave travelling in a direction making angles α, β and δ with the x, y and z axes $l = \cos \alpha$, $m = \cos \beta$ and $n = \cos \delta$. We have

$$\cos^2\alpha + \cos^2\beta + \cos^2\delta = 1$$

which is the three-dimensional counterpart of an equation in the preceding section. Hence we find that

$$2/\lambda = \sqrt{(p^2/X^2 + q^2/Y^2 + r^2/Z^2)}$$

by writing down the three conditions for stationary waves in the x, y and z directions and

$$f_{pqr} = (c/2)\sqrt{(p^2/X^2 + q^2/Y^2 + r^2/Z^2)} \qquad (5.23)$$

f_{pqr} being the frequency of the pqr mode. This is the three-dimensional equivalent of *Equation (5.16)*.

111

In the enclosure there are three kinds of standing waves:

(*a*) *Oblique*, for which *p*, *q* and *r* are not zero. The oblique stationary wave is formed from eight travelling waves which are reflected from all six walls.

(*b*) *Tangential*, for which either *p* or *q* or *r* is zero. For example, if *p* is zero but *q* and *r* are not, the standing wave is parallel to the *yz* plane and is composed of four waves travelling in this plane and being reflected from four walls.

(*c*) *Axial*, for which only one of the integers does not equal zero. If *p* and *q* are zero, the standing wave is parallel to the *z* axis and consists of two waves travelling in opposite senses in this direction reflected from two walls.

A vector **V** may be resolved into three components $\hat{i}V_a$, $\hat{j}V_g$ and $\hat{k}V_a$ where

$$\mathbf{V} = \hat{i}V_x + \hat{j}V_y + \hat{k}V_z$$

or

$$V = \sqrt{(V_x^2 + V_y^2 + V_z^2)}.$$

Comparison of the last equation with (*5.23*) suggests that each frequency f_{pqr} behaves as a vector in 'frequency space' having components $cp/2X$, $cq/2Y$ and $cr/2Z$. A particular mode of vibration is

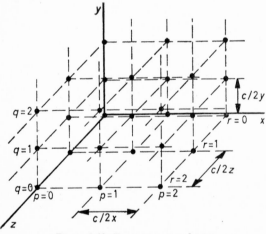

Figure 5.10. Frequency space lattice

represented by a point in frequency space having these co-ordinates, the distance of the point from the origin equalling the frequency of the mode. *Figure 5.10* shows a few of the points corresponding to vibrational modes. They are situated at the intersections of a rectangular lattice of spacings $c/2X$, $c/2Y$ and $c/2Z$. The number of such points contained in an octant of radius f gives the number of modes having frequencies below and equal to f.

The volume of the lattice corresponding to one vibration is that defined by adjacent points which are at the corners of the volume. Thus the volume equivalent to one vibration is $(c/2X)(c/2Y)(c/2Z)$ which is $c^2/8XYZ$. The volume of an octant of radius f is $\frac{1}{8}(4\pi f^3/3)$ which equals $\pi f^3/6$. Hence the number of modes having frequencies below and equal to $f = (\pi f^3/6)/(c^3/8XYZ) = (4\pi f^3/3c^3)XYZ = N(f)$, or

$$N(f) = 4\pi f^3 V/3c^3 \qquad (5.24)$$

where V is the volume of the enclosure. Thus

$$\delta[N(f)] = (4\pi f^2 V/c^3)\delta f \qquad (5.25)$$

$\delta[N(f)]$ being the number of modes having frequencies between f and $f+\delta f$. Since $c = f\lambda$

$$\delta[N(\lambda)] = (4\pi V/\lambda^4)\delta\lambda \qquad (5.26)$$

from which the Rayleigh–Jeans electro-magnetic radiation formula can be derived after doubling this result. Doubling allows for the polarization of the electro-magnetic standing waves in two perpendicular directions, thus giving twice the number of independent vibrational modes. The kind of acoustic wave considered here cannot be polarized because it is longitudinal.

In a rectangular room having edges which are rational multiples, many of the frequencies of modes given by *Equation (5.25)* coincide. There is thus much degeneracy, which becomes greatest for a cubical room, and although the total number of vibrational modes is large there are considerably less characteristic frequencies. These are widely spaced and there is strong resonance at them, unless the walls of the room are highly absorptive. An acoustically 'dead' room is not usually desirable and, fortunately, pronounced resonances are often sufficiently reduced by furniture, both by absorption and reflection, without making the room like an anechoic chamber.

For small rooms, a large error in *Equation (5.24)*, and the ones following, is found when experimental results are compared with those obtained from this equation. Experimental values of $N(f)$ are higher than the calculated values. A more accurate equation is

$$N(f) = 4\pi f^3 V/3c^3 + \pi Af^2/4c^2 + Df/8c + 0(f) \qquad (5.27)$$

where A is the total surface area of the enclosure walls, D the total length of the edges, and $O(f)$ is an irregular step function of order f. The second term in *Equation (5.27)* represents the inclusion of the part of frequency space outside the octant $\pi f^3/6$ associated with lattice points lying on the planes formed by the x, y and z axes. The third term allows for the frequency space containing the points lying on the x, y and z axes. The fourth term gives the graph connecting the number of modes with frequency a stepped form which would be expected, instead of the smooth curve that is otherwise obtained.

5.7. Vibrations of a Bar

Longitudinal vibrations in a bar or rod have already been examined in sections **4.2.** and **5.4.** Transverse (lateral) vibrations require special consideration, for allowance has to be made for rigidity which could be neglected for strings. The wave equation thereby differs from *(4.6)*.

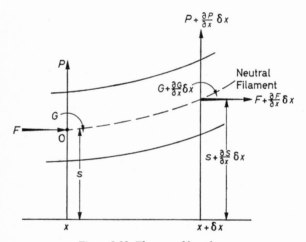

Figure 5.11. Element of bent bar

Figure 5.11 depicts an element of a vibrating bar of density ρ, area of cross-section A, and radius of gyration k for a cross-section about the neutral filament. The shearing forces, bending moments and longitudinal forces at x and $x+\delta x$ are P, $P+(\partial P/\partial x)\delta x$; G, $G+(\partial G/\partial x)\delta x$ and F, $F+(\partial F/\partial x)\delta x$. The damping of oscillations, due to the viscosity of the surrounding medium or to internal losses in the rod, are ignored.

114

The equation of transverse motion of the element is

$$P - [P + (\partial P/\partial x)\delta x] = \rho A \delta x \, \partial^2 s/\partial t^2$$

or

$$\partial P/\partial x = -\rho A \, \partial^2 s/\partial t^2 \tag{5.28}$$

The equation of longitudinal motion is

$$F - [F - (\partial F/\partial x)\delta x] = \rho A \delta x \, \partial^2 s'/\partial t^2$$

as for plane longitudinal waves, treated in section **4.2.**, s' being the longitudinal displacement of the plane at x. Such a displacement is negligible if the displacement amplitude of the transverse oscillation is small. Thus

$$\partial F/\partial x = -\rho A \, \partial^2 s'/\partial t^2 \simeq 0.$$

If I is the moment of inertia of the element δx about an axis through 0 in *Figure 5.11*, normal to the plane of the diagram, the product of I and the angular acceleration of the element about 0 is

$$G + (\partial G/\partial x)\delta x - G - [P + (\partial P/\partial x)\delta x + F + (\partial F/\partial x)\delta x](\partial s/\partial x)\delta x$$

which is also nearly zero. Hence

$$\partial G/\partial x - P \simeq 0 \tag{5.29}$$

neglecting terms containing δx^2, $\partial s/\partial x$ being of the same order as δx in transverse oscillations of small amplitude.

We have

$$G = Ak^2 E/R \tag{5.30}$$

where E is Young's modulus for the material of the rod, and R is the radius of curvature of the rod which is very nearly $1/\partial^2 s/\partial x^2$, as shown in section **4.6.** Differentiating *Equation (5.29)* with respect to x gives

$$\partial^2 G/\partial x^2 - \partial P/\partial x = 0 \tag{5.31}$$

or, using *Equation (5.28)*

$$\partial^2 G/\partial x^2 + \rho A \, \partial^2 s/\partial t^2 = 0.$$

On substituting for G from *Equation (5.30)* this becomes

$$k^2 E \, \partial^4 s/\partial x^4 + \rho \partial^2 s/\partial t^2 = 0$$

or

$$\partial^2 s/\partial t^2 + (k^2 E/\rho)\partial^4 s/\partial x^4 = 0 \tag{5.32}$$

which differs from the wave equation *(4.6)* previously found.

The velocity of longitudinal vibrations in the bar is c, which equals $\sqrt{(E/\rho)}$, so *Equation (5.32)* can be written

$$\partial^2 s/\partial t^2 + k^2 c^2 \partial^4 s/\partial x^4 = 0 \qquad (5.33)$$

from which the velocity v of transverse waves can be found, by assuming as a solution

$$s = A \cos\left[2\pi(x \pm vt)/\lambda\right]$$

where A is now a constant. Then

$$\partial^2 s/\partial t^2 = -4\pi^2 v^2 s/\lambda^2$$

$$\partial^4 s/\partial x^4 = 16\pi^4 s/\lambda^4$$

so that, by substitution in *Equation (5.33)*

$$v = 2\pi kc/\lambda. \qquad (5.34)$$

Thus transverse waves are *dispersed*, since short waves will travel faster than long ones.

A conclusion derived from experiments is that s is a harmonic function of t, since repetitive motion of the bar is found to occur about an equilibrium position. Hence we assume that

$$s = F(x) \cos \omega t \qquad (5.35)$$

Thus

$$\partial^2 s/\partial t^2 = -\omega^2 F(x) \cos \omega t$$

and

$$\partial^4 s/\partial x^4 = (\cos \omega t)\partial^4 F/\partial x^4$$

where $F = F(x)$. Putting these in *Equation (5.33)* yields

$$\partial^4 F/\partial x^4 - \omega^2 F/k^2 c^2 = 0 \qquad (5.36)$$

a solution of which is

$$F(x) = A \cos bx + B \sin bx + C \cosh bx + D \sinh bx \qquad (5.37)$$

where $b^2 = \omega/kc$, ω still being undetermined, and A, B, C and D are arbitrary constants to be evaluated according to the end conditions:

(*i*) At a *free* end G is zero, hence from *Equation (5.30)* $\partial^2 s/\partial x^2$ is zero. P is also zero, so that from *Equations (5.30)* and *(5.31)* $\partial^3 s/\partial x^3$ is zero.

(*ii*) At a *clamped* end s and $\partial s/\partial x$ may be arranged to equal zero or other convenient values.

116

(*iii*) At a *supported* end, for example at a knife-edge, G is zero, so that $\partial^2 s/\partial x^2$ equals zero. s can be chosen to equal zero or any other suitable value.

Suppose the bar is clamped at $x = 0$ and free at $x = L$. At $x = 0$, s may be taken as zero and is then necessarily zero at all times, since the clamp must be assumed to be perfectly rigid. Thus from *Equation* (5.35) $F(x)$ is zero at $x = 0$, and using (5.37) gives

$$0 = A + C.$$

At $x = 0$, $\partial s/\partial x$ can be assumed to be zero at all times, and *Equation* (5.35) gives here $\partial F/\partial x = 0$. Hence from (5.37)

$$0 = B + D$$

and *Equation* (5.37) becomes

$$F(x) = A \cos bx + B \sin bx - A \cosh bx - B \sinh bx. \quad (5.38)$$

At $x = L$

$$\partial^2 s/\partial x^2 = \partial^3 s/\partial x^3 = 0$$

at all times. Thus from *Equation* (5.35)

$$\partial^2 F/\partial x^2 = \partial^3 F/\partial x^3 = 0$$

so from (5.38)

$$A(\cos bL + \cosh bL) + B(\sin bL + \sinh bL) = 0$$

$$A(\sin bL - \sinh bL) - B(\cos bL + \cosh bL) = 0$$

or

$$\cos^2 bL + \cosh^2 bL + 2 \cos bL \cosh bL = \sinh^2 bL - \sin^2 bL$$

Thus

$$\cos bL \cosh bL + 1 = 0. \quad (5.39)$$

This transcendental equation cannot be solved precisely, but approximate solutions can be obtained by finding where graphs of $\cosh bL$ and $-\sec bL$, both plotted against bL, intersect. The graphs are indicated in *Figure 5.12*, which is not drawn to scale. The values of bL for which *Equation* (5.39) holds are in the region of odd multiples of $\pi/2$ and become closer as bL increases.

For a bar clamped or free at both ends, the equation corresponding to (5.39) is

$$\cos bL \cosh bL - 1 = 0 \quad (5.40)$$

the roots of which are also indicated in *Figure 5.12*. A few roots of *Equations* (*5.39*) and (*5.40*) are set out in *Table 5.1* The results for a

Table 5.1. *Roots of cosh* bL = −*sec* bL *and sec* bL.

Fixed–free bar, $bL =$	1·875	4·694 (= $3\pi/2$)	7·855 (= $5\pi/2$)
Free–free or fixed–fixed bar $bL =$	0	4·730	7·853

bar free at both ends is not only of academic interest, as might be thought initially, for the results apply approximately to a long body suspended in a fluid of small viscosity, such as submarine or aircraft.

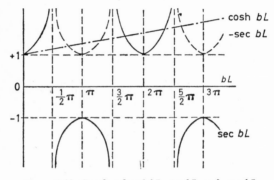

Figure 5.12. Graphs of cosh bL, *sec* bL *and*−*sec* bL

The frequency of oscillations $f = \omega/2\pi = kcb^2/2\pi$ so the frequencies of the higher overtones (partials) are roughly directly proportional to the squares of odd integers, and thus do not form a harmonic series. The fundamental for a fixed–free bar is f_T which equals $1·875^2 ck/2\pi L^2$ compared with f_L, which is $c/4L$, for longitudinal vibrations in the same bar.

$$f_T/f_L = (1·875^2 ck/2\pi L^2)4L/c = 2·24k/L.$$

Usually k is very much smaller than L, so that the fundamental frequency of transverse vibrations is lower than that of longitudinal ones. The same is true for other corresponding modes.

Figure 5.13. depicts the first three vibrational modes of fixed–free and free–free bars, the solid lines indicating the limits of the vibrations. When a free–free bar is bent, the nodes of the fundamental mode approach each other as shown in *Figure 5.14*. The final positions, when the two parts of the bar are parallel and close together, approximate closely to those of the nodes of the fundamental mode of a tuning fork, which could thus be imagined to be a bent free–free bar. Unfortunately none of the nodes of the second

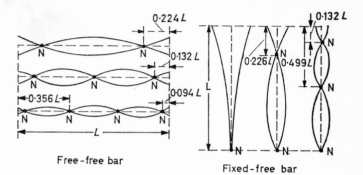

Free-free bar

Fixed-free bar

Figure 5.13. Modes of transverse vibration of bars

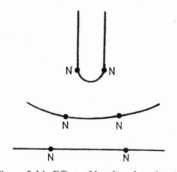

Figure 5.14. Effect of bending free–free bar

mode of vibration of a tuning fork is observed to be at the stem, which would correspond to the centre of a free–free bar. The absence of a node at the stem also excludes the representation afforded by a pair of fixed–free bars. Moreover their nodes for the fundamental are nearer the ends than those observed for a tuning fork, which would thus appear not to be simply analogous to bent or fixed bars when vibrations are studied.

I   119

Figure 5.15 indicates the nodes observed by Chladni for the first three vibrational modes of a tuning fork. Vibration in the first mode seems to be very much easier than in the others, and in fact the tone emitted by a tuning fork is very nearly of a single frequency unless the vibrational amplitude is large.

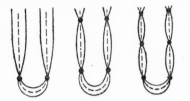

Figure 5.15. Vibrational modes of a tuning fork

References

[1] W. H. GEORGE and H. E. BECKETT *Proc. Roy. Soc.*, *A* **114**, 111, 1927.
[2] W. E. KOCK *J. acoust. Soc. Amer.* **8**, 227, 1937.

6

WAVE PROPERTIES

6.1. Interference of Waves

In the preceding chapter the resultant of two plane waves, travelling in opposite senses but otherwise identical, has been examined. The component waves are present simultaneously in the medium but do not affect one another, the displacement of the medium anywhere and at any time being simply the resultant of the component displacements. Beats, examined in section 2.5., may occur. This *principle of superposition* may be extended to any number of waves of any frequency travelling in any direction providing that the medium, if present, is devoid of non-linear properties, such as the decrease of compressibility with increase in pressure when sound wave transmission is being studied. The principle applies not only to displacements, but generally to vectors associated with waves such as velocities, pressures, and electric or magnetic vectors. It does not apply to their scalar products, for example energies or intensities.

The two component waves have been shown to give a stationary wave—the resultant displacements follow a wave variation along an x axis. There are points at which the displacement is always zero and others in between where the displacement can be a maximum. The phenomenon is described generally as *interference*, and the two waves are said to *interfere*. Both terms are misleading for the waves do not affect each other, and the zero and maximum amplitudes are only a direct consequence of the superposition principle. Because these terms are well-established there would seem to be no objection to their use, providing that the restricted meaning is perceived; but the terms 'constructive' and 'destructive' interference are of very doubtful utility.

The standing waves previously investigated were the resultants of two identical waves travelling in opposite senses. The superposition principle applies to waves travelling in any direction, and thus standing waves can also occur when identical waves travel in the same sense. This happens in optics and acoustics experiments in which a single source emitting waves covering a very small frequency range ('monochromatic') is arranged to give two narrow beams. The beams pass along paths of slightly different lengths and eventually combine

121

to form an interference pattern, usually in the form of straight or circular *fringes* of alternate maximum and minimum intensity. The paths might be actually different in length, or effectively different because of the beams passing through different media. The effect in both instances is to produce a phase difference, independent of time increases, between the disturbances caused by the two beams if these are *coherent* in the region of the disturbances.

The amount of coherence between two beams coming from the same source to some point depends on whether their paths are slightly or greatly different in length. Light sources do not emit continuous wave trains but send out a succession of trains of finite lengths, there being no fixed phase relation between successive trains. When the paths are nearly the same length, the superposed disturbances will have left the source at nearly the same time, that is within about 10^{-8} sec. Consequently the phase difference between them depends only on the path difference and does not change randomly with time. The disturbances are coherent and can interfere in the sense that a standing wave can be formed.

When the difference in path length exceeds a few metres the disturbances must have left the source at times differing by 10^{-8} sec at least, and the light belonging to one train is superposed on that from another. There is no fixed phase difference between them so the disturbances are *incoherent* and do not interfere. Disturbances coming from separate sources are necessarily incoherent.

Between the two extremes of path length difference, actual or effective, there are intermediate values corresponding to *partial coherence.* Then the abrupt phase changes in one disturbance occur between those of the other, and there is partial interference. A standing wave is combined with a travelling wave, so that the maxima and minima are superposed on a background of uniform intensity and are less distinctive.

Sources of acoustic and radio waves mostly emit continuous wave trains, so that beams derived from the same source are everywhere coherent. Even disturbances coming from two separate but identical sources are coherent if they are of the same frequency, but in practice synchronization of the sources would be necessary to counteract slight frequency drifts.

There is a simple relation between path length difference and phase difference which can be obtained by bearing in mind previous conclusions. In a single wave, particles whose distances apart are $\lambda/2, 3\lambda/2, 5\lambda/2, \ldots (2n-1)\lambda/2$, where n is an integer, are moving completely out of phase. The phase angle difference is $\pi, 3\pi, 5\pi, \ldots$

$(2n-1)\pi$ radians, all of which are equivalent to π radians. Particles whose distances apart are $\lambda, 2\lambda, 3\lambda, \ldots n\lambda$ are moving in phase. Thus if two waves of the same frequency and wavelength, and originally in phase, travel to the same point along paths differing in length by $\lambda/2, 3\lambda/2, 5\lambda/2, \ldots (2n-1)\lambda/2$ they will combine to form a minimum disturbance, whereas if the paths differ by $\lambda, 2\lambda, 3\lambda, \ldots n\lambda$ a maximum results. The intensities of the minimum or maximum depend on the amplitudes of the waves, the degree of coherence, nature of polarization, if any, and possibly on the directions of the waves. The reference to particles in the preceding reasoning does not preclude its application to electro-magnetic waves. Although in them there is no particle motion, there are electric and magnetic disturbances which are analogous to particle motion.

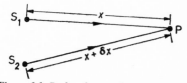

Figure 6.1. Paths of waves from two sources

Suppose plane waves are emitted from S_1 and S_2, shown in *Figure 6.1*, which have the same amplitude, frequency, wavelength and phase, and are unpolarized or similarly polarized. At P the disturbances can be expressed in terms of the scalars s_1 and s_2 where

$$s_1 = a \sin 2\pi(t/T - x/\lambda)$$

$$s_2 = a \sin 2\pi[t/T - (x + \delta x)/\lambda].$$

The assumptions now made depend on the kind of waves leaving S_1 and S_2. For longitudinal sound waves $S_1 S_2$ should be small or $S_2 P - S_1 P$ should be large. For light waves, which are transverse, there is only a practical restriction on $S_1 S_2$ but $S_2 P - S_1 P$ should be sufficiently small to ensure coherency. This restriction may not be required for radio waves. Suitable assumptions can be made for other kinds of wave. The purpose of making such assumptions is that the superposition principle can then be easily applied, and the resultant disturbance at P is $s_1 + s_2$ given by

$$s_1 + s_2 = a\{\sin 2\pi(t/T - x/\lambda) + \sin 2\pi[t/T - (x + \delta x)/\lambda]\}$$

$$= 2a[\cos (\pi\delta x/\lambda)] \sin 2\pi[t/T - (x + \delta x/2)/\lambda].$$

The mean path difference is here incorporated, and the amplitude

123

$2a \cos \pi\delta x/\lambda$ depends on the path difference δx. If $\delta x = 0$, λ, 2λ, 3λ, ... $n\lambda$, where n is an integer, the amplitude of the resultant is $2a$. If $\delta x = \lambda/2$, $3\lambda/2$, $5\lambda/2$, ... $(2n-1)\lambda/2$, the resultant is zero at all times, since the sine term cannot exceed unity. These conclusions are in accord with those previously reached.

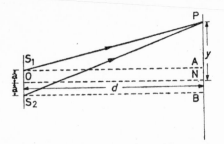

Figure 6.2. Geometry of Young's two-slit experiment

In Young's two-slit experiment, a single source is used to illuminate two slits which are equivalent to S_1 and S_2 in the preceding discussion. The resultant illumination at a point P on a plane AB normal to ON which is of length d, as shown in Figure 6.2, is considered. From Figure 6.2

$$S_2P^2 = d^2 + (y+a)^2$$

and

$$S_1P^2 = d^2 + (y-a)^2$$

Thus

$$S_2P^2 - S_1P^2 = 4ya$$

or

$$S_2P - S_1P = 4ya/(S_2P + S_1P)$$

$$= \text{path length difference.}$$

If a and y are small in comparison with d, the path difference is nearly $4ya/2d$. For a maximum at P

$$2ya/d = n\lambda$$

and for a minimum

$$2ya/d = (2n-1)\lambda/2.$$

Practically, the values of y and n relating to individual fringes would not be found in order to determine λ but a difference $y_2 - y_1$ would be measured, and the corresponding difference in n would be found by counting the number of fringes between those for which y_1 and y_2 were obtained. We find that, from either of the two preceding equations

$$\lambda = 2a(y_2 - y_1)/(n_2 - n_1)d \qquad (6.1)$$

which thus holds if y_1 and y_2 both refer to maxima or to minima. $n_2 - n_1$ is the number of fringes between those for which y_2 and y_1 have been noted plus one. The value of λ obtained from *Equation (6.1)* is averaged over the $n_2 - n_1$ fringes.

In optics λ is usually of the order of 6×10^{-7} metre, and d may be between 1 and 2 metres, so that $y_2 - y_1$ has to be measured with a travelling microscope even if a is made as small as possible. AB is then the focal plane of the microscope, which is of low power, and either has a calibrated scale incorporated in it or can be moved parallel to plane AB over an external scale. The interference pattern is seen as a set of alternate light and dark bands parallel to the slits forming the sources S_1 and S_2, which are assumed to be normal to the plane of *Figure 6.2*.

In acoustics, the various distances are scaled up considerably since λ could be a few centimetres, with a about 5 cm, d a few metres and the slits themselves about one centimetre wide. A suitable detector is a Rayleigh disc or a small microphone connected through an amplifier to a valve-voltmeter. A slit parallel to the ones forming S_1 and S_2 is moved along plane AB with the detector on the side remote from the sources. These are slits in an absorbent baffle, the sound energy being derived from a loudspeaker. Alternatively S_1 and S_2 could be two small loudspeakers fed from the same amplifier. If they are not connected so that their cones move in phase then there is a minimum at N in *Figure 6.1* and the other maxima and minima are interchanged. A tuning fork also generates an interference pattern. The waves sent out by the tines, which move out of phase, combine to produce silent zones. These can be detected by rotating a vibrating fork close to the ear, and can be shown to be due to interaction between the tines by carefully placing a small cylinder over one of them, when the silent zones disappear.

There are many other optics and acoustics experiments for finding wavelengths, refractive indexes and so on based on the interference of waves, but they will not be discussed as the main principles have been enunciated. Various interference experiments can also be done with radio waves.

125

6.2. Reflection of Waves

(*a*) Reflection at a rigid (unyielding) boundary.

In section **5.1.** reflection at a rigid boundary has been examined. There was supposed never to be any displacement at $x = 0$ and at $x = L$. The wave travelling in the positive x direction was found to be completely out of phase with the one travelling in the opposite sense.

The same conclusion can be reached if the solution of *Equation (4.6)*

$$\partial^2 s/\partial t^2 = c^2 \partial^2 s/\partial x^2$$

having greater generality is used. This is *Equation (4.7)*

$$s = f_1(ct-x) + f_2(ct+x).$$

If there is a rigid boundary at $x = 0$, the particle displacement s is always zero at $x = 0$. Thus, from *Equation (4.7)*

$$0 = f_1(ct) + f_2(ct)$$

or

$$f_1(ct) = -f_2(ct)$$

which holds for all values of t. The functions thus have the same form but opposite sign so that

$$f_1(ct-x) = -f_2(ct-x)$$

and

$$s = f_2(ct+x) - f_2(ct-x). \tag{6.2}$$

The wave $f_2(ct+x)$ can be regarded as incident on the boundary at $x = 0$ and is reflected into a wave of the same form, $f_2(ct-x)$, travelling in the opposite sense and being completely out of phase with the incident one. There has been no obligation to specify an angle of incidence, for any value of which the conclusions hold. We are at present unable to state the relative amplitudes of the incident and reflected waves, and no account can yet be taken of a refracted wave. The results apply in optics when both the incident and reflected waves are in a medium of smaller refractive index than the one on the other side of the boundary.

The particle velocity is also reversed. For the incident wave

$$\partial s_i/\partial t = c f_2'(ct+x)$$

from *Equation (6.2)* and for the reflected wave

$$\partial s_r/\partial t = -c f_2'(ct-x)$$

where $f_2' = \partial f_2/\partial t$, s_i and s_r being the particle displacements of the incident and reflected waves. At the boundary $x = 0$, so that

$$\partial s_i/\partial t = cf_2'(ct)$$

and

$$\partial s_r/\partial t = -cf_2'(ct).$$

Hence

$$\partial s_r/\partial t = -\partial s_i/\partial t.$$

The wave velocity is also reversed at the boundary.

In sound waves having an amplitude comparable with or larger than their wavelength, the density ρ of the medium through which the waves travel varies instantaneously to a sufficient extent to make untenable the assumption of a constant static value ρ_0. The *condensation S* becomes appreciable and is defined by

$$\rho = \rho_0(1+S).$$

For a plane wave $S = -\partial s/\partial x$, which is shown as follows.

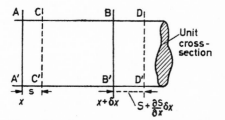

Figure 6.3. Element of medium. Plane waves

AA' and BB' represent planes containing undisplaced particles, as in section **4.2.**, *Figure 4.2. Figure 6.3* is this figure redrawn with the forces omitted. CC' and DD' are planes containing displaced particles, and we consider unit cross-section of the wave. The undisplaced volume of medium is δx, while the displaced volume is $\delta x + (\partial s/\partial x)\delta x$. Since the mass of gas is the same in both volumes

$$\rho_0\delta x = \rho(1+\partial s/\partial x)\delta x$$

or

$$\rho = \rho_0(1+\partial s/\partial x)^{-1} \simeq \rho_0(1-\partial s/\partial x).$$

But by definition $\rho = \rho_0(1+S)$ so that

$$S \simeq -\partial s/\partial x. \qquad (6.3)$$

127

If p, which equals δP as used in section **4.2.**, is the pressure excess required to give a condensation S, that is a volume strain $-\partial s/\partial x$, the elastic modulus of the medium κ equals $p/(-\partial s/\partial x)$ or

$$p = \kappa S. \qquad (6.4)$$

Now a conclusion can be reached regarding the condensations in the incident and reflected waves. That in the incident wave is

$$S_i = -\partial s_i/\partial x = -f_2'(ct+x)$$

and in the reflected wave

$$S_r = -\partial s_r/\partial x = -f_2'(ct-x)$$

both being obtained from *Equation (6.2)*. At the boundary $x = 0$ so that

$$S_i = -f_2'(ct)$$
$$S_r = -f_2'(ct).$$

Hence the condensations are equal and in phase as are the instantaneous pressures, because $p = \kappa S$ according to *Equation (6.4)*.

(b) Reflection at a free (yielding) boundary.

For a free boundary at $x = 0$, the particle displacement amplitude is a maximum since there is no constraint. From *Equation (4.7)*

$$\partial s/\partial x = -f_1'(ct-x)+f_2'(ct+x)$$

and at $x = 0$

$$\partial s/\partial x = -f_1'(ct)+f_2'(ct)$$

$$= 0 \text{ for a numerical maximum.}$$

Thus

$$f_1'(ct) = f_2'(ct)$$

which shows that the first derivatives of the functions have the same form. Hence

$$f_1'(ct+x) = f_2'(ct+x)$$

which can be integrated to give

$$f_1(ct+x) = f_2(ct+x)+\text{a constant.}$$

so that *Equation (4.7)* becomes

$$s = f_1(ct-x)+f_1(ct+x)+\text{a constant.}$$

The constant represents a displacement of the medium as a whole and can be made zero by altering the origin of s. Thus

$$s = f_1(ct-x) + f_1(ct+x).$$

The incident wave $f_1(ct+x)$ is therefore reflected into a wave $f_1(ct-x)$ travelling in the opposite sense but of the same phase. This result also applies in optics to reflection at a boundary when both the incident and the reflected waves are in a medium of greater refractive index than the one on the other side of the boundary.

The particle velocities $\partial s_i/\partial t$ and $\partial s_r/\partial t$ are also in phase, but the condensations S_i and S_r are completely out of phase, as are the excess pressures p, because

$$S_i = -\partial s_i/\partial x = -f_1'(ct+x)$$

$$S_r = -\partial s_r/\partial x = f_1'(ct-x)$$

and *Equation (6.4)* is

$$p = \kappa S.$$

The same conclusions regarding condensation and excess pressure can be reached by remembering that, at a free boundary, the resultant condensation and excess pressure must be zero.

6.3. Reflection and Transmission of Waves at a Boundary

Although the following analysis depends on certain features of sound waves, some of these are also possessed by light waves so that a number of results apply to both kinds of wave. Plane waves are incident on the interface of two media of densities ρ_1 and ρ_2, as indicated in *Figure 6.4*, the dimensions of the boundary being very much larger than the wavelength λ, so that the geometrical laws of reflection and refraction can be applied. Thus the angle of reflection equals the angle of incidence and from Snell's law

$$(\sin i)/\sin r = c_1/c_2 \qquad (6.5)$$

where i and r are the angles of incidence and refraction, c_1 and c_2 being the wave velocities in the two media.

If a_i, a_r and a_t are the amplitudes of the incident, reflected and transmitted displacements, the normal components of these must total zero algebraically at the boundary if it is not disturbed. Thus

$$a_i \cos i - a_r \cos i = a_t \cos r. \qquad (6.6)$$

Energy may be assumed to be conserved at the boundary, that is the incident sound wave energy is the sum of the reflected and transmitted energies. A plane wave, if travelling along an x axis in a positive sense, can be described by

$$s = a \cos 2\pi(t/T - x/\lambda)$$

and

$$\partial s/\partial t = -(2\pi a/T) \sin 2\pi(t/T - x/\lambda)$$
$$= -\omega a \sin 2\pi(t/T - x/\lambda)$$

where ω, the angular frequency, is $2\pi/T$. $\partial s/\partial t$ can be regarded as the velocity of a layer of medium normal to the direction of wave travel

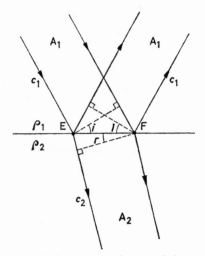

Figure 6.4. Reflection and refraction of plane waves

at a distance x from the origin and of thickness δx. The kinetic energy of this layer per unit area is $\frac{1}{2}\rho_0 \delta x (\partial s/\partial t)^2$ and the kinetic energy of a length λ of the wave of unit cross-section is E_λ given by

$$E_\lambda = \frac{1}{2}\rho_0 \int_0^\lambda (\partial s/\partial t)^2 \mathrm{d}x$$
$$= \frac{1}{2}\rho_0 \int_0^\lambda \omega^2 a^2 \sin^2 2\pi(t/T - x/\lambda) \mathrm{d}x$$
$$= \frac{1}{4}\rho_0 \omega^2 a^2 \int_0^\lambda [1 - \cos 4\pi(t/T - x/\lambda)] \mathrm{d}x.$$

But

$$\int_0^\lambda \cos 4\pi(t/T - x/\lambda) \mathrm{d}x = 0$$

so that

$$E_\lambda = \tfrac{1}{4}\rho_0\omega^2 a^2\lambda \qquad (6.7)$$

and the kinetic energy per unit volume is

$$E = \tfrac{1}{4}\rho_0\omega^2 a^2.$$

We have, from the analysis preceding *Equation (6.4)*

$$p = -\kappa\partial s/\partial x$$

where p is the pressure excess producing a volume strain $-\partial s/\partial x$ and κ is the elastic modulus of the medium through which the waves are travelling, the work per unit area done by p being

$$-p\delta s = -p(\partial s/\partial x)\delta x = -\kappa(\partial s/\partial x)^2\delta x.$$

Over a distance λ the work done by p is W_λ per unit area, given by

$$W_\lambda = \tfrac{1}{2}\int_0^\lambda \kappa(\partial s/\partial x)^2 \mathrm{d}x$$

as the average excess pressure over a distance λ is $p/2$. Using the sinusoidal description of a plane wave as before, we get

$$\partial s/\partial x = (2\pi a/\lambda)\sin 2\pi(t/T - x/\lambda).$$

Thus

$$W_\lambda = (2\pi^2 a^2\kappa/\lambda^2)\int_0^\lambda \sin^2 2\pi(t/T - x/\lambda)\mathrm{d}x$$

$$= (\pi^2 a^2\kappa/\lambda^2)\lambda$$

or the potential energy per unit volume $W = \pi^2 a^2\kappa/\lambda^2$. From *Equation (4.2)* $\kappa = \rho_0 c^2$ and $c^2/\lambda^2 = f^2$ where f is the wave frequency. Thus $W = \tfrac{1}{4}\rho_0\omega^2 a^2$ and is equal to E, the kinetic energy per unit volume. Hence the total energy per unit volume of plane waves is $E + W$ where

$$E + W = \tfrac{1}{2}\rho_0\omega^2 a^2. \qquad (6.8)$$

The energy reaching the interface per unit time is thus $\tfrac{1}{2}\rho_1 A_1 c_1 a_i^2\omega^2$, while the reflected and transmitted energies are respectively $\tfrac{1}{2}\rho_1 A_1 c_1 a_r^2\omega^2$ and $\tfrac{1}{2}\rho_2 A_2 c_2 a_t^2\omega^2$ where A_1 and A_2 are the areas of the waves. The angular frequency ω is not altered when a wave is reflected or refracted. If energy is conserved at the interface

$$\rho_1 A_1 c_1 a_i^2 = \rho_1 A_1 c_1 a_r^2 + \rho_2 A_2 c_2 a_t^2. \qquad (6.9)$$

The width of the waves normal to the plane of *Figure 6.4* is unaltered. Let it be unity. Then

$$EF = A_1/\cos i = A_2/\cos r \qquad (6.10)$$

and combining this with *Equation (6.9)* gives

$$\rho_1 c_1 (a_i^2 - a_r^2) = \rho_2 c_2 a_t^2 (\cos r)/\cos i$$

which becomes, in terms of the amplitude ratio R which is a_r/a_i

$$\rho_1 c_1 a_i^2 (1 - R^2) = \rho_2 c_2 a_t^2 (\cos r)/\cos i.$$

If *Equation (6.6)* is squared we have

$$a_i^2 (1 - R)^2 \cos^2 i = a_t^2 \cos^2 r.$$

Thus

$$(1 + R)/(1 - R) = (\rho_2 c_2/\rho_1 c_1)(\cos i)/\cos r$$

$$= (\rho_2/\rho_1)(\cot i)/\cot r$$

using *Equation (6.5)*. Hence

$$R = [\rho_2/\rho_1 - (\cot r)/\cot i]/[\rho_2/\rho_1 + (\cot r)/\cot i]. \qquad (6.11)$$

For complete transmission R is zero which occurs when

$$[\rho_2/\rho_1 - (\cot r)/\cot i] = 0.$$

Thus

$$(\rho_2/\rho_1)\cot i = \cot r$$

or

$$(\rho_2^2/\rho_1^2)\cot^2 i = \operatorname{cosec}^2 r - 1$$

$$= (c_1^2/c_2^2)\operatorname{cosec}^2 i - 1$$

using *Equation (6.5)*. Hence

$$(\rho_2^2/\rho_1^2)\cot^2 i = (c_1^2/c_2^2)(\cot^2 i + 1) - 1$$

and

$$\cot^2 i = (c_1^2/c_2^2 - 1)/(\rho_2^2/\rho_1^2 - c_1^2/c_2^2)$$

which is positive for real values of ρ_1, ρ_2, c_1 and c_2 if

$$1 \leqslant c_1/c_2 \leqslant \rho_2/\rho_1.$$

This holds when both media are gases because $c = \sqrt{(\gamma P_0/\rho_0)}$, and for simple gases γ is roughly the same. Thus, for the same pressures

$$c_1/c_2 = \sqrt{(\rho_2/\rho_1)}$$

and

$$\cot^2 i = (\rho_2/\rho_1 - 1)/(\rho_2^2/\rho_1^2 - \rho_2/\rho_1) = \rho_1/\rho_2$$

which is positive. For other similar media complete passage is possible, but is very unlikely if the two media are different.

We have, if the media are both gases

$$c_1/c_2 = \sqrt{(\rho_2/\rho_1)}$$

which equals $(\sin i)/\sin r$ from *Equation (6.5)*, so that substitution in *Equation (6.11)* gives

$$R = [\tan(i-r)]/\tan(i+r). \tag{6.12}$$

This is also the Fresnel relation for the reflection of light polarized normally to the plane of incidence, as shown in section **8.11.**

Equation (6.11) can also be written

$$R = (\rho_2 c_2 \cos i - \rho_1 c_1 \cos r)/(\rho_2 c_2 \cos i + \rho_1 c_1 \cos r) \tag{6.13}$$

either from the analysis preceding *Equation (6.11)* or by combining *Equation (6.5)* with *(6.11)*. *Equation (6.13)* can be written in terms of the impedances of the media. We have

$$Y_m = v/F \tag{2.40a}$$

where Y_m is the admittance, v the velocity and F a corresponding force in a mechanical system. The analogous acoustical equation is

$$Y_a = v_a/p$$

which may be written in terms of impedance Z_a

$$Z_a = p/v_a$$

p being the excess pressure and v_a the volume velocity which equals Av, as mentioned in section **2.6.**, where A is an area normal to the direction of travel of a wave and v is the particle velocity. For a plane wave $p = \kappa S$ from *Equation (6.4)*. Hence $p = \rho_0 c^2 S$ because $c = \sqrt{(\kappa/\rho_0)}$ and

$$Z_a = \rho_0 c^2 S/Av.$$

A plane wave may be described by

$$s = a \sin 2\pi(t/T - x/\lambda).$$

Thus v, which equals $\partial s/\partial t$, is $(2\pi a/T) \cos 2\pi(t/T - x/\lambda)$ and S, which is $-\partial s/\partial x$ from *Equation (6.3)*, is given by

$$S = (2\pi a/\lambda) \cos 2\pi(t/T - x/\lambda).$$

Hence

$$Z_a = (\rho_0 c^2 / A)(2\pi a / \lambda)/(2\pi a / T) = (\rho_0 c^2 / A)T/\lambda$$

$$= (\rho_0 c^2 / A)/f\lambda = \rho_0 c / A$$

since $c = f\lambda$. Thus the *unit area impedance*, otherwise *specific* or *characteristic impedance*, Z, is $\rho_0 c$. Hence for the two media $\rho_1 c_1 = Z_1$ and $\rho_2 c_2 = Z_2$. *Equation (6.13)* becomes

$$R = (Z_2 \cos i - Z_1 \cos r)/(Z_2 \cos i + Z_1 \cos r). \qquad (6.14)$$

For normal incidence cos i and cos r are both unity and *Equation (6.14)* becomes

$$R = (Z_2 - Z_1)/(Z_2 + Z_1). \qquad (6.15)$$

If there is complete transmission R is zero, so that Z_2 equals Z_1. With this in mind a special rubber having nearly the same impedance as water has been developed. It is used to protect underwater transducers without reducing their efficiencies by energy reflection. For media of widely differing impedances, one of intermediate impedance is placed between them in order to increase energy transfer. Ideally the intermediate impedance should be the geometric mean of the other two, and the thickness of the additional medium should be one quarter of the length of the waves used. There is thus an analogy between such a method of increasing the transmission of acoustic energy and the way in which the amount of light passing through lenses is increased. The lenses are coated with a $\lambda/4$ thickness of material whose refractive index is the geometric mean of the indexes of air and the lens glass.

Equation (6.15) can be written

$$R = (1 - Z_1/Z_2)/(1 + Z_1/Z_2)$$

and if Z_1 is very much smaller than Z_2

$$R \simeq (1 - Z_1/Z_2)^2 \simeq 1 - 2Z_1/Z_2. \qquad (6.16)$$

For air $Z \simeq 40 \, \mathrm{g \, cm^{-2} sec^{-1}}$ and for water $Z \simeq 1.5 \times 10^5$, in the same units. Hence the amplitude ratio for waves travelling in air and being reflected from a water surface is

$$R = 1 - 80/(1.5 \times 10^5) = 99.95\%.$$

A small critical angle i_c, which equals $\sin^{-1} c_1/c_2$, would be expected because the air–water velocity ratio, c_1/c_2, is about 1:5. For air $c_1 \simeq 3.3 \times 10^4 \, \mathrm{cm \, sec^{-1}}$ and for water $c_2 \simeq 1.5 \times 10^5 \, \mathrm{cm \, sec^{-1}}$, so that $i_c \simeq 12°$. For angles of incidence greater than this all the incident energy is reflected, so that the transmission of acoustic energy from air into water is almost negligible at all angles. For steel $Z \simeq 4.7 \times 10^6$ g cm^{-2}sec^{-1} and for waves in water being reflected from steel, *Equation (6.16)* will still be of sufficient accuracy. R is found to be 94 per cent, which is sufficiently large for underwater steel objects to be detected by echo methods. Many dense solids have impedances of the same order as that for steel so they can also be detected, but ice, for which Z is nearly 2×10^5, reflects very little energy for waves in water. The amplitude ratio for waves in water reflected from ice has to be found from *Equation (6.15)*, since the impedances are comparable, and is 14·3 per cent. In echo methods the detector responds to the energy of the reflected wave. Since, from *Equation (6.8)*, the total wave energy is directly proportional to the square of the amplitude, R^2 is required here. R^2 is only 2 per cent, so that the detection of underwater ice would appear to be very difficult, but fortunately icebergs usually contain rock and air pockets so the reflected energy is considerably increased.

6.4. Superposition of SHMs in the Same Direction

There are assumed to be n SHMs of the same angular frequency p but with different amplitudes $a_1, a_2, a_3, \ldots a_n$ and phase angles $e_1, e_2, e_2, \ldots e_n$ given by

$$s_1 = a_1 \cos (pt + e_1)$$
$$s_2 = a_2 \cos (pt + e_2)$$
$$\cdots \cdots \cdots \cdots$$
$$s_n = a_n \cos (pt + e_n).$$

If these vibrations are in the same direction, the resultant s is given by

$$s = s_1 + s_2 + \ldots s_n$$

$$= \cos pt \sum_{n=1}^{n} a_n \cos e_n - \sin pt \sum_{n=1}^{n} a_n \sin e_n.$$

Let

$$\sum_{n=1}^{n} a_n \cos e_n = A \cos \phi$$

and

$$\sum_{n=1}^{n} a_n \sin e_n = A \sin \phi.$$

Then

$$s = A \cos (pt + \phi)$$

and the resultant vibration is simple harmonic of amplitude A and phase angle ϕ where

$$A = \left[\left(\sum_{n=1}^{n} a_n \cos e_n \right)^2 + \left(\sum_{n=1}^{n} a_n \sin e_n \right)^2 \right]^{\frac{1}{2}} \qquad (6.17)$$

and

$$\tan \phi = \left(\sum_{n=1}^{n} a_n \sin e_n \right) \Big/ \left(\sum_{n=1}^{n} a_n \cos e_n \right). \qquad (6.18)$$

If there are only two vibrations and they have the same amplitude a

$$A = a[2 + 2 \cos (e_1 - e_2)]^{\frac{1}{2}} \qquad (6.19)$$

where $e_1 - e_2$ is the phase angle difference. If $e_1 - e_2$ equals zero or $2q\pi$, where q is any integer, A equals $2a$. If $e_1 - e_2$ is $(2q-1)\pi$, A is zero.

The phase difference is often due to two waves arriving at the point where SHM can occur after travelling along paths of different lengths. Interference then results, as mentioned in section **6.1**. If the path length difference is δx the phase angle difference $e_1 - e_2$ is $2\pi\delta x/\lambda$; $A = 2a$ if $\delta x = 0$ or $q\lambda$, while $A = 0$ if $\delta x = (2q \pm 1)\lambda/2$. These conclusions were reached in section **6.1**.

When diffraction occurs there are usually superposed a large number n of vibrations of the same direction, amplitude a and angular frequency p, but with a common phase angle difference e, in contrast with the small number, usually two, in interference. Then

$$A \cos \phi = a \cos e + a \cos 2e + \ldots a \cos ne$$

$$A \sin \phi = a \sin e + a \sin 2e + \ldots a \sin ne.$$

Multiplying the second equation by j [equals $\sqrt{(-1)}$] and adding and subtracting yields

$$A \exp j\phi = a(\exp je + \exp 2je + \ldots \exp nje)$$

$$= a(\exp je)(1 - \exp nje)/(1 - \exp je)$$

and

$$A \exp -j\phi = a(\exp -je + \exp -2je + \ldots \exp -nje)$$

$$= a(\exp -je)(1 - \exp -nje)/(1 - \exp -je)$$

since both the series are geometrical progressions having common ratios exp je and exp −je. Thus

$$A^2 = a^2(1-\exp nje)(1-\exp -nje)/(1-\exp je)(1-\exp -je)$$
$$= a^2\,[2-(\exp nje+\exp -nje)\,]/\,[2-(\exp je+\exp -je)\,]$$
$$= a^2(1-\cos ne)/(1-\cos e)$$

or

$$A = a(\sin \tfrac{1}{2}ne)/\sin \tfrac{1}{2}e. \tag{6.20}$$

If n is very large and e is very small, the total phase angle difference $(n-1)e \simeq ne = 2\alpha$ and we have from *Equation (6.20)*

$$A = a(\sin \alpha)/\sin (\alpha/n)$$
$$= na(\sin \alpha)/\alpha$$

since α/n is very small. Hence

$$A = R(\sin \alpha)/\alpha \tag{6.21}$$

where R equals *na* which is the sum of the amplitudes, if all the component motions are in phase.

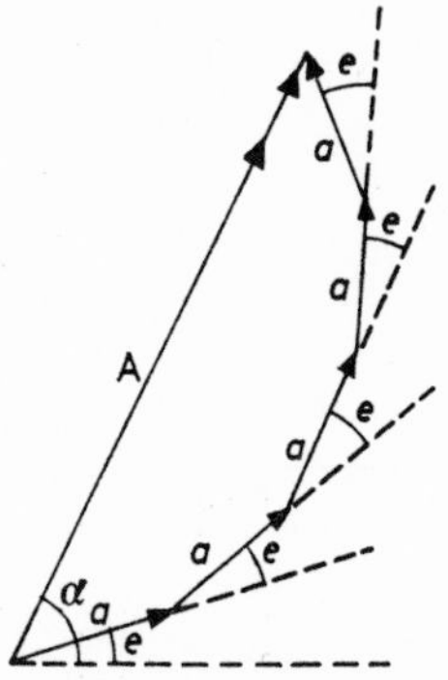

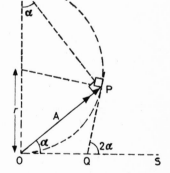

Figure 6.5. Vector polygon of displacements

Fig. 6.6. Equivalent vector diagram of displacements

If α equals $m\pi$, where m is an integer, the polygon shown in *Figure 6.5* is closed and A is zero. When a and e are very small and n is very large, the polygon becomes a continuous curve—part of the circumscribing circle—closed by a chord of length A. The circle is replaced by a spiral if successive amplitudes of the component motions gradually diminish. The geometry of the circle shown in *Figure 6.6*.

137

leads to *Equation (6.21)*. $\angle$PQS $= ne = 2\alpha$ and OP $= A = 2r \sin \alpha$, where r is the radius of the circumscribing circle. For the first vibration A would become a, and α would be $\frac{1}{2}e$. Hence

$$a = 2r \sin \tfrac{1}{2}e$$

$$= 2r \sin (\alpha/n)$$

$$= (A/\sin \alpha) \sin (\alpha/n)$$

or

$$A = a(\sin \alpha)/\sin (\alpha/n)$$

which can be developed as before.

6.5. Diffraction of Waves at a Slit

Associated with progressive waves is a *wave-front* which is imagined to move at the velocity with which the waves are advancing. The shape of the wave-front is a description of the kind of wave. For example, plane waves have a plane wave-front, spherical waves a spherical wave-front and so on. Huyghens in 1690 gave a construction by which, if a position of a wave-front was known, its position could be found at any subsequent time. All the points on the wave-front were imagined to be secondary sources. The envelope of all the secondary waves diverging from these sources gave the wave-front at later times. On this basis reflection and refraction of waves, the passage of light through very small holes, and approximately rectilinear propagation through large apertures can be explained. But Huyghen's principle is not sufficient to explain the apparent departure from rectilinear propagation when diffraction occurs, or to explain why the waves do not travel in the opposite sense, for the secondary sources presumably emit waves in all directions.

Fresnel imagined the wave-front to be suitably divided into *zones*, each contributing to illumination ahead of the wave-front. He was thus able to explain the phenomenon of *diffraction* which occurs when the wave-front meets an obstacle. The wave appears to bend round the edges of the obstacle, so that energy is found behind the barrier where none would be expected if the wave propagation were rectilinear. For example, the intensity of a shadow cast by an obstacle varies considerably with position near the edges of the shadow, particularly if the obstacle has a size comparable with the length of the incident waves. Diffraction thus has a large influence on the radiation and obstruction of sound waves, but the effect is less pronounced for light waves, which have a much shorter wavelength.

Fresnel's division of the wave-front will be discussed later. For the present suppose that unpolarized waves, coming from a distant source or produced by collimation, are normally incident on a slit QR of width *d*, indicated in *Figure 6.7*, the length of the slit being normal to the plane of the diagram. P is a distant point, such that the lines QP and RP may be thought to be parallel. The front of the incident

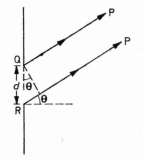

Figure 6.7. Extreme rays from a slit

waves will fill the slit at a particular instant. Suppose then that the wave-front is divided into a set of *n* equal elementary strips parallel to the length of the slit. The contributions of these to the disturbance at P will be nearly equal, but there will be a progressive difference in phase and the resultant amplitude at P will be given by *Equation (6.21)*

$$A = na(\sin \alpha)/\alpha$$

where *a* is the amplitude due to each strip, and 2α is the phase angle difference between the first and last strips.

For rays emerging at angle θ, the path length difference ranges between zero for QP, and $d \sin \theta$ for RP. The phase angle difference 2α is thus given by

$$2\alpha = 2\pi d(\sin \theta)/\lambda. \tag{6.22}$$

The maximum numerical values for the resultant A are found according to $dA/d\alpha = 0$. Numerical maxima are considered because the wave energy depends on the square of the amplitude, as shown earlier for acoustic waves, the same being true for light waves. Thus

139

minima, which are negative, become energy maxima when they are squared. For numerical maxima

$$\frac{d}{d\alpha}\left(\frac{\sin \alpha}{\alpha}\right) = 0$$

since na is a constant for a particular intensity of illumination at the slit. Hence

$$(\cos \alpha)/\alpha - (\sin \alpha)/\alpha^2 = 0$$

or

$$(\alpha \cos \alpha - \sin \alpha)/\alpha^2 = 0$$

the solution of which is the transcendental equation

$$\alpha = \tan \alpha \qquad (6.23)$$

since $1/\alpha^2$ is not generally zero. Exact solutions cannot be computed but approximate solutions can be found by plotting $\tan \alpha$ and α

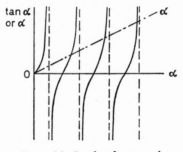

Figure 6.8. Graphs of tan α and α
against α

against α, as in *Figure 6.8* and noting the intersections of the two graphs. From *Figure 6.8* $\alpha = 0$ or

$$\alpha \simeq \pm 3\pi/2, \ \pm 5\pi/2, \ \ldots \pm (2p-1)\pi/2$$

where p is any positive integer but unity. Hence, from (6.22)

$$\pi d(\sin \theta)/\lambda = 0, \ \pm 3\pi/2, \ \pm 5\pi/2, \ \ldots \pm (2p-1)\pi/2$$

and

$$\sin \theta = 0, \ \pm 3\lambda/2d, \ \pm 5\lambda/2d, \ \ldots \pm (2p-1)\lambda/2d$$

from which angles relating to the various maxima can be found if λ and d are known. The angles differ appreciably if λ and d are comparable, as they can easily be for sound waves. For light waves a very fine slit is required to give distinct maxima.

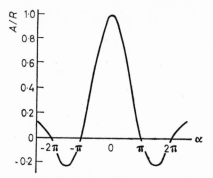

Figure 6.9. Graph of amplitude ratio against α for slit diffraction

A graph of the amplitude ratio A/R, where R is na, the central maximum, against $α$ is given in *Figure 6.9*. For the second numerical maxima

$$A/R = (\sin α)/α \simeq (\sin 3π/2)/(3π/2) = -2/3π.$$

For the third maxima

$$A/R = (\sin 5π/2)/(5π/2) = 2/5π$$

and so on. Most of the wave passes straight through, as would be expected. A result for an obstacle of width d can be similarly obtained, but the fringe pattern is substantially different because most of the incident plane wave-front has to be allowed for instead of a narrow strip of the wave-front defined by the slit.

If the plane wave is incident at an angle $φ$, measured on the opposite side of the normal to $θ$, the same treatment holds, and *Equation (6.22)* becomes

$$α = πd(\sin θ - \sin φ)/λ \qquad (6.24)$$

where

$$(\sin θ - \sin φ) = 0, \pm 3λ/2d, \pm 5λ/2d, \ldots \pm (2p-1)λ/2d.$$

The diffraction pattern is no longer symmetrical about the beam passing straight through, and is expanded on one side and compressed on the other.

141

The preceding analysis does not apply only to monochromatic waves. For different values of λ there will be corresponding values of θ for each value of p. A spectrum is thus produced from incident white light by the diffraction effect. The beam passing straight through is unaffected.

From *Equation (6.21)* A is zero if

$$\alpha = q\pi$$

where q is a positive or negative integer. Thus, using *Equation (6.22)*, minima are given by

$$\pi d(\sin \theta)/\lambda = q\pi$$

or

$$\sin \theta = q\lambda/d. \tag{6.25}$$

The first dark bands, one on either side of the central maximum, thus correspond to

$$\sin \theta = \pm \lambda/d \tag{6.26}$$

for monochromatic radiation. For a circular aperture the first dark ring corresponds to

$$\sin \theta = 0{\cdot}61\lambda/r \tag{6.27}$$

where r is the radius of the aperture. These two results are of importance when the directional properties of acoustic radiators are being examined. Although both results are obtained by considering secondary sources on an incident plane wave-front, they both apply to radiation from a diaphragm of appropriate dimensions if all the diaphragm is vibrating in phase. Most of the energy radiated will be contained in a wedge of semi-angle θ, given by *Equation (6.26)*, for a slit radiator, or in a cone of semi-angle θ, given by *(6.27)*, for a circular radiator. A moving-coil direct radiator loudspeaker is usually circular, so that *Equation (6.27)* applies. For elliptical loudspeakers *(6.27)* would apply roughly to the two perpendicular directions, r equalling the major and minor semi-axes, or if the ellipse is very thin *Equation (6.26)* could be used.

At high frequencies the sound energy is concentrated in a narrow beam, which widens as the frequency is reduced, and hence the wavelength is increased. If a highly directional radiator is required, for example in echo-sounding, the size required for a given acoustic output frequency can be found. Usually a compromise has to be made, for even at frequencies near 50 kc/s, r has to be about 10 cm for a semi-angle of 10° of radiated waves in sea-water. The radiator would be very bulky, and a diaphragm of radius 10 cm is not easily driven at such a high frequency at the amplitudes required for echo-sounding. Unless the diaphragm were extremely rigid it would not vibrate in the same phase all over, and *Equation (6.27)* would not apply.

6.6. Diffraction Grating

An optical transmission diffraction grating consists essentially of a number of fine rulings, closely spaced and parallel, on an optical flat; transparent plastic film replicas, which are in common use, can be made from such a master grating. *Figure 6.10* represents a section of a grating, the spacing being *d*.

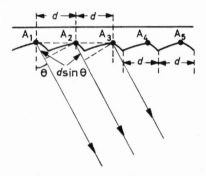

Figure 6.10. Section of a diffraction grating

Suppose plane unpolarized waves are normally incident on the plane side, and some emerge at an angle θ as shown. Rays passing from the plane face to the surface of each ruling all have a different phase since they traverse different thicknesses of glass, but there will be points A_1, A_2, A_3, . . at which a resultant can be found. The rulings can be assumed to have the same profile so that A_1A_2 = A_2A_3 = A_3A_4 = . . = d. The phase angle difference between the resultants coming from A_1, A_2, A_3, . . . is

$$(2\pi d/\lambda) \sin \theta$$

as for the rays coming from the edges of the slit in the preceding analysis. Even with a grating having a large number of lines per unit length this difference cannot be regarded as sufficiently small to

143

justify the use of *Equation (6.21)* which was used for the treatment of the slit. *Equation (6.20)* must be used

$$A = a(\sin \tfrac{1}{2}ne)/\sin \tfrac{1}{2}e$$

where e, the phase angle difference between successive disturbances, is here $(2\pi d/\lambda) \sin \theta$. a is the amplitude of the resultant through each ruling and n is the number of resultants, that is the total number of rulings. The maximum amplitude is na, which equals R as before, so that

$$A/R = (\sin \tfrac{1}{2}ne)/n(\sin \tfrac{1}{2}e).$$

Let $A/R = (\sin n\beta)/n(\sin \beta)$. A equals R when $n \sin \beta = \sin n\beta$, which is a condition for maxima since A cannot exceed R. This equa-

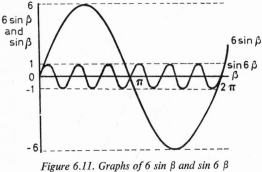

Figure 6.11. Graphs of $6 \sin \beta$ and $\sin 6\beta$
against β

tion can be solved graphically by taking a small number, such as six, for n, and plotting $6 \sin \beta$ and $\sin 6\beta$ against β, as shown in *Figure 6.11*. The solutions are given by

$$\beta = m\pi$$

where m is an integer or zero, and are unaltered by n being very large. In practice n is usually at least several thousand. $(\sin n\beta)/n(\sin \beta)$ would appear to be indeterminate for $\beta = m\pi$, but the limiting value of this fraction as β approaches $m\pi$ is easily shown to be unity. Because β has replaced $\tfrac{1}{2}e$ we now have

$$e = 2m\pi = (2\pi d/\lambda) \sin \theta.$$

Hence

$$d \sin \theta = m\lambda \qquad (6.28)$$

which is the usual equation for a diffraction grating and can be obtained by a simplified treatment.

The path difference between two adjacent rays coming from A_1 and A_2, A_2 and A_3 and so on is $d \sin \theta$. For the rays to reinforce in a direction defined by θ this path length difference should equal a whole number of wavelengths. Thus $d \sin \theta = m\lambda$ as before.

A deficiency in this simple treatment is that there are actually large numbers of small maxima between the main ones given by *Equation (6.28)*. Writing as before

$$A/R = (\sin n\beta)/n(\sin \beta)$$

we have

$$dA/d\beta = R[n(\cos n\beta)/\sin \beta - (\sin n\beta)(\cos \beta)/\sin^2 \beta]/n$$

and for a numerical maximum $dA/d\beta$ is zero. Thus

$$n(\cos n\beta) \sin \beta - (\sin n\beta) \cos \beta = 0$$

since $\sin \beta$ is not generally zero. Hence for a numerical maximum

$$n \tan \beta = \tan n\beta$$

which is solved approximately by taking a small value for n, as before, and plotting graphs of $\tan \beta$ and $\tan n\beta$ against β, as in *Figure 6.12* where n has been taken as six. Over the interval $\beta = 0$

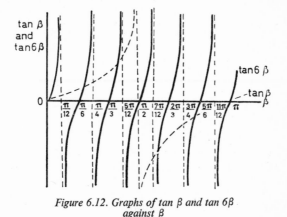

Figure 6.12. Graphs of tan β and tan 6β against β

to $\beta = \pi$ there are six maxima for $n = 6$. Maxima have been shown to occur at $\beta = 0$ and $\beta = \pi$; the other four are subsidiary maxima in between the principal ones. Generally there are $n-2$ subsidiary maxima of very small intensity between the principal maxima of very much greater intensity, so that only the principal ones are of experimental interest. The amplitudes of the principal maxima are not equal, even though equality might be inferred from the preceding analysis giving their positions. The amplitude ratio A/R, where A is the amplitude of an image of order m, is given by

$$A/R = (\sin \pi d'm/d)/\pi d'm/d \qquad (6.29)$$

for an ideal grating in which there are perfectly transparent strips of width d', separated by opaque ones of width $d-d'$. For the direct image $m = 0$ and $A = R$. Particular values of d'/d will cause images of a certain order not to appear. For example, if $d'/d = \frac{1}{2}$ the even order images disappear. Practically the rulings may be such that, because of reflection or refraction, light is concentrated in a particular direction which may coincide with a principal maximum.

The analysis leading to *Equation (6.28)* is substantially the same if waves are incident at angle ϕ on the grating. The phase angle difference is then

$$(2nd/\lambda)(\sin \theta - \sin \phi)$$

if ϕ is measured on the opposite side of the normal to θ, and *Equation (6.28)* becomes

$$d(\sin \theta - \sin \phi) = m\lambda. \qquad (6.28a)$$

The diffraction pattern is altered in that there is a greater angular spacing between the various orders on one side of the zero-order image, and a smaller spacing on the other. As with the slit, spectra corresponding to the various orders, except zero, are produced if white light is used.

The foregoing analysis also applies to acoustical gratings, which can be of much larger dimensions. The spacing d can be a few centimetres instead of the order of 10^{-4} cm. Such gratings can be used to alter the directional properties of acoustic radiators, for practical demonstrations or for wavelength measurement, the latter being the main use of single optical gratings.

6.7. Diffraction of Light by Acoustic Waves

When sound waves pass through a fluid, compressions and rarefactions are set up in the manner indicated in *Figure 5.5*. Fluid particles congregate in regions where the particle displacements change from positive to negative through zero, and disperse from those where the displacement change is from negative to positive. Thus there are in the fluid regions of larger and smaller densities than the static density ρ_0, separated by regions of density ρ_0 and corresponding to regions of larger and smaller refractive indexes. The path lengths of light rays passing through these regions differ, so that the fluid through which sound waves are passing can be used as a diffraction grating. The spacing between, and difference in magnitude of, the density maxima and minima have to be suitable, and satisfactory gratings were discovered in 1932 by Lucas and Biquard in France, and Debye and Sears in America. For the small spacing required, ultrasonic waves are necessary at frequencies of one megacycle per second or greater. Quartz crystal and other small transducers can be coupled efficiently at such frequencies to liquids

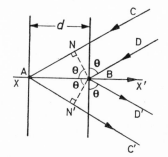

Figure 6.13. Rays reflected from density maxima

in which waves are thereby formed. Focussing and diffraction effects can be exploited to produce intense beams of ultrasonic waves in the liquid, a limiting factor being *cavitation*, which occurs when the wave intensity is so large that voids are formed in the liquid. Optical diffraction patterns can be produced by progressive or stationary acoustic waves, for the velocity of sound is so much smaller than that of light that the compressions and rarefactions in a progressive wave can be regarded as stationary. The patterns resulting from the two kinds of wave are considerably different. The light waves are usually sent through the liquid at about right-angles to the acoustic beam.

The complete theory of the ultrasonic diffraction grating contains many difficulties and will not be examined here but, as with the diffraction of X-rays in crystals, can be simplified by supposing the process to be caused by reflection at a series of parallel planes corresponding to maximum compression, as indicated in *Figure 6.13*.

CAC′ and DBD′ are light rays collimated from a single slit and having wave-fronts NB and N′B. θ is the angle between these wave-fronts and the direction XX′ in which the sound waves are advancing. The path length difference between successive reflected wave-fronts is 2AN which is $2d \sin \theta$, where d is the separation of the compression maxima, that is the length of the acoustic waves. There will be reinforcement in a direction specified by θ for a wavelength λ of light if

$$2d \sin \theta = m\lambda \qquad (6.30)$$

where m is an integer. *Equation (6.30)* is known as Bragg's law in X-ray diffraction when the planes AE and BF are crystal planes.

For light passing through the ultrasonic beam and incident normally to the wave velocity, the path length difference is $d \sin \theta$ so that

$$d \sin \theta = m\lambda \qquad (6.31)$$

which may be compared with *Equation (6.28)* for a plane transmission diffraction grating. The ultrasonic grating is roughly analogous to a grating made of a transparent solid having a sinusoidal surface like a piece of corrugated iron. In *Equations (6.30)* and *(6.31)* m is limited to the first few integers because of the sinusoidal variation in density. θ is only a few degrees even for very high ultrasonic frequencies. In practice many more diffraction maxima are observed than would be expected from either of the two equations, so the process is clearly not completely described by the preceding simple treatment. The equations are generally used to obtain d, the length of the acoustic waves, the other quantities being known. If the acoustic frequency is known, the wave velocity can be found, which has been done for a large number of liquids. Only a small volume of liquid through which the waves are passing can be observed, which may be a disadvantage if the passage of the acoustic wave is to be examined.

An experiment devised by Bär and Meyer enabled a much larger volume of liquid to be studied. The illumination was provided by a number of pinholes regularly distributed over an opaque screen and illuminated from a common source. The light from these travelled parallel to the acoustic wave-front. Each pinhole source gave a set of diffracted images, the interpretation of which yielded considerable information. The separation of the images gave the length of the sound waves; the intensity of the pattern and the number of visible diffraction images was a measure of the sound wave intensity, which became attenuated as the liquid was traversed; and the line joining the diffracted images of the same pinhole source gave the direction of the sound wave velocity. The effects of obstacles, slits, diffraction gratings and the like in the path of the sound waves were studied. Later Bär and Bez-Bardili used this technique to study the refraction of ultrasonic waves at boundaries between different liquids.

6.8. Half-period Zones. Zone Plate

The diffraction phenomena so far discussed are included in *Fraunhofer diffraction* which occurs when the diffraction pattern is formed in a plane conjugate to the source. The preceding examples belong to a special category in that the source and the plane in which the patterns are formed are at, or effectively at because of the action of a lens, a very large distance from the diffracting object. *Fresnel diffraction* occurs when the source or the diffracted image plane or both are at finite but not conjugate distances from the diffracting object, and there is usually no lens in the diffraction system. Such diffraction is now examined.

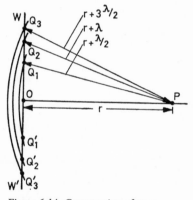

Figure 6.14. Construction of zones on a plane wave-front

In section **6.5.** a brief reference has been made to the division of a plane wave-front into zones, suggested by Fresnel. Annular zones were originally postulated and are constructed as follows. Suppose WW' is a section of the front of a plane wave of length λ advancing towards a point P at velocity c, as shown in *Figure 6.14*. The front is instantaneously at a distance r from P and is normal to OP. With centre P and radii $r+\lambda/2$, $r+\lambda$, $r+3\lambda/2$, . . . draw circles cutting WW' at Q_1Q_1', Q_2Q_2', Q_3Q_3', . . . In three dimensions the circles would become spheres which intersect the plane wave-front in circles of radii OQ_1, OQ_2, OQ_3, . . . thus forming annular zones. Fresnel then supposed that the contribution that any such zone on the wave-front made to the disturbance at P had an amplitude proportional to that at the zone and to the area of the zone, but was inversely proportional the mean distance of the zone from P. The wave amplitude is the same all over the wave-front, and the increase in area as the radius of the zone increases is balanced by the increase in the mean distance from P, shown as follows.

Let the radii OQ_1, OQ_2, OQ_3, . . . be q_1, q_2, q_3, . . . The area of the central circular zone is

$$\pi q_1^2 = \pi[(r+\lambda/2)^2 - r^2] \simeq \pi r\lambda$$

if r greatly exceeds λ. The area of the first annular zone is

$$\pi(q_2^2 - q_1^2) = \pi\{[(r+\lambda)^2 - r^2] - [(r+\lambda/2)^2 - r^2]\}$$
$$= \pi(2r+3\lambda/2)(\lambda/2) \simeq \pi r\lambda.$$

The area of the nth annular zone is

$$\pi(q_{n+1}^2 - q_n^2) = \pi\{[(r+(n+1)\lambda/2)^2 - r^2] - [(r+n\lambda/2)^2 - r^2]\}$$
$$= \pi[2r+(2n+1)\lambda/2](\lambda/2) \simeq \pi r\lambda.$$

The difference in area between the nth and the $(n-1)$th zones is

$$(\pi\lambda/2)\{[2r+(2n+1)\lambda/2] - [2r+(2n-1)\lambda/2]\} = \pi\lambda^2/2.$$

Hence the fractional increase in area $\simeq (\pi\lambda^2/2)/\pi r\lambda$

$$\simeq \lambda/2r.$$

The increase in the mean distance of the zones from P is $\lambda/2$ for successive zones, and the fractional increase in distance near the nth zone is $(\lambda/2)/(r+n\lambda/2)$ which is very nearly $\lambda/2r$, because otherwise, as we have assumed that r greatly exceeds λ, n would have to be very large. Since the two increases are nearly the same, the reduction in amplitude of the disturbance at P is nullified by the increased amplitude due to the enlargement of zonal area.

There is however a gradual reduction in the amplitude of the contribution at P from each zone as the distance increases. The inclination of the zones to the radii $r+\lambda/2$, $r+\lambda$, $r+3\lambda/2$, . . . differs gradually in such a way that the contributions from the zones decrease slowly as the mean zonal radii increase. The dependence of the contributions on inclination partly removes a difficulty inherent in Huyghen's construction. At points behind the wave-front the inclination factor is always small. The contributions from the secondary sources are therefore small behind the wave-front and the wave is propagated almost entirely in a forward sense. Although the decrease in the contributions from the zones as their mean radii increase is not uniform, since a sine or cosine factor is involved, the resultant disturbance at P can be found by summing the series

$$a = a_0 - a_1 + a_2 - a_3 + a_4 - a_5 \ldots \qquad (6.32)$$

where $a_0, a_1, a_2, \ldots$ are all positive, and are the amplitudes of the contributions from the central zone of radius q_1 and from the annular zones. The difference in sign arises because of the phase difference between the contributions from the various zones. The mean path length of light travelling from the central circular zone is $r + \lambda/4$. That from the first annular zone is $r + 3\lambda/4$ so that there is a path length difference of $\lambda/2$ and hence a phase angle difference of π radians. There is the same difference between all adjacent zones so that the contributions from alternate zones reinforce. From the phase angle difference of π, which corresponds to a phase difference of half the period of vibration, arises the name *half-period zones*. They are otherwise known as *Fresnel zones*.

The series (6.32) can be summed by grouping the terms and then showing that the sum lies between two limits. Whether there are an odd or even number of terms, and whether each term is greater or less than the mean of the preceding and following ones, has necessarily to be considered and treated separately. Approximations are also required, and the following treatment because of its brevity would seem to be more appropriate here

$$a = a_0 - a_1 + a_2 - a_3 + a_4 - a_5 \ldots$$
$$= \tfrac{1}{2}a_0 + [\tfrac{1}{2}(a_0 + a_2) - a_1] + [\tfrac{1}{2}(a_2 + a_4) - a_3] \ldots$$

The terms $[\tfrac{1}{2}(a_0 + a_2) - a_1]$, $[\tfrac{1}{2}(a_2 + a_4) - a_3]$, $\ldots$ are very close to zero and become even closer as the suffixes increase, because a reasonable assumption is that the contributions from the outer zones become negligible. Thus we get

$$a \simeq a_0/2 \qquad (6.33)$$

a result which can also be obtained graphically. In *Figure 6.15* OA_0 is proportional to a_0, A_0A_1 to a_1, A_1A_2 to a_2 and so on. The phase difference is allowed for by drawing the vectors as shown. The sequence of points A_0, A_1, A_2, $\ldots$ ultimately reaches A, the mid-

L   151

point of OA_0, so that the resultant a is proportional to OA. But $OA = \frac{1}{2}OA_0$ and $a = \frac{1}{2}a_0$ as before. Furthermore the diagram shows that the final vector is in the same sense as the first one OA_0, so the resultant of all the contributions has the same phase as the one from the central zone. There is a gradual change of phase between rays

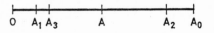

Figure 6.15. Vector diagram of resultant zonal contributions

coming from different points across each zone, and the vectors OA_0, A_0A_1, A_1A_2, ... represent the resultants for each zone. The complete vector diagram consists of a spiral starting at O, passing through A_0, A_1, A_2, ... and terminating at A. A spiral vector diagram is obtained in many examples of diffraction and can sometimes be identified approximately with Cornu's spiral, mentioned in section **6.10**.

The radius q_n is given by

$$q_n = \sqrt{[(r+\tfrac{1}{2}n\lambda)^2 - r^2]}$$
$$= \sqrt{(rn\lambda + \tfrac{1}{4}n^2\lambda^2)}$$

and if n is small

$$q_n = \sqrt{(rn\lambda)} \qquad (6.34)$$

or

$$q_n \propto \sqrt{n}$$

for particular values of r and λ. A number of concentric circles can be drawn on white card or paper such that this relation is followed and, if the central zone and alternate annular zones are blackened and then photographed, the negative on the film can be used as a *zone plate*. Collimated monochromatic light normally incident on such a negative would become 'focused' at a small region on the other side at a distance r, given by *Equation (6.34)*, because the transparent zones all contribute light of the same average phase. The vector diagram, *Figure 6.15*, then consists only of the vectors OA_0, A_1A_2 and so on in the same sense, so that the resultant would be large. The focused spot intensity could be made larger if the opaque zones were replaced by a transparent material of sufficient thickness to give an average phase angle difference of π radians between the rays emerging from these zones and the rays coming from the zones which were

152

originally transparent. This modification gives what is known as a *phase reversal zone plate*.

For a particular zone plate and wavelength of incident light, r can be calculated from *Equation (6.34)*. At a point distant $r/3$ from the plate each transparent zone transmits three Fresnel zones of the incident waves. The two near the outer edges of the transparent zone contribute light in phase at the point, while the contribution of the middle zone is π radians out of phase. The three contributions are of nearly equal amplitude so the resultant is nearly the contribution from one Fresnel zone. There will be similar contributions from the other transparent zones of the same phase, so there is a maximum at $r/3$. A similar reasoning indicates that there will be maxima at $r/5$, $r/7$ and so on, but nearly zero amplitudes at $r/2, r/4, \ldots$ since each transparent zone then transmits an even number of Fresnel zones. These maxima are smaller than the one at a distance r. The zone plate thus behaves as a converging lens having a principal focal length r and subsidiary focal lengths which are odd submultiples of r. The plate is not as efficient as a lens, for an appreciable amount of the incident light is not transmitted and the principal maximum is smaller than might be inferred from the preceding reasoning, as there is a phase difference between the contributions arriving at the focus from each zone. When light is transmitted through a lens all the light reaches the focus in phase. Furthermore the zone plate is considerably less achromatic than even a simple lens because the focal length r is, from *Equation (6.34)*, inversely proprtional to λ.

Fresnel's construction applies to sound waves, and a zone plate can be made for focusing them. The dimensions are very much larger. An acoustic zone plate with a microphone at the principal focus can be used for finding the direction of a source emitting waves covering a small frequency range. Maximum response would be obtained when the source is on the axis of the zone plate.

6.9. Diffraction at a Straight Edge

In *Figure 6.16* S is a slit source, the length of the slit being normal to the plane of the diagram. Cylindrical waves can be assumed to be radiated from S. The disturbance at P is found by dividing the wavefront WW' into half-period strips, the lengths of which are parallel to that of S along the wave-front. As with the preceding annular zones $PQ_1 = r + \lambda/2$, $PQ_2 = r + \lambda$, $PQ_3 = r + 3\lambda/2, \ldots PQ_n = r + n\lambda/2$. Here there are pairs of strips, one above and one below O. The phase angles of the resultants from adjacent strips reaching P differ by π radians.

On the plane wave-front the half-period zones have roughly equal areas, but here the half-period strips have areas which decrease as n increases. There is also a greater decrease in the contributions to the illumination at P due to the increased change of inclination of the strips, and because the distance of the strips from P increases more rapidly than for the plane wave-front. Thus the contributions a_0, a_1, a_2, ... from successive zones here decrease more rapidly than for the plane wave-front, and the effect of the whole wave is only very roughly half the effect of the first pair of strips.

If an obstacle is placed at O, as shown in *Figure 6.17.*, the disturbance at any point ahead of the obstacle is caused by the components coming from unobstructed strips. A straight edge of an opaque

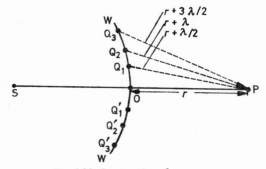

*Fig. 6.16. Construction of zones on a
cylindrical wave-front*

screen parallel to a slit source and normal to the plane of the diagram is placed at O. The screen is sufficiently large to cut off waves from the source S below SP. At P only half the wave-front is effective and the amplitude is one-half (the intensity I one-quarter) that due to the unobstructed wave.

At a point P′ in the geometrical shadow the strips above O again contribute illumination, but only those near O are effective because of the rapid decrease previously mentioned. The resultant illumination thus decreases quickly for negative values of Y, the distance of points on the plane through P measured from P.

In order to find the illumination at a point P″, for which Y is positive, the cylindrical wave-front is divided into half-period strips starting from Q″. All those on the side remote from O are effective and contribute illumination at P″ equal to that at P. The contribution from the part Q″O of the wave-front depends on the number of strips contained in this length. If there is one, its contribution is added to that from half the wave, because such a contribution is in phase with that of the strip on the other side of Q'' with which it forms a pair. The average phase of this pair determines the phase of the total illumination as their contribution is larger than that from any other pair. The resultant illumination at P'' is then greater than that from the complete wave-front, which can be verified by imagining the contribution of the first strip to be detached from that of the remainder of the half wave-front. The contribution from the second strip, while less than that of the first, is greater than any other and is π radians out of phase with the first. The resultant contribution of

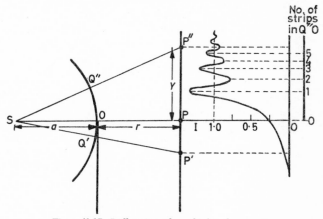

*Figure 6.17. Diffraction of a cylindrical wave at a
straight edge*

the second and remaining strips is thus π radians out of phase with that of the first, as can be verified by a vector diagram such as *Figure 6.15*. The total contribution from the half wave-front is hence less than that from the first strip alone.

If there are two strips in Q''O, these give illuminations of opposite phase and somewhat different amplitudes, the resultant contribution being small and of the same phase as that from the other half of the wave. Thus although the resultant illumination at P'' is then greater than that at P, it is less than that when there is only one strip in Q''O and is less than that from the whole wave-front. The effect of the second strip is no longer partly nullified by the remainder of the half wave-front, which would give illumination in phase with the contribution from the first strip.

155

There is thus a series of maxima and minima which rapidly converges to a value representing the illumination from the whole wavefront, the maxima being obtained from an odd number of strips in the distance $Q''O$ and the minima from an even number, as shown in *Figure 6.17*. The convergence to the illumination given by the whole wave-front, taken as unity, occurs because if P'' is far from P the obstructed zones below O are only the outer ones, which have little effect.

If there is a minimum at P'' when there is an even number of strips in $Q''O$ we have

$$OP'' - Q''P'' = m\lambda$$

where m is an integer, since the strips are half-period ones and OP'', $Q''P''$ are measured to the remote edges of these strips. Because $SO = SQ'' = a$, the radius of the wave-front

$$(SO + OP'') - (SQ'' + Q''P'') = m\lambda.$$

Thus

$$[a + \sqrt{(r^2 + Y^2)}] - \sqrt{[(a+r)^2 + Y^2]} = m\lambda$$

or

$$a + r + Y^2/2r - [a + r + Y^2/2(a+r)] \simeq m\lambda$$

if r and $a+r$ greatly exceed Y^2. Hence

$$[1/r - 1/(a+r)]Y^2/2 \simeq m\lambda$$

or

$$\left.\begin{array}{c} Y^2 \simeq r(a+r)2m\lambda/a. \\[2mm] Y^2 \simeq r(a+r)(2m-1)\lambda/a \end{array}\right\} \tag{6.35}$$

Similarly

since for an odd number of strips in $Q''O$

$$OP'' - Q''P'' = (m + \tfrac{1}{2})\lambda.$$

Besides the approximations to the binomial expansions, there is a further approximation in the first equation because the strips do not make equal contributions and

$$OP'' - Q''P'' = m\lambda$$

does not accurately define a minimum. The equations (6.35) hold only for a few fringes near P and a more rigorous analysis follows.

Q and Q' represent, in *Figure 6.18*, two points on a cylindrical wave-front of radius a. The wave is obstructed by a straight edge at O. P' is a point on a plane normal to the plane of the diagram, dis-

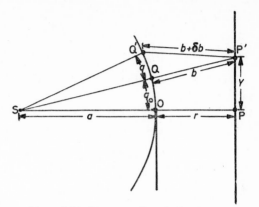

Figure 6.18. Geometry of a cylindrical wave at a straight edge

tance b from Q and $b+\delta b$ from Q'. Applying the cosine rule to triangle P'Q'S yields

$$(b+\delta b)^2 = a^2 + (a+b)^2 - 2a(a+b) \cos (q/a)$$

since q/a is the angle subtended by QQ' at the source S. a must be large if S is a point source and a cylindrical wave is considered as before. If S is a slit source, a still has to be large if the curvature of the wave-front in a direction normal to the plane of the diagram is to approach zero. We have $\cos \alpha = \sqrt{(1-\sin^2 \alpha)}$ so that

$$\cos q/a \simeq \sqrt{(1-q^2/a^2)} \simeq 1 - q^2/2a^2$$

because q/a is small. Hence

$$b^2 + 2b\delta b \simeq a^2 + a^2 + 2ab + b^2 - 2a(a+b)(1-q^2/2a^2)$$
$$\simeq b^2 + (a+b)q^2/a.$$

Thus

$$\delta b \simeq (a+b)q^2/2ab$$
$$\simeq (1/b + 1/a)q^2/2$$

or, since $1/a$ is very small

$$\delta b \simeq q^2/2b. \qquad (6.36)$$

Suppose that the vibrations on the cylindrical wave-front vary as $\sin(2\pi t/T)$, T being the period of oscillation. Then the vibration at

157

P' due to a strip δq at Q' varies as $\sin[2\pi(t/T-(b+\delta b)/\lambda)]$. If the origin is taken at Q, QO is $-q_0$, QW is q_1 and the vibration at P' due to the whole wave-front varies as

$$\int_{-q_0}^{q_1} \sin 2\pi[t/T-(b+\delta b)\lambda]\mathrm{d}q.$$

Because only δb depends on q, the vibration at P' varies as

$$[\sin 2\pi(t/T-b/\lambda)]\int_{-q_0}^{q_1} \cos (2\pi\delta b/\lambda)\mathrm{d}q$$

$$-[\cos 2\pi(t/T-b/\lambda)]\int_{-q_0}^{q_1} \sin (2\pi\delta b/\lambda)\mathrm{d}q$$

which is of the form $A \sin [2\pi(t/T-b/\lambda)-\theta]$ where

$$A \sin \theta = \int_{-q_0}^{q_1} \sin (2\pi\delta b/\lambda)\mathrm{d}q$$

$$A \cos \theta = \int_{-q_0}^{q_1} \cos (2\pi\delta b/\lambda)\mathrm{d}q.$$

The intensity of the resultant vibration varies as A^2 so that the intensity is proportional to

$$\left[\int_{-q_0}^{q_1} \sin (2\pi\delta b/\lambda)\mathrm{d}q\right]^2+\left[\int_{-q_0}^{q_1} \cos (2\pi\delta b/\lambda)\mathrm{d}q\right]^2 \qquad (6.37)$$

Relative values of intensity could hence be found by computation for particular values of q since, from *Equation (6.36)*

$$\delta b \simeq q^2/2b.$$

Evaluation is laborious and fortunately similar integrals, *Fresnel's integrals*, have been expressed in series form and tabulated for various values of the upper limit.

6.10 Fresnel's Integrals. Cornu's Spiral
Fresnel's integrals are

$$\left.\begin{array}{l} x = \displaystyle\int_0^l \cos (\pi l^2/2)\mathrm{d}l \\[20pt] y = \displaystyle\int_0^l \sin (\pi l^2/2)\mathrm{d}l \end{array}\right\} \qquad (6.38)$$

Values of these have been tabulated for various values of l, and *Equation (6.37)* can be evaluated after a suitable substitution has been made. In *Equation (6.37)*

$$2\pi\delta b/\lambda \simeq \pi q^2/b\lambda$$

using *Equation (6.36)*. Thus the substitutions are

$$\left. \begin{array}{l} l = q\sqrt{(2/b\lambda)} \\ l_1 = q_1\sqrt{(2/b\lambda)} \\ -l_0 = -q_0\sqrt{(2/b\lambda)} \end{array} \right\} \qquad (6.39)$$

and the tabulated values can be used since

$$\int_{l_0}^{l_1} = \int_0^{l_1} - \int_0^{l_0}$$

The integrals *(6.38)* define *Cornu's spiral* which can be used for a graphical evaluation of the integrals. Some geometrical properties of the spiral are first examined. From *Equations (6.38)*

$$dx/dl = \cos \pi l^2/2$$

and

$$dy/dl = \sin \pi l^2/2.$$

If ψ is the gradient at any point

$$\tan \psi = dy/dx = \tan \pi l^2/2.$$

or, if only the simplest solution is considered

$$\psi = \pi l^2/2 \qquad (6.40)$$

which is the intrinsic equation of the spiral as l is measured along the curve. This is not apparent from the preceding work, so let L be the distance measured along the curve $y = f(x)$. Then

$$\delta L^2 = \delta x^2 + \delta y^2$$

and

$$dL/dx = \sqrt{[1+(dy/dx)^2]}.$$

Here

$$dL/dx = \sqrt{(1+\tan^2\pi l^2/2)}$$

$$= \sec \pi l^2/2 = dl/dx$$

and integrating, $L = l+$a constant. If $L = 0$ when $l = 0$ the integration constant is zero. Hence $l = L$, the distance measured along the curve. The radius of curvature at any point is $dL/d\psi = dl/d\psi = \pi l$, from *Equation (6.39)*. Furthermore

$$\int_0^\infty \cos(\pi l^2/2)dl = \int_0^\infty \sin(\pi l^2/2)dl = \tfrac{1}{2}.$$

Hence the spiral has asymptotic points $(\tfrac{1}{2},\tfrac{1}{2})$ and $(-\tfrac{1}{2},-\tfrac{1}{2})$. The graph is shown in *Figure 6.19* and from it relative illumination intensities can be estimated.

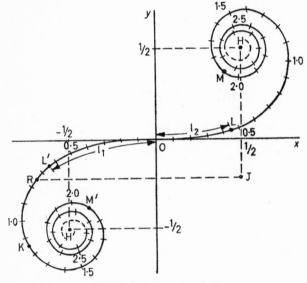

Figure 6.19. Cornu's spiral

If the radius a of the cylindrical wave incident on a straight edge is large, q_1, the upper limit in *Equation (6.37)*, will be large. The wavelength λ for light waves is very small so that, according to *Equation (6.39)*, l_1 is very large and may be assumed to be infinitely large. Then

$$RJ = \int_{-l_0}^\infty \cos(\pi l^2/2)dl$$

and

$$JH = \int_{-l_0}^\infty \sin(\pi l^2/2)dl.$$

The intensity of the disturbance at P′ in *Figure 6.18.* is proportional to $RJ^2 + JH^2$, which equals RH^2. Suppose P' is moved along the plane, starting well into the shadow. $-l_0$ is then $+\infty$ so that R is at H. As P' is moved towards P, R moves along the spiral and RH gradually increases. When P' is at P, R is at O on the spiral. R then reaches K, which corresponds to the first maximum, and as R moves round the lower spiral the other maxima and minima are defined. A

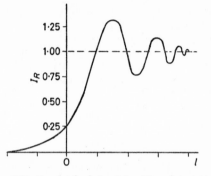

Figure 6.20. Graph of relative intensities of straight-edge diffraction maxima

steady value of the illumination is reached when R is at H', which corresponds to P' being far from P. The intensity is then four times that at P, as shown in the simple analysis. There is some error in the assumption that R starts at H, but intensity values obtained from the spiral by measuring RH agree well with those computed from the tables of Fresnel's integrals. *Figure 6.20.* shows the relative intensity I_R plotted against l.

If, in *Figure 6.18*, $PP' = Y$

$$Y = [(a+r)/a]q_0 \simeq q_0$$

since a must be very much larger than r in the preceding analysis. Thus, from *Equation (6.39)*

$$Y = l_0\sqrt{(b\lambda/2)}.$$

Suppose P' is in the geometric shadow and take b as one metre, which is also roughly the distance of the plane from the straight edge. RH is then very small. For example, if R is at the point $l_0 = 2$ on the spiral, RH^2 is about 0.025. Y is then $\sqrt{(2\lambda)}$ roughly, λ being measured in metres. If λ is 5000 Å, $Y = \sqrt{(2 \times 5 \times 10^{-7})} = 10^{-3}$ metre $= 1$ mm. Thus if the source S is far away from the straight edge, the relative intensity of illumination falls to about 0.025 at a point 1 mm inside

161

the geometric shadow, if the wavelength of the incident light is 5000 Å. For acoustic waves the point must be a much greater distance in the geometric shadow, since λ is very much larger. The distance can be found as shown, and is one metre at a frequency of 660 c/s.

The Cornu spiral can also be used to elucidate the diffraction patterns produced by single slits or opaque strips. For the slit the effective part of the spiral is that lying between $l = l_1$ and $l = l_2$ where l_1 and l_2 are determined by q_1 and q_2, the values of q at the edge of the slit. $q_2 - q_1$ is constant at all points on a plane on the side of the slit remote from the source, so that $l_2 - l_1$ is constant. Thus the nature and intensity distribution of the diffraction pattern can be found by drawing a constant arc length LL' along various parts of the spiral, and measuring the length of the chord drawn between the ends of the arc. As an aid to marking the arc length on various parts of the spiral, a piece of thread of the required length can be used. The square of the chord length is proportional to the intensity of illumination. From equation (6.39)

$$l_1 = q_1\sqrt{(2/b\lambda)} \text{ and } l_2 = q_2\sqrt{(2/b\lambda)}.$$

Hence

$$l_2 - l_1 = (q_2 - q_1)\sqrt{(2/b\lambda)}.$$

For a distant source $q_2 - q_1$ is roughly the width of the slit, and since λ is very small $l_2 - l_1$ is large in comparison with $q_2 - q_1$ which is advantageous when plotting the arc on the spiral.

For particular slit widths a minimum may occur at the centre of the fringe system. If L and L' are at M and M', for example, the chord length and hence the intensity are minimal, since the chord length increases if more of either spiral is described, which occurs when the intensities at other points on the plane are found. For wide slits there are other minima and maxima in the geometrically illuminated region, while for very wide slits the fringe system is that of two superposed straight edge patterns meeting at the centre of the bright region.

If the slit having a width corresponding to $l_2 - l_1$ is replaced by an opaque strip of the same width, the whole of the spiral in *Figure 6.19* is effective except for the arc LL', which is moved along the spiral as the intensities at points off the axis are found. The resultant amplitude is the vector sum of the chords HL and H'L', and the intensity is proportional to the square of this resultant. The fringe system can thus be seen to differ considerably from that of a slit of the same width, as was suggested in section **6.5**.

ACOUSTICAL WAVE PHENOMENA

7.1. Velocity of Moderate Amplitude Waves in a Gas

Equation (*6.3*) is

$$S \simeq -\partial s/\partial x$$

where S, the condensation, is given by

$$\rho = \rho_0(1+S)$$

ρ and ρ_0 being the instantaneous and static densities. For adiabatic changes the pressure and density of a gas are related by

$$p/P_0 \simeq (\rho/\rho_0)^\gamma$$

where p and P_0 are the excess and static pressures and γ is the ratio of the specific heat of the gas at constant pressure to that at constant volume. Hence

$$p/P_0 \simeq (1+S)^\gamma$$

$$\simeq (1+\partial s/\partial x)^{-\gamma}$$

and if both sides are differentiated with respect to x

$$\partial p/\partial x \simeq -\gamma P_0(\partial^2 s/\partial x^2)(1+\partial s/\partial x)^{-(\gamma+1)}.$$

From the analysis concerning plane longitudinal waves in section **4.2.** there comes

$$A\rho_0 \partial^2 s/\partial t^2 = -\partial F/\partial x$$

or

$$\partial^2 s/\partial t^2 = -(1/\rho_0)\partial p/\partial x \qquad (7.1)$$

since $p = F/A$. (*7.1*) is an acceleration equation, and is a simplified form of a general one which is obtained in hydrodynamics. Substituting for $\partial p/\partial x$ in *Equation* (*7.1*) gives

$$\partial^2 s/\partial t^2 \simeq (\gamma P_0/\rho_0)(1+\partial s/\partial x)^{-(\gamma+1)}\partial^2 s/\partial x^2$$

and the comparison of this non-linear equation with the one-dimensional wave equation

$$\partial^2 s/\partial t^2 = c^2 \partial^2 s/\partial x^2 \qquad (4.6)$$

suggests that the wave velocity c_a is given approximately by

$$c_a = \sqrt{[(\gamma P_0/\rho_0)(1+\partial s/\partial x)^{-(\gamma+1)}]}.$$

In section **4.2.** the velocity c for small amplitude waves has been shown to equal $\sqrt{(\gamma P_0/\rho_0)}$ so that

$$c_a \simeq c(1+\partial s/\partial x)^{-\frac{1}{2}(\gamma+1)}$$

or

$$c_a \simeq c(1+S)^{\frac{1}{2}(\gamma+1)} \qquad (7.2)$$

which is for plane waves. For spherical waves the amplitude decreases as the waves advance, and *Equation (7.2)* has to be modified. While (7.2) is of limited quantitative use, it does indicate that plane waves travel at a speed c only if the condensation S is negligible.

S is dependent on the wavelength λ as well as on the particle displacement amplitude a, and can be expressed in terms of the ratio a/λ. For a plane sinusoidal wave

$$s = a \sin 2\pi(t/T - x/\lambda)$$

according to section **5.1.** Hence

$$\partial s/\partial x = -(2\pi a/\lambda) \cos 2\pi(t/T - x/\lambda)$$

$$\simeq -S$$

from *Equation (6.3)*. The maximum condensation S_{max} is thus given by

$$S_{max} = 2\pi a/\lambda. \qquad (7.3)$$

The ratio a/λ thus gives a measure of the departure of c_a from c.

Consider waves of amplitude a, which equals 5×10^{-5} cm, travelling in air. c is about 330 m sec^{-1} and at a frequency of 2 Mc/s, λ is $1 \cdot 65 \times 10^{-2}$ cm. Then

$$S_{max} = 2\pi \times 5 \times 10^{-5}/1 \cdot 65 \times 10^{-2} \simeq 2 \times 10^{-2}.$$

Taking γ as $1 \cdot 4$ gives $c_a \simeq c(1 \cdot 02)^{1 \cdot 2}$ or $c_a \simeq 1 \cdot 024c$. The increase in speed is thus about $2\frac{1}{2}$ per cent. For a frequency in the region of the upper limit of audibility, 20 kc/s, the increase in speed is only $0 \cdot 02$ per cent because S_{max} is about 2×10^{-4}. The excess pressures corresponding to the values of S_{max} obtained can be calculated by using *Equation (6.4)*

$$p = \kappa S$$

where κ, the elastic modulus of the medium, is for a gas γP_0 according to *Equation* (*4.3*) and the preceding reasoning. Hence a displacement amplitude of 5×10^{-5} cm in air at a frequency of 20 kc/s corresponds to a maximum condensation of 2×10^{-4}, the maximum excess pressure being

$$p_{max} = 1 \cdot 4 \times 76 \times 13 \cdot 6 \times 981 \times 2 \times 10^{-4}$$
$$= 2 \cdot 8 \times 10^2 \text{ dynes/cm}^2.$$

For a sinusoidal wave, the root-mean-square value of pressure is $p_{max}/\sqrt{2}$ which here equals 2×10^2 dynes/cm^2, a pressure in the region of the threshold of feeling for the human ear.

Equation (*7.2*) shows that in a wave of moderate amplitude the propagation velocity is greater at compressions, which correspond to positive values of S, than at rarefactions, where S is negative. The form of the wave changes as it advances, the process being described as the *overtaking effect* since the crests tend to overtake the troughs. The change of form is indicated in *Figure 7.1*, which shows a part of

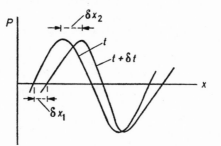

Figure 7.1. Change of wave form

the wave at time t and at a later time $t + \delta t$. During the time δt points along the x axis have advanced a distance δx_1 where $\delta x_1 = c\delta t$, and the crest has advanced a distance δx_2, given by $\delta x_2 = c_a \delta t$. Hence

$$\delta x_2 - \delta x_1 = (c_a - c)\delta t$$

and from *Equation* (*7.2*)

$$c_a \simeq c + \tfrac{1}{2}(\gamma + 1)cS_{max}$$

because at crests the condensation has the maximum value S_{max}. Thus

$$\delta x_2 - \delta x_1 \simeq \tfrac{1}{2}(\gamma + 1)c\delta t S_{max}$$

or

$$\delta x_2 - \delta x_1 \simeq \tfrac{1}{2}(\gamma + 1)\delta x_1 S_{max}. \tag{7.4}$$

165

γ, δx_1 and S_{max} are all positive, so the wave changes form in the manner indicated in *Figure 7.1* as it advances, the pressure gradient at the wave front becoming very large and thus a *shock wave* can be formed. According to *Equation (7.4)* a wave would change form even for a very small S_{max} if δx_1 were sufficiently large, but no account has been taken of energy loss as the wave advances. For large amplitude waves the energy loss is considerable and, unless the wave is initially of very large amplitude, energy dissipation will rapidly decrease the amplitude of the travelling wave below that necessary for the production of a shock. Sound waves coming from explosions are sometimes of sufficient amplitude for a shock wave to be formed.

The large pressure gradient is associated with a big density gradient in the medium in which the wave is travelling. Light is refracted appreciably where the density gradient is large, and there are various optical methods for investigating large amplitude and shock waves. Shock waves will be examined again in section **7.4**.

The overtaking effect is often seen when large amplitude sea waves approach a slightly shelving beach. The wave velocity varies with the depth of the water according to *Equation (4.31)*. In shallow water there will be a large difference in depth, and thus in velocity, between the crests and the troughs, which are overtaken by the crests. The crests become shorter and increase in amplitude until their faces become vertical and fall into the preceding troughs.

7.2. Maximum Power Transmission in Fluids

If p_{max}, the excess pressure amplitude in a fluid, is greater than the static pressure P_0, voids are formed in the fluid during the minima in the cyclic variation of the excess pressure p with time t. *Cavitation* is then said to occur, as mentioned in section **6.7**. The transmission of energy is thus limited because energy is used in forming the voids. The transmitted energy is a maximum when p_{max} equals P_0.

For a plane sinusoidal wave travelling parallel to an x axis

$$s = a \sin 2\pi(t/T - x/\lambda)$$

and, as in the preceding section

$$S = (2\pi a/\lambda) \cos 2\pi(t/T - x/\lambda).$$

The particle velocity v is given by

$$v = (2\pi a/T) \cos 2\pi(t/T - x/\lambda)$$

so that

$$v/S = \lambda/T = \lambda f = c \qquad (7.5)$$

166

where f and c are the frequency and velocity of the wave. *Equation (6.4)* is

$$p = \kappa S$$

and, from *Equation (4.2)*

$$\kappa = \rho_0 c^2.$$

Thus

$$v = p/\rho_0 c \qquad (7.6)$$

when S is eliminated from *Equation (7.5)*.

The total energy per unit volume of a plane wave is $\frac{1}{2}\rho_0 \omega^2 a^2$ according to *Equation (6.8)*. ωa is $2\pi f a$ or $2\pi a/T$, the maximum particle velocity v_{max}. The maximum energy transmitted across unit area per unit time is

$$\frac{1}{2}\rho_0 \omega^2 a^2 c = \frac{1}{2}\rho_0 v_{max}^2 c = \frac{1}{2}p_{max}^2/\rho_0 c$$

using *Equation (7.6)*, and this is also the maximum power W_{max} crossing unit area. Thus

$$W_{max} = \frac{1}{2}p_{max}^2/\rho_0 c. \qquad (7.7)$$

$\rho_0 c$ is the unit area acoustical impedance of the fluid as noted in section **6.3.**, so there is a similarity between *Equation (7.7)* and the electrical equation

$$W_e = \frac{1}{2}I^2/Y$$

where W_e is the power developed or dissipated in an electrical circuit, I the current, and Y the admittance as mentioned in section **2.6.**

The values for $\rho_0 c$ previously quoted in section **6.3.** can be used in *Equation (7.7)* to find the maximum power that can be transmitted through unit area in air or in water near the surface. p_{max} will equal P_0, atmospheric pressure, which can be taken as 10^6 dynes/cm^2. For air $\rho_0 c$, which equals Z, is about 40 g cm^{2}sec^{-1} and is $1 \cdot 5 \times 10^5$ for water in the same units. Hence for air

$$W_{max} = \frac{1}{2} \times 10^{12}/40 = 1 \cdot 25 \times 10^{10} \text{ erg sec cm}^{-2}$$

$$= 1 \cdot 25 \text{ kW/cm}^2.$$

For water

$$W_{max} = \frac{1}{2} \times 10^{12}/1 \cdot 5 \times 10^5$$

$$= 3 \cdot 33 \times 10^{-4} \text{ kW/cm}^2.$$

Thus the maximum power that can be transmitted by water without

M

cavitation occurring is very much smaller than that which can pass through air at the same pressure. Generally much more power can be passed through gases than through liquids.

The maximum power transmitted is independent of frequency, but the displacement amplitude associated with maximum power is not. We have

$$v = (2\pi a/T) \cos 2\pi(t/T - x/\lambda)$$

for a plane wave and, from *Equation (7.6)*

$$v = p/\rho_0 c.$$

Hence

$$p_{max}/\rho_0 c = 2\pi a/T = 2\pi f a$$

or

$$a = P_0/2\pi f Z$$

since p_{max} equals P_0 when the maximum power is transmitted. For air a is thus nearly 20 cm at 200 c/s and 2 mm at 20 kc/s, both of which are much too large to be generated by present-day transducers, although such amplitudes could be reached in waves from explosions near the source if the explosion were sufficiently large.

For water near the surface the corresponding figures are 5.3×10^{-3} cm and 5.3×10^{-5} cm, while at an ultrasonic frequency of 200 kc/s the particle displacement amplitude corresponding to maximum power transmission is only 5.3×10^{-6} cm. Such an amplitude is easily attained because a transducer can be efficiently coupled to a liquid. The radiation impedance of the transducer and the impedance of the liquid can usually be matched more closely than when transducers radiate into gases. Thus, at ultrasonic frequencies, cavitation can easily occur in water and in many other liquids. If the liquid contains dissolved gases these give rise to streams of bubbles in a standing wave system at the pressure antinodes, even when p_{max} is smaller than P_0. If the dissolved gases have been previously removed, vapour bubbles may be generated from the liquid surrounding pressure antinodes when p_{max} is smaller than P_0. Because of one or both of these effects the figures for maximum power can be significantly less than the preceding figures, which were obtained by assuming that W_{max} is reached when p_{max} equals P_0.

The coupling between a transducer and a gas into which radiation occurs is inefficient, because of the large discrepancy between their impedances. For a direct radiator loudspeaker the radiation efficiency is only a few per cent and, if impedances are matched more closely by fitting a horn to the loudspeaker, the maximum efficiency does not rise to more than about thirty per cent. Thus in practice the maximum power that can be transmitted through gases at usual pressures and temperatures is very much less than $1\cdot2$ kW/cm^2, so cavitation is not approached. Moreover energy dissipation is very large at large vibrational amplitudes in fluids and in solids, for which transducer coupling is also inefficient although it can be improved by using a medium, usually an oil, between the transducer and the solid. Contact between the transducer and the solid is thereby improved and energy transfer can be further facilitated if the medium is of intermediate acoustic impedance, as suggested in section **6.3.** If the solid itself forms part of the transducer, for example in some magnetostrictive transducers, dissipation limits severely the amount of energy that can be transmitted.

7.3. Doppler Effect. Waves from Projectiles

Large amplitude waves are often radiated from projectiles, including jet aircraft, and travel with an increased velocity as shown in section **7.1.** There is in addition, even if the velocity of the projectile is constant, an apparent change in the frequency of the emitted waves which is known as the *Doppler effect*, although Russell, Fizeau and possibly Babinet discovered the effect independently. The effect was originally invoked to explain the change in colour of stars. Their colour depends partly on whether they are approaching or receding from the earth, from which they are observed. The explanation was unsound, in that a relative velocity would be required which was much greater than that estimated and because the simple Doppler effect does not accurately apply to electro-magnetic waves. More success was later obtained when the shift of the spectral lines in light from stars was explained with reference to the Doppler effect, but again a relativistic correction to the effect is required for the explanation to be complete. Briefly, according to Einstein's special theory of relativity there is a time and a length dilatation in a system of moving co-ordinates, so that a frequency f_0 becomes reduced to f given by

$$f = f_0 \sqrt{(1 - u^2/c_0^2)}$$

where u is the velocity of the co-ordinate system and c_0 is the velocity of light in free space. Thus a moving source suffers a frequency reduction independent of and supplementary to that from the Doppler effect. The same result applies if the source is stationary and an observer is moving. u cannot exceed c_0, in contrast to sound waves when the velocity of the source or observer may exceed the wave velocity. The relativistic correction is negligible if u is very much smaller than c_0.

Doppler's effect can be demonstrated by fixing a sound source near the edge of a gramophone turntable. To an observer in the plane of rotation of the source, its velocity varies between $\pm 2\pi r n$, where r is the radius of the circle of rotation and n is the number of revolutions per unit time. n should be small if frequency measurements are to be made. Such an experiment was originally devised by Mach.

The apparent frequency as recorded by an observer is easily calculated when the velocities of the source and observer are in the same direction, providing that the amplitude of the emitted sound is sufficiently low for the wave velocity c to be the same everywhere in the acoustic field. In *Figure 7.2* S and O are the initial positions of

Figure 7.2. Motion of source and observer

the source and observer and S', O' their positions unit time later. Their velocities u_s and u_0, the wave velocity c and that of the medium through which the waves are travelling, w, are all in the same sense. If f is the frequency of waves generated by the source, while it is moving from S to S' the f waves emitted have reached P. These f waves occupy the distance S'P which equals $c + w - u_s$ and the length of the waves is

$$(c + w - u_s)/f$$

which will be the same at all points ahead of the source. If the source were stationary, the f waves would be contained in the distance SP which equals $c + w$. The effect of the motion of the source is thus to reduce the length of the waves travelling in the same sense, while those travelling in the opposite sense are increased in length.

Only the f' waves passing the observer would be heard by him, and they are contained in the distance O'Q which is $c+w-u_0$ so their effective wavelength is

$$(c+w-u_0)/f'.$$

Hence

$$(c+w-u_s)/f = (c+w-u_0)/f'$$

or

$$f' = f(c+w-u_0)/(c+w-u_s). \tag{7.8}$$

If u_0, u_s or w are in the opposite sense, they merely have to be replaced by $-u_0$, $-u_s$ or $-w$ where they occur in *Equation (7.8)*. Thus if the source and the observer were travelling in the opposite sense to that shown in *Figure 7.2*, *Equation (7.8)* would become

$$f' = f(c+w+u_0)/(c+w+u_s). \tag{7.9}$$

f' given by *Equation (7.8)* is different from that given by *(7.9)* if the speeds remain the same, and hence the velocity of S relative to O is the same. The significance lies not in the velocity of S relative to O, but in the velocities of S and O relative to the sound wave. If u_0 equals u_s and they are both in the same sense, the velocity of the medium has, if it remains constant, no effect on frequency.

From *Equation (7.8)* as u_s increases continuously from zero, f' increases regularly from $f(c+w-u_0)/(c+w)$ until u_s equals $c+w$. Then all the waves travel with the source and reach the observer simultaneously, so that f' may be said to be infinite. The increase in f' is not noticed above the upper frequency limit of audibility, about 20 kc/s, but the increase could be recorded, the frequency response of the recording apparatus being the limiting factor. If u_s is greater than $c+w$, f' decreases in magnitude but is always negative. The interpretation is that then the waves are received in the reverse order, the source having outstripped the emitted waves. If u_s is in the opposite sense, *Equation (7.9)* applies and f' decreases to zero as u_s increases.

As u_0 increases from zero, f' decreases to zero according to *Equation (7.8)*. If u_0 is greater than $c+w$, f' increases in magnitude but is negative. The observer then overtakes the waves, which are received in the reverse order. If the observer is approaching the source, *Equation (7.9)* applies and f' increases as u_0 increases.

If the source and observer are not moving in the same direction, f' can be obtained from *Equation (7.8)* by replacing u_s and u_0 with the component velocities of S and O in the direction of the sound

171

wave. For example, if u_0 and w are zero and u_s is as shown in *Figure 7.3*

$$f' = f(c)/(c - u_s \cos \theta) \qquad (7.10a)$$
$$= f[(c - u_s \cos \theta)/c]^{-1}$$

or

$$f' = f(c + u_s \cos \theta)/c \qquad (7.10b)$$

if u_s is small in comparison with c. A similar allowance can be made if w is not in the same direction as c. Then the component velocity of the medium in the direction of the sound wave is required in *Equation (7.8)*.

If u_s is constant in magnitude and direction and is as shown in *Figure 7.3*

$$f' = f(c + u_s)/c$$

when PS is very large, and decreases as P is approached. When S is at P $f' = f$. As S recedes from P on the other side f' decreases to $f(c - u_s)/c$. For a particular u_s the frequency f' changes gradually if OP is large, and more rapidly if OP is small, but in both instances the change is continuous.

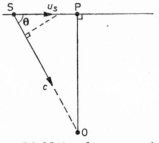

Figure 7.3. Motion of source away from stationary observer

An equation such as *(7.10a)* can be used for a projectile if u_s is constant and if the waves coming from the projectile are of a sufficiently small amplitude for the wave velocity c to be constant everywhere. The frequencies of the sounds emitted may be functions of the speed of the projectile, while for modern projectiles u_s and c are usually comparable and u_s is often greater than c. If the trajectory is as shown in *Figure 7.3* and u_s is greater than c, at some point in the path $u_s \cos \theta$ could equal c. The waves generated in the region of this point arrive simultaneously at O. The result is a sharp, intense sound—

a *shock wave*, nowadays often called a 'supersonic bang', and is the first sound to be heard if the starting of the projectile is inaudible because of a long distance between the starting point and the observer. $u_s \cos \theta$ is greater than c for small values of θ if u_s is greater than c, and the projectile outstrips its own waves until it becomes sufficiently close to the observer.

The shock wave is a compression pulse and is examined in more detail in section **7.4**. Such waves are produced continuously from both the nose and tail of the projectile, their paths lying instantaneously along cones having their apices close to the nose and tail.

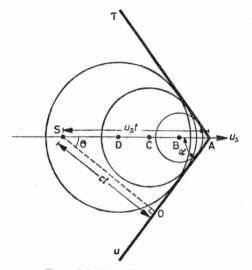

Figure 7.4. Waves from a projectile

The width of intersections of these cones on the surface of the earth from projectiles travelling above is often of the order of a quarter of a mile. The picturesque term 'breaking the sound barrier' is misleading if shock wave production is associated with the noise of 'breaking', although there is a 'sound barrier' in the sense that airflow past the projectile, and hence the force acting on it, is substantially altered when u_s exceeds c.

The speed of the projectile can be found by measuring α, the semiangle of a cone defining a shock wave path, indicated in *Figure 7.4*. Suppose A is the position of a projectile at time t, which equals OS/c, where OS is the distance of the projectile from O when the

173

shock wave is received, the time zero being when the projectile is at S. Along its trajectory, points B, C, D, . . . are found such that AB $= u_s t'$, AC $= 2u_s t'$, AD $= 3u_s t'$, . . . where t' is any convenient time interval, perhaps unity. With centres B, C, D, . . . and radii ct', $2ct'$, $3ct'$, . . . circles are drawn which are coplanar with u_s and O. There are common tangents AT and AU to these circles, one of which passes through O. We have

$$\cos \theta = ct/u_s t$$

or

$$u_s \cos \theta = c$$

which is a relation previously quoted. We also find that

$$\sin \alpha = \cos \theta = c/u_s.$$

The ratio u_s/c is known as the *Mach number* and is greater than unity for speeds exceeding that of sound.

Figure 7.4 in three dimensions would show a cone enveloping spheres of radii ct', $2ct'$, $3ct'$, . . . By Huyghen's construction this cone is the resultant wave of all those emitted at points along AS and is the 'nose-wave' of the projectile travelling in the direction indicated. Such a wave, together with one coming from the tail, can actually be photographed when generated by small projectiles such as rifle bullets if a suitable lighting arrangement is devised. Then α can be measured, and u_s calculated if c is known. α should not be measured very close to the nose, because there the condensation is large and c is increased to c_a according to *Equation (7.2)*. Thus near the nose α is higher than that giving the true Mach number, such an effect being increased by a blunt-nosed projectile.

7.4. Shock Fronts and Waves

The *overtaking effect* has been mentioned in section **7.1**. The term is used to describe the change of form of a wave of appreciable amplitude as it advances, and also applies to pulses of a large excess pressure increase. The leading edge of the pulse cannot become normal to the direction of travel, for then energy would be dissipated by viscosity and thermal conduction processes at an infinite rate, but a pulse from, for example, an explosion can have a very steep leading edge. Dissipation in this region cannot be ignored in a theoretical investigation although energy losses in the remainder of the pulse may be negligible. The steep region, which corresponds to a large pressure gradient, is known as a *shock-front*, the pressure change being spread over a distance of the order of ten to a hundred molecular diameters.

Rankine and *Hugoniot* showed that a shock-front can be described uniquely in terms of propagation velocity, stream velocity and magnitude of the pressure change. The rate of dissipation of energy during the passage of the shock-front was found without the actual values of viscosity and thermal conductivity for the surrounding fluid being required, although they were assumed to be finite but small. A simplified analysis follows.

The pressure in the undisturbed fluid is assumed to be P_0 and a shock is moving into the fluid at a velocity U. The stream velocity immediately behind the shock is u and the densities of the fluid in front of and behind the shock are ρ_0 and ρ. The shock is brought to rest by imposing a velocity U on the fluid, so that the undisturbed fluid arrives at the shock with a velocity U and leaves with a velocity $U-u$, as indicated in *Figure 7.5*.

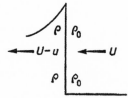

Figure 7.5. Moving shock-front

For the conservation of mass of the fluid

$$\rho(U-u) = \rho_0 U. \qquad (7.11)$$

In unit time the momentum $\rho_0 U \times U$ is brought up to unit area of the shock, while $\rho(U-u) \times (U-u)$ is carried away. The difference between these two momenta is, according to Newton's second law of motion, the force acting on unit area of the shock. Thus

$$P + \rho(U-u)^2 = P_0 + \rho_0 U^2$$

and by substituting for $\rho(U-u)$ in this equation from *(7.11)* we have

$$P - P_0 = \rho_0 U u. \qquad (7.12)$$

A third equation can be obtained by a reasoning similar to that used in the investigation of the Joule–Thomson effect for the passage of a gas through a porous plug. The undisturbed fluid passes into the shock at pressure P_0, is suddenly compressed and leaves at a pressure P. Because P_0 and P are steady, each element of the fluid suffers the

175

same change. The work done on unit mass entering the shock is the product of P_0 and the volume of unit mass, that is P_0/ρ_0. The work done by unit mass of the fluid on leaving the shock is P/ρ. The difference between these two quantities is the sum of the changes in kinetic and internal energies of unit mass of the fluid. As in the porous-plug experiment the corresponding temperature change differs from that for a reversible change of pressure from P_0 to P. If energy is conserved

$$P_0/\rho_0 + \tfrac{1}{2}U^2 + E_0 = P/\rho + \tfrac{1}{2}(U-u)^2 + E \qquad (7.13)$$

where E_0 and E are the internal energies of the fluid on either side of the shock-front.

If the specific heats and the equation of state, which relates pressures, densities and temperatures, are known, *Equations (7.11)*, *(7.12)* and *(7.13)* are sufficient for the calculation of P, ρ, U and u, if one of these is known in addition to P_0 or ρ_0 and the corresponding temperature. The equations can be used to find the rate of dissipation of energy of the shock which, for weak shocks, is directly proportional to the cube of the pressure difference. They can also be used to show that in any ordinary fluid, for which $\partial P/\partial \rho$ increases with pressure, a pulse of an excess pressure decrease (P less than P_0) is not feasible since the direct conversion of heat into mechanical energy would be implied. Such a pulse becomes smoothed out, as

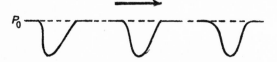

Figure 7.6. Change of form of a trough

indicated in *Figure 7.6*, because regions of low pressure travel less rapidly than those of high pressure, according to the treatment in section **7.1**.

From *Equation (7.11)*

$$u = U(\rho - \rho_0)/\rho = (U-u)(\rho - \rho_0)/\rho_0$$

so that, using *Equation (7.12)*

$$P - P_0 = U(U-u)(\rho - \rho_0). \qquad (7.14)$$

176

We have

$$\rho_0(P-P_0)/(\rho-\rho_0) = (P-P_0)/(\rho-\rho_0)/\rho_0$$
$$\simeq (P-P_0)/(\rho-\rho_0)/\rho = (P-P_0)/(1/\rho_0 - 1/\rho)/1/\rho_0$$
$$= (P-P_0)/(V_0-V)/V_0$$

which equals κ, the bulk modulus of elasticity, because, for a constant mass of fluid, the volume V or V_0 is directly proportional to the density ρ or ρ_0. Hence

$$(P-P_0)/(\rho-\rho_0) = \kappa/\rho_0 = c^2$$

from *Equation (4.2)*, where c is the velocity of small amplitude sound waves. Thus, using *Equation (7.14)*

$$U^2 - Uu \simeq c^2 \text{ or } U \simeq c + \tfrac{1}{2}u.$$

The velocity of a shock-front is hence greater than that of small amplitude sound waves. The last result applies to fluids generally and to gases in particular, when it differs from a result obtained from *Equation (7.2)*

$$c_a \simeq c + \tfrac{1}{2}(\gamma+1)cS.$$

From section **7.2.** the ratio of the particle velocity to the condensation S has been shown to equal c in a plane sinusoidal wave, so that here u ought to be roughly cS and U, which is equivalent to c_a, should be given by

$$U \simeq c + \tfrac{1}{2}(\gamma+1)u$$

using the preceding result from *Equation (7.2)*. The discrepancy between this result and the one from the present analysis occurs because no allowance has been made for energy changes in the analysis leading to *Equation (7.2)*, there being some approximations and relations which hold for plane sinusoidal waves which cannot be applied here without modification. The division by a shock-front of a region of fluid flow in which the stream velocity exceeds the velocity of sound from one in which it is less is indicated, and is a usual property of shock-fronts. Thus in *Figure 7.5* fluid flows into the shock at velocity U which equals $c + \tfrac{1}{2}u$, and leaves at $U - u$ which is $c - \tfrac{1}{2}u$.

7.5. Radiation Pressure

When waves impinge on a surface, a force is exerted which tends to move the surface towards a region where there are no waves. The force can be described as a *radiation pressure* which depends on the energy of the wave and is independent of any vibrations conferred on the surface particles by the wave.

Consider a plane longitudinal sound wave incident normally on a plane surface S_1S_2 which is normal to the plane of *Figure 7.7*. A_1A_2 is a plane containing undisplaced particles and is parallel to and distant $2a$ from S_1S_2. B_1B_2 and C_1C_2 mark the limits of vibration of the particles contained in A_1A_2, a being the displacement amplitude. When the vibrating particles lie in the plane B_1B_2 the fluid pressure acting on S_1S_2 is $2P_0$; when they are in C_1C_2 the pressure is $2P_0/3$, P_0 being the static pressure and Boyle's law being assumed to hold, for simplicity. The net pressure on the surface is $4P_0/3$ which is the radiation pressure. Actually the radiation pressure is very much smaller, because the motions of fluid particles near stationary

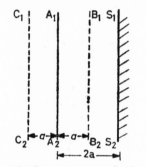

Figure 7.7. Plane wave near a fixed surface

surfaces are almost negligible in comparison with those in the main body of the fluid, but the illustration, due to Poynting, indicates the existence of radiation pressures.

Radiation pressure can be found in terms of the wave energy by a method devised by Larmor. A reflecting boundary is assumed to move in the positive x direction at a velocity u against an incident plane wave given by

$$s_i = a_i \sin k_i(x+ct)$$

where k_i is $2\pi/\lambda_i$, the wave travelling in the negative x direction. The reflected wave has a higher frequency because of the Doppler effect, and hence a greater *activity*—energy per unit area per unit time. The energy increase is presumed to be due to work being done by the reflector against the radiation pressure.

The reflected wave is

$$s_r = a_r \sin k_r(x - ct)$$

where k_r is $2\pi/\lambda_r$. At the surface of the reflector the total particle displacement can be taken as zero. Thus

$$s_i + s_r = 0$$

and if the reflector started moving from the origin at $t = 0$, $x = ut$ so we have

$$a_i \sin k_i t(u+c) + a_r \sin k_r t(u-c) = 0$$

which is true at any time so that

$$a_i = a_r \quad \text{and} \quad k_i(u+c) = -k_r(u-c)$$

for the smallest values. Hence

$$(c-u)/(c+u) = k_i/k_r = \lambda_r/\lambda_i. \tag{7.15}$$

According to *Equation (6.8)* the total energy per unit volume of plane waves is directly proportional to ω^2, ω being the angular frequency of the wave. Thus

$$E_i/E_r = \omega_i^2/\omega_r^2 = \lambda_r^2/\lambda_i^2 = (c-u)^2/(c+u)^2 \tag{7.16}$$

where E_i and E_r are here the total incident and reflected energies, and $\lambda_i = 2\pi c/\omega_i$, $\lambda_r = 2\pi c/\omega_r$, because if the reflector is perfect no energy is absorbed by it. Hence

$$E_r = E_i(c+u)^2/(c-u)^2$$

or

$$E_i + E_r = E_i[1 + (c+u)^2/(c-u)^2]$$

that is

$$E_i + E_r = 2E_i(c^2 + u^2)/(c-u)^2. \tag{7.17}$$

The activities of the waves are e_i and e_r given by

$$e_i = E_i(c+u) \tag{7.18}$$

$$e_r = E_r(c-u). \tag{7.19}$$

Thus, using *Equation (7.16)*

$$e_r/e_i = (c+u)/(c-u). \tag{7.20}$$

The work done by the reflector per unit area per unit time is $P_R u$, where P_R is the radiation pressure. This work is the difference between the activities of the reflected and incident waves so that

$$P_R u = e_r - e_i = e_i[2u/(c-u)]$$

from *Equation (7.20)*. Hence

$$P_R = 2e_i/(c-u) = 2E_i(c+u)/(c-u)$$

from *Equation (7.18)* and using *Equation (7.17)* we get

$$P_R = (E_i + E_r)(c^2 - u^2)/(c^2 + u^2). \qquad (7.21)$$

For a perfect reflector at rest $u = 0$, and $E_i = E_r = E$ because $\lambda_r = \lambda_i$. Then

$$P_R = 2E. \qquad (7.22)$$

If the boundary is a perfect absorber $E_r = 0$ and, putting $E_i = E$ as before

$$P_R = E. \qquad (7.23)$$

This equation is apparently identical with (*7.22*) if E is taken as the *total* energy density, but the distinction is preferable in order that confusion may be avoided.

Brillouin and Langevin obtained the last two equations by considering waves in an infinite medium. Such a condition usually corresponds closely to those in which radiation pressure measurements are made, and the results are independent of the equation of state of the fluid in which the experiments are done. Hence the last two equations usually apply more accurately than, for example, Rayleigh's equation

$$P_R = (\gamma + 1)E \qquad (7.24)$$

which refers to a perfect reflector in a gas. This equation agrees with (*7.22*) for isothermal conditions.

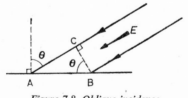

Figure 7.8. Oblique incidence

The incident wave has so far been assumed to be normal to the reflecting or absorbing surface. *Oblique incidence* is indicated in *Figure 7.8*. AB represents a plane surface which is a perfect absorber, a plane wave of unit cross-sectional area being incident at angle θ. The total force on AB is the same as on a plane BC normal to the wave, but the area of AB is greater than unity by an amount sec θ because $AB = BC \sec \theta$. Hence the pressure on AB is smaller, the normal component of pressure being $(E \cos \theta) \cos \theta$ which is $E \cos^2 \theta$, while the tangential component is $(E \sin \theta) \cos \theta$. If there is complete reflection at AB the normal component of pressure is doubled, but the resultant tangential pressure is zero because the two components are in opposite senses.

From *Equation (6.8)* the total energy per unit volume, which is here denoted by E, of a plane wave is $\frac{1}{2}\rho_0\omega^2 a^2$ and for a plane wave u_{max}, the maximum particle velocity, is ωa, which can be shown by taking

$$s = a \sin 2\pi(t/T - x/\lambda)$$

and differentiating with respect to t. Thus

$$E = \tfrac{1}{2}\rho_0 u_{max}^2$$

and, for a perfect reflector

$$P_R = 2E = \rho_0 u_{max}^2.$$

Writing *Equation (7.6)* in terms of the maximum particle velocity and excess pressure p_{max} we have

$$u_{max} = p_{max}/\rho_0 c.$$

Thus

$$P_R = u_{max}p_{max}/c$$

or

$$P_R/p_{max} = u_{max}/c. \tag{7.25}$$

This equation shows that P_R is very small in comparison with p_{max} as the maximum particle velocity is greatly exceeded by the wave velocity in small-amplitude waves. Such a conclusion also follows from the following extension.

From section **7.2.**

$$u_{max}/S_{max} = c.$$

Hence, from *Equation (7.25)*

$$P_R = p_{max}S_{max}.$$

But according to *Equation (6.4)*

$$p_{max} = \kappa S_{max}$$

so that

$$P_R = \kappa S_{max}^2. \tag{7.26}$$

181

For small-amplitude waves S_{max} is almost negligible, so that P_R is very small. Even for moderate-amplitude waves P_R is still very small. Using, for example, some of the data for waves of moderate amplitude from section 7.1., S_{max} is 2×10^{-2} for waves in air of amplitude 5×10^{-5} cm and frequency 2 Mc/s. κ is γP_0 and is roughly $1 \cdot 4 \times 10^6$ dynes/cm^2 at normal atmospheric pressure. Hence

$$P_R = 1 \cdot 4 \times 10^6 \times 4 \times 10^{-4}$$

which is $5 \cdot 6 \times 10^2$ dynes/cm^2 or about $4 \cdot 2 \times 10^{-2}$ cm of mercury. Radiation pressures of this order can be measured with an *acoustic radiometer* which consists of a disc attached to and counterbalanced on the horizontal arm of a torsion balance having a very fine suspension. The diameter of the disc should be large compared with the length λ_i of the incident wave, in order to eliminate diffraction effects. At low frequencies a baffle surrounding, but not touching, the disc renders an inconveniently large disc unnecessary. The acoustic field may be appreciably altered by the presence of the radiometer.

Equations (7.22) and (7.23) also apply to electro-magnetic waves, although their derivation is then substantially different. The radiation pressure of electro-magnetic waves was predicted and calculated by Maxwell and is very much smaller than that for acoustic waves. For solar radiation at the earth's surface, the normal radiation pressure for normal incidence on a good reflector is only about 10^{-4} dyne/cm^2. Hence measurement, by Lebedew, Nicholls and Hull and others, was delayed until about the beginning of this century. Optical masers, mentioned in section 9.2., can be developed to emit very intense monochromatic beams, and presumably the intensities could be such as to facilitate comparison by radiometers instead of by conventional photometric methods.

ELECTRO-MAGNETIC WAVES

8.1. General. Maxwell's Equations

Electro-magnetic waves cover a vast range of wavelengths—from about 10^{-12} to 10^8 cm for those at present known, as indicated in *Figure 8.1*. All these waves can be described by some equations which are later obtained, but many effects which depend on wavelength or

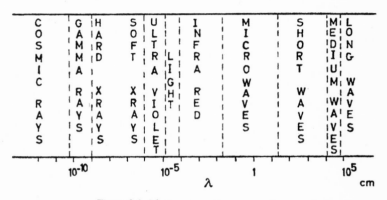

Figure 8.1. Electro-magnetic wave spectrum

frequency differ widely between the various categories of the waves.

The units employed in the following treatment are those of the rationalized MKS system in which the absolute permittivity ε of a dielectric is given by

$$\varepsilon = \varepsilon_r \varepsilon_0$$

where ε_r, the relative permittivity ('dielectric constant'), is dimensionless and equals unity for a perfect vacuum or free space. ε_0 is the absolute permittivity of free space and equals $8 \cdot 854 \times 10^{-12}$ farad metre^{-1}. Similarly the absolute permeability μ of a medium is $\mu_r \mu_0$ where μ_r is the relative permeability, equal to unity for free space, and μ_0 is the absolute permeability of free space which is $4\pi \times 10^{-7}$ or $1 \cdot 256 \times 10^{-6}$ henry metre^{-1}.

N

Flux—Figure 8.2 shows an elementary area δS in an electric field **E**. The *electric flux* over δS is $(\mathbf{E}.\hat{n})\delta S$ where $\hat{n}$ is the unit normal to δS. Thus the electric flux is

$$E(\hat{E}.\hat{n})\delta S = E(\cos\theta)\delta S.$$

θ is the angle between **E** and $\hat{n}$ as shown in *Figure 8.2* and $\hat{E}$ is a unit vector defining the direction of **E**, which equals $E\hat{E}$, E being the magnitude of **E**. $E\cos\theta$ is the magnitude of the component of **E** normal to δS and equals E_n. Hence the flux through δS is $E_n\delta S$. **E** is measured in volt metre^{-1} so the flux is in volt metre.

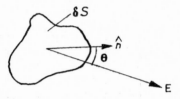

Figure 8.2. Flux through an elementary area

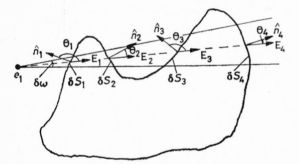

Figure 8.3. Charge outside a closed surface

Gauss' theorem—Suppose $\mathbf{E}_1$, $\mathbf{E}_2$, $\mathbf{E}_3$, . . . are the fields at δS_1, δS_2, δS_3, . . . at distances r_1, r_2, r_3, . . . from a charge e_1, as indicated in *Figure 8.3*. Then the total flux through these areas is

$$(\mathbf{E}_1.\hat{n}_1)\delta S_1 + (\mathbf{E}_2.\hat{n}_2)\delta S_2 + (\mathbf{E}_3.\hat{n}_3)\delta S_3 + \ldots$$

where

$$\mathbf{E}_1 = (e_1/4\pi\varepsilon r_1^2)\hat{r}_1;\ \mathbf{E}_2 = (e_1/4\pi\varepsilon r_2^2)_2\hat{r};$$

$$\mathbf{E}_3 = (e_1/4\pi\varepsilon r_3^2)\hat{r}_3;\ \ldots.$$

184

since, assuming an inverse square law, the force between two charges e_1 and e_2 is $(e_1 e_2/4\pi\varepsilon r^2)\hat{r}$ and E is defined as the force on unit charge, which is $(e_1/4\pi\varepsilon r^2)\hat{r}$ due to e_1. Hence the flux through the areas is

$$(e_1/4\pi\varepsilon)[(\hat{r}_1.\hat{n}_1)\delta S/_1 r_1^2 + (\hat{r}_2.\hat{n}_2)\delta S_2/r_2^2 + \ldots]$$

$$= (e_1/4\pi\varepsilon)[\delta S_1(\cos\theta_1)/r_1^2 + \delta S_2(\cos\theta_2)/r_2^2 + \ldots]$$

where θ_1 is the obtuse angle between $\hat{n}_1$ and $\hat{r}_1$,

θ_2 is the acute angle between $\hat{n}_2$ and $\hat{r}_2$,

. . . .

The total flux across the areas is thus

$$(e_1/4\pi\varepsilon)(-\delta\omega + \delta\omega - \delta\omega + \ldots)$$

$\delta\omega$ being the elementary solid angle subtended by the areas δS_1, δS_2, δS_3, . . . at e_1.

If e_1 is outside the surface there will be an even number of areas, and hence an even number of terms $\delta\omega$ whose sum is zero. Thus the total flux through a closed surface from a point charge outside is zero, because the preceding analysis could be repeated until all the area of the surface has been treated.

If e_1 is inside the surface, the elementary flux is $e_1\delta\omega/4\pi\varepsilon$ and the total flux is

$$\int_S (e_1/4\pi\varepsilon)d\omega$$

which equals e_1/ε because $\int_S d\omega$ is 4π, S being the total area of the closed surface. For a number of charges e_1, e_2, e_3, . . . e_n the total flux is

$$(1/\varepsilon)\sum_{n=1}^{n} e_n$$

which is a statement of *Gauss' theorem*. The total flux is also referred to as the *total normal induction* or as the *surface integral of force*

(*field*), which is $\int E.\hat{n}dS$. Thus

$$\int_S E.\hat{n}dS = (1/\varepsilon)\sum_{n=1}^{n} e_n. \tag{8.1}$$

185

If the charge per unit volume in the volume V of the closed surface of area S is ρ then

$$\sum_{n=1}^{n} e_n = \int_V \rho \mathrm{d}V. \tag{8.2}$$

Suppose a surface δS encloses a volume δV. The flux leaving δS is $\mathbf{E}.\hat{n}\delta S$ which also equals $(\mathrm{div}\ \mathbf{E})\delta V$, since the divergence of a vector is defined as the amount of flux, due to the vector, leaving unit volume. Hence

$$\int_S \mathbf{E}.\hat{n}\mathrm{d}S = \int_V (\mathrm{div}\ \mathbf{E})\mathrm{d}V \tag{8.3}$$

for a finite volume V enclosed by a surface S. From *Equations (8.1)* and *(8.2)*

$$\int_S \mathbf{E}.\hat{n}\mathrm{d}S = (1/\varepsilon)\int_V \rho \mathrm{d}V.$$

Hence

$$\int_V (\mathrm{div}\ \mathbf{E})\mathrm{d}V - (1/\varepsilon)\int_V \rho \mathrm{d}V = 0$$

or

$$\int_V (\mathrm{div}\ \mathbf{E} - \rho/\varepsilon)\mathrm{d}V = 0.$$

ρ is assumed to be constant throughout the volume V so that div $\mathbf{E}$ will also be constant in this volume. Thus

$$\mathrm{div}\ \mathbf{E} - \rho/\varepsilon = 0$$

or

$$\mathrm{div}\ \mathbf{E} = \rho/\varepsilon.$$

If the dielectric is *isotropic* ε is constant and

$$\mathrm{div}\ \varepsilon\mathbf{E} = \rho.$$

$\varepsilon\mathbf{E}$ is Maxwell's *electric displacement vector* $\mathbf{D}$ so we have

$$\mathrm{div}\ \mathbf{D} = \rho \tag{8.4}$$

which is another statement of Gauss' theorem.

186

Steady current—Figure 8.4 shows a current i, constant with time, flowing between points A and B distance δl apart in a conductor, the resistance between these points being R. v_A and v_B are the potentials at A and B, v_A being larger than v_B.

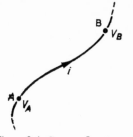

Figure 8.4. Current flow in a wire

From Ohm's law of current flow

$$i = (1/R)(v_A - v_B)$$

where R is $(1/\sigma)\delta l/\delta S$, the cross-sectional area of the conductor being δS and the conductivity σ. Thus

$$i = \sigma(\delta S/\delta l)(-\delta v)$$

the minus sign allowing for the decrease in potential in the sense of current flow. The current density in the conductor is $i/\delta S$, i being normal to δS, so the last equation can be written

$$i/\delta S = -\sigma \delta v/\delta l$$

or vectorially

$$\mathbf{i} = \sigma \mathbf{E} \qquad (8.5)$$

since E, the field in the conductor, is $-\delta v/\delta l$, (generally $\mathbf{E} = -\text{grad } v$), the vectors $\mathbf{i}$ and $\mathbf{E}$ being in the same sense in an isotropic conductor. $\mathbf{i}$ is the *current density vector* given by

$$i = \int_S \mathbf{i}.\hat{n}dS$$

where $\hat{n}$ is the unit normal to δS.

i may also be written in terms of the charge density ρ, since i is the time rate of change of charge. Thus

$$i = -\frac{\partial}{\partial t}\left(\int_V \rho dV\right).$$

187

The minus sign is required since ρ decreases in time, equilibrium ultimately being established when ρ is zero. But

$$i = \int_S \mathbf{i}.\hat{n}\mathrm{d}S = \int_V (\mathrm{div}\ \mathbf{i})\mathrm{d}V$$

using *Equation (8.3)* with **E** replaced by **i**, Thus

$$\int_V (\mathrm{div}\ \mathbf{i} + \partial\rho/\partial t)\mathrm{d}V = 0.$$

The volume V is arbitrary so that

$$\mathrm{div}\ \mathbf{i} = -\partial\rho/\partial t \tag{8.6}$$

and combining this with *Equation (8.4)* we get

$$\mathrm{div}\ \mathbf{i} = -\frac{\partial}{\partial t}(\mathrm{div}\ \mathbf{D})$$

$$= -\mathrm{div}\ (\partial\mathbf{D}/\partial t).$$

Hence

$$\mathrm{div}\ (\mathbf{i} + \partial\mathbf{D}/\partial t) = 0 \tag{8.7}$$

or

$$\mathrm{div}\ \mathbf{c} = 0$$

where

$$\mathbf{c} = \mathbf{i} + \partial\mathbf{D}/\partial t$$

Equation (8.7) being true at every point in the medium. According to Maxwell **c** is the *total current* and is the vector sum of the *conduction current* **i** and the *displacement current* $\partial\mathbf{D}/\partial t$. For most media one of the components approaches zero. In insulators **i** is negligible, whereas in conductors $\partial\mathbf{D}/\partial t$ is very small.

In magnetism the equation corresponding to *(8.4)* is

$$\mathrm{div}\ \mathbf{B} = 0 \tag{8.8}$$

because in the formulation of the MKS system no isolated poles are assumed to exist, a pole, if such were possible, being equivalent to an electric charge. In *Equation (8.8)* **B** equals μH where **B** is the *magnetic flux density*, otherwise *magnetic induction*, units weber metre^{-2} or newton amp^{-1} metre^{-1}, μ is the absolute permeability of the medium as previously mentioned and **H** is the *magnetic field*, units amp metre^{-1}.

Oersted found in 1820 that an electric current is always accompanied by a magnetic field. That due to the current in a long straight wire is circular, the circles joining points of equal magnitude of field being concentric with the wire and with their planes perpendicular to it. The sense of **H** relative to the current follows a right-hand screw rule. **H** is not irrotational and the line integral $\oint H_l dl$ is not zero for a path surrounding the wire. We find that, using MKS units

$$\oint \mathbf{H}.d\mathbf{l} = i \qquad (8.9)$$

where i is the current in the wire measured in amperes. This result applies generally to any path passing once through the plane of a circuit, which may have any boundary. For a path of radius r concentric with and outside a long straight wire $2\pi r H = i$ or $H = i/2\pi r$, a result that is well-known.

The current density vector **i** is given by

$$i = \int_S \mathbf{i}.\hat{n}dS$$

and

$$i = \oint \mathbf{H}.d\mathbf{l}$$

which is *Equation (8.9)*. Hence, using Stokes' theorem

$$\int_S \mathbf{i}.\hat{n}dS = \int_S (\text{curl}\mathbf{H}).\hat{n}dS$$

S can be any arbitrary surface, since *Equation (8.9)* holds for all points outside and inside the wire. Thus

$$\text{curl } \mathbf{H} = \mathbf{i}.$$

Generally the total current **c**, which is always solenoidal, replaces **i**. Then the last equation applies to all media. Hence

$$\text{curl } \mathbf{H} = \mathbf{i} + \partial\mathbf{D}/\partial t. \qquad (8.10)$$

Faraday found in 1831 that an electric current is generated in a closed conducting circuit when a magnet in its vicinity is moved. Suppose R is the resistance of the circuit and S is a surface whose perimeter of length l is bounded by the circuit but is otherwise arbitrary. The sense of a current in the circuit and the positive directions

189

of δl and a normal $\hat{n}$ to an element δS of the surface are consistent with a right-hand screw rule. We have, from Faraday's experiments

$$iR = -\frac{\partial}{\partial t}\left(\int_S \mathbf{B}.\hat{n}\mathrm{d}S\right)$$

the minus sign being required because the induced emf equals the time rate of *decrease* of the flux. The potential difference across an element δl of the conductor is δv which equals $-i\delta R$ if there is no additional source of emf along δl, that due to induction resulting in i. But, as before, E is $-\delta v/\delta l$. Thus

$$i\delta R = E\delta l$$

or

$$iR = \oint \mathbf{E}.\mathbf{dl}$$

since i is constant along the conductor. Hence, with no additional source of emf in the circuit

$$\oint \mathbf{E}\mathbf{dl} = -\frac{\partial}{\partial t}\left(\int_S \mathbf{B}.\hat{n}\mathrm{d}S\right)$$

$$= \int_S (\text{curl } \mathbf{E}).\hat{n}\mathrm{d}S$$

by Stokes' theorem. The integrand $\mathbf{B}$ can be differentiated with respect to t, and because S is arbitrary we get

$$\text{curl } \mathbf{E} = -\partial\mathbf{B}/\partial t. \qquad (8.11)$$

Maxwell's equations have now been established. They are

$$\text{div } \mathbf{D} = \rho \qquad (8.4)$$

$$\text{div } \mathbf{B} = 0 \qquad (8.8)$$

$$\text{curl } \mathbf{H} = \mathbf{i} + \partial\mathbf{D}/\partial t \qquad (8.10)$$

$$\text{curl } \mathbf{E} = -\partial\mathbf{B}/\partial t. \qquad (8.11)$$

These, together with the constitutive relations

$$\mathbf{D} = \varepsilon\mathbf{E}$$

$$\mathbf{i} = \sigma\mathbf{E} \qquad (8.5)$$

$$\mathbf{B} = \mu\mathbf{H}$$

are used in the study of electro-magnetic radiation.

8.2. Waves in Dielectrics

For an isotropic dielectric in which there are no free charges Maxwell's equations are

$$\text{div } \mathbf{B} = 0 \tag{8.8}$$

$$\text{curl } \mathbf{E} = -\partial \mathbf{B}/\partial t \tag{8.11}$$

$$\text{div } \mathbf{D} = 0 \tag{8.12}$$

$$\text{curl } \mathbf{H} = \partial \mathbf{D}/\partial t \tag{8.13}$$

since ρ and σ are both zero. We have

$$\text{curl curl } \mathbf{E} = \text{grad div } \mathbf{E} - \text{div grad } \mathbf{E}$$

or, using *Equations (8.11) and (8.8)*

$$\text{curl } (-\mu \partial \mathbf{H}/\partial t) = 0 - \nabla^2 \mathbf{E}$$

which becomes

$$\mu \frac{\partial}{\partial t}(\text{curl } \mathbf{H}) = \nabla^2 \mathbf{E}.$$

Thus, using equation *(8.13)*

$$\partial^2 \mathbf{E}/\partial t^2 = (1/\mu \varepsilon)\nabla^2 \mathbf{E}. \tag{8.14}$$

Similarly

$$\partial^2 \mathbf{H}/\partial t^2 = (1/\mu \varepsilon)\nabla^2 \mathbf{H}. \tag{8.15}$$

These equations represent waves travelling with velocity $c = 1/\sqrt{(\mu \varepsilon)}$ in three dimensions. In vacuo or in free space

$$c_0 = 1/\sqrt{(\mu_0 \varepsilon_0)} = 2 \cdot 998 \times 10^8 \text{ metres/sec.}$$

The ratio

$$c_0/c = \sqrt{(\mu \varepsilon/\mu_0 \varepsilon_0)} = \sqrt{(\mu_r \mu_0 \varepsilon_r \varepsilon_0/\mu_0 \varepsilon_0)} = \sqrt{(\mu_r \varepsilon_r)}.$$

But this ratio is the refractive index n of the dielectric, and for waves in the visible region of the spectrum μ_r is nearly unity so that

$$n^2 = \varepsilon_r \tag{8.16}$$

which is known as *Maxwell's relation* and holds roughly for many transparent dielectrics near the red end of the optical range, but usually not so well at higher frequencies.

Consider the equation

$$\partial^2 \mathbf{s}/\partial t^2 = c^2 \nabla^2 \mathbf{s} \tag{8.17}$$

where $\mathbf{s}$ is $\mathbf{E}$ or $\mathbf{H}$ and c^2 is $1/\mu \varepsilon$. The solution of such an equation in

191

terms of a scalar s has already been indicated in sections **4.4.** and **5.1.** and is not materially altered if s is a vector. The functions f_1, f_2 and so on merely need to have vector properties. We have shown that f_1 and f_2 can have simple harmonic form, and vector properties can be conferred by making the amplitude a vector whose magnitude is the maximum value of **s** and whose sense is the same. Accordingly a solution of *Equation (8.17)* is

$$\mathbf{s} = \mathbf{a} \cos k(Lx + My + Nz - ct) \qquad (8.18a)$$

where L, M and N are direction cosines ($L^2 + M^2 + N^2 = 1$), **a** is a real constant and k is $2\pi/\lambda$. In exponential form this solution is

$$\mathbf{s} = \mathbf{a} \exp jk(Lx + My + Nz - ct) \qquad (8.18b)$$

the real part being required, and, for a plane wave travelling parallel to the x axis, *Equation (8.18b)* becomes

$$\mathbf{s} = \mathbf{a} \exp jk(x - ct). \qquad (8.19)$$

Hence

$$\partial\mathbf{s}/\partial t = -jkc\mathbf{a} \exp jk(x - ct) = -jkc\mathbf{s}$$

and

$$\partial\mathbf{s}/\partial x = jk\mathbf{a} \exp jk(x - ct) = jk\mathbf{s}.$$

Thus here the operator $\partial/\partial t$ is equivalent to the multiplier $-jkc$ while $\partial/\partial x$ is equivalent to jk. The operators $\partial/\partial y$ and $\partial/\partial z$ both give zero when applied to *Equation (8.19)*.

From *Equation (8.12)* div **E** = 0 or

$$\partial E_x/\partial x + \partial E_y/\partial y + \partial E_z/\partial z = 0.$$

Thus

$$jkE_x + 0 + 0 = 0$$

or

$$E_x = 0.$$

From *Equation (8.8)* div **H** = 0 so that H_x is also zero. The plane wave is thus *transverse* because there is no component of **E** or **H** in the direction in which the wave is travelling.

From *Equation (8.13)* curl **H** $= \varepsilon\partial\mathbf{E}/\partial t$ which is, in component form

$$\partial H_z/\partial y - \partial H_y/\partial z = \varepsilon\partial E_x/\partial t \qquad (8.20x)$$

$$\partial H_x/\partial z - \partial H_z/\partial x = \varepsilon\partial E_y/\partial t \qquad (8.20y)$$

$$\partial H_y/\partial x - \partial H_x/\partial y = \varepsilon\partial E_z/\partial t. \qquad (8.20z)$$

Using the previously obtained equivalents of the operators *Equation* (*8.20x*) gives

$$0 - 0 = 0$$

while from *Equations* (*8.20y*) and (*8.20z*)

$$0 - jkH_z = -jkc\varepsilon E_y$$

$$jkH_y - 0 = -jkc\varepsilon E_z.$$

Thus we find

$$H_z = \varepsilon c E_y \qquad (8.21a)$$

$$H_y = -\varepsilon c E_z. \qquad (8.21b)$$

In a similar manner from *Equation* (*8.11*) we find that

$$E_z = -\mu c H_y \qquad (8.22a)$$

$$E_y = \mu c H_z \qquad (8.22b)$$

the four equations not being independent, since c is $1/\sqrt{(\mu\varepsilon)}$. The scalar product $\mathbf{E}.\mathbf{H} = E_y H_y + E_z H_z$ since $E_x = H_x = 0$. Thus

$$\mathbf{E}.\mathbf{H} = (\mu c H_z)(-\varepsilon c E_z) + E_z H_z$$

$$= -E_z H_z + E_z H_z = 0.$$

But neither $\mathbf{E}$ nor $\mathbf{H}$ equals zero, so the smaller angle included between them must be $\pi/2$ radians for their scalar product to be zero.

From *Equation* (*8.21a*)

$$E_y = [\sqrt{(\mu\varepsilon)}/\varepsilon] H_z = \eta H_z \qquad (8.23a)$$

and from *Equation* (*8.21b*)

$$E_z = -[\sqrt{(\mu\varepsilon)}/\varepsilon] H_y = -\eta H_y \qquad (8.23b)$$

where η, which has units of volt amp^{-1} or ohms, is called the *intrinsic, characteristic* or *wave impedance*. For a vacuum or free space

$$\eta_0 = \sqrt{(\mu_0/\varepsilon_0)} \simeq \sqrt{(4\pi \times 10^{-7} \times 36\pi \times 10^9)}$$

$$\simeq 120\pi \simeq 377 \text{ ohms.}$$

The minus sign in *Equation* (*8.23b*) indicates that $\mathbf{E}$ and $\mathbf{H}$ are perpendicular, as shown before, the system $\mathbf{x}$, $\mathbf{E}$ and $\mathbf{H}$ conforming to a right-hand screw rule. Generally we have

$$E = \eta H \qquad (8.24)$$

so that

$$\partial E/\partial t = \eta \partial H/\partial t$$

Thus E and H vary with time in phase. Alternatively, they can be said to be in phase because they both satisfy

$$\mathbf{s} = \mathbf{a} \cos k(x - ct).$$

Thus for plane electro-magnetic waves in isotropic dielectrics the following conditions apply:
(a) The wave is transverse. There is no component of $\mathbf{E}$ or $\mathbf{H}$ in the direction of travel.
(b) $\mathbf{E}$ and $\mathbf{H}$ are perpendicular, and their magnitudes are related by $E = \eta H$ where $\eta = \sqrt{(\mu/\varepsilon)}$.
(c) $\mathbf{E}$ and $\mathbf{H}$ vary with time in phase.
These conclusions were partly verified for radio waves travelling in air in the experiments of Hertz in 1885.

8.3. Polarized Waves

For waves travelling parallel to the x axis, *Equation (8.18a)* becomes

$$\mathbf{s} = \mathbf{a} \cos k(x - ct)$$

which is a particular solution of

$$\partial^2 \mathbf{s}/\partial t^2 = c^2 \partial^2 \mathbf{s}/\partial x^2.$$

Suppose $\mathbf{s}$ is replaced by $\mathbf{H}$. We then have, since there is no x component

$$H_y = a_y \cos k(x - ct) \qquad (8.25y)$$

$$H_z = a_z \cos k(x - ct). \qquad (8.25z)$$

Using *Equations (8.22a)* and *(8.22b)* we get

$$E_y = \mu c a_z \cos k(x - ct) \qquad (8.26y)$$

$$E_z = -\mu c a_y \cos k(x - ct). \qquad (8.26z)$$

If a_z is zero, H_z and E_y are zero at all times, but H_y and E_z are not generally zero. The wave is then *plane polarized* in the xy plane, according to the convention in which the plane of polarization is the one containing the magnetic vector and the axis parallel to the direction of travel of the wave. The alternative is to specify the electric vector instead of the magnetic one, as in radio and radar wave study, but there is no difficulty in changing from one convention to the other. If a_y were zero the wave would then be polarized in the xz plane, because there would be only H_z and E_y.

If a_y and a_z are both not zero, the description of the kind of polarized wave depends on the figure imagined to be traced on a plane parallel to the yz plane by the tips of the **H** or **E** components. There are in effect two vibrations of the same frequency at right angles, given by the variations in H_y and H_z or by E_y and E_z with time. The loci of the tips of the vectors can be found by using the conclusions reached regarding Lissajous' figures in section **2.5**. Thus the *Equations* (*8.25y*) to (*8.26z*) represent a plane polarized wave. The figure on a plane parallel to the yx plane is a pair of coincident straight lines, since there is zero phase difference between the **H** components and an angular difference of π radians between the **E** components. Furthermore the coincident straight lines for the **H** components, along which the resultant **H** vector may be imagined to expand and to contract, are at an angle of $\tan^{-1} a_z/a_y$ to the y axis, the plane of polarization $y/z = a_y/a_z$ having the same gradient. The tip of the resultant **E** vector follows a similar locus at right angles to the **H** vector.

If the phases of H_y and H_z, or of E_y and E_z, differ an ellipse is traced, and the wave is said to be *elliptically polarized*. If a_y equals a_z and the angular phase difference between either pair of components is $\pi/2$ or $3\pi/2$ a circle is traced, and the wave is *circularly polarized*. The equations for the components could then be

$$H_y = a \cos k(x-ct) \tag{8.27y}$$

$$H_z = a \sin k(x-ct) \tag{8.27z}$$

$$E_y = \mu ca \sin k(x-ct) \tag{8.28y}$$

$$E_z = -\mu ca \cos k(x-ct). \tag{8.28z}$$

If the loci of the tips of the pairs of vectors have shapes which vary randomly with time, the wave is unpolarized although the wave is instantaneously at least elliptically polarized. A partially polarized wave has a polarized component impressed on an unpolarized one, so the figure traced would contain a stable part superposed on a random variation.

8.4. Waves in Conductors

Equation (8.10) is

$$\varepsilon \partial \mathbf{E}/\partial t + \sigma \mathbf{E} = \text{curl } \mathbf{H}$$

or

$$\text{div } (\varepsilon \partial \mathbf{E}/\partial t + \sigma \mathbf{E}) = \text{div curl } \mathbf{H}.$$

Thus

$$\text{div } [(\varepsilon \partial/\partial t + \sigma)\mathbf{E}] = \nabla.\nabla \times \mathbf{H}$$

$$= \nabla \times \nabla.\mathbf{H}$$

$$= 0.$$

But $(\varepsilon \partial/\partial t + \sigma)$ is not zero so that

$$\text{div } \mathbf{E} = 0 \qquad\qquad (8.29)$$

which would be expected since any distribution of charge in a conductor would rapidly disappear. There is an exponential decay of charge density, shown as follows.

Combining *Equations (8.5)* and *(8.6)* gives

$$\text{div } \sigma \mathbf{E} = -\partial \rho/\partial t$$

or, for an isotropic conductor

$$\sigma \text{ div } \mathbf{E} = -\partial \rho/\partial t.$$

From *Equation (8.4)*

$$\text{div } \mathbf{E} = \rho/\varepsilon$$

so that

$$-\partial \rho/\partial t = (\sigma/\varepsilon)\rho$$

which may be integrated as a total differential equation, since ρ is here being considered only as a function of time. If $\rho = \rho_0$ at $t = 0$

$$\rho = \rho_0 \exp(-\sigma t/\varepsilon)$$

or

$$\rho = \rho_0 \exp(-t/T) \qquad\qquad (8.30)$$

where T is ε/σ and is known as the *modulus of decay* or *relaxation time* and is the time in which the charge density decays to $1/e$ of its original value. For metals T/ε, is of the order of 10^{-19} sec, increasing to about 10^{-6} sec for water. The decay of charge is thus very rapid and is independent of electro-magnetic disturbances in the conductor, so that div $\mathbf{E}$ does not differ appreciably from zero.

Using *Equation (8.11)*

$$\text{curl curl } \mathbf{E} = \text{curl } (-\partial \mathbf{B}/\partial t)$$
$$= \text{grad div } \mathbf{E} - \text{div grad } \mathbf{E}$$

which

$$= 0 - \nabla^2 \mathbf{E}$$

if *Equation (8.29)* is employed. Thus

$$\mu \frac{\partial}{\partial t} (\text{curl } \mathbf{H}) = \nabla^2 \mathbf{E}$$

or, substituting for curl **H** from *Equation (8.10)*

$$\mu \frac{\partial}{\partial t} (\varepsilon \partial \mathbf{E}/\partial t + \sigma \mathbf{E}) = \nabla^2 \mathbf{E}$$

which becomes

$$\mu\varepsilon \partial^2 \mathbf{E}/\partial t^2 + \mu\sigma \partial \mathbf{E}/\partial t = \nabla^2 \mathbf{E} \tag{8.31}$$

Similarly, by using *Equations (8.10)* and *(8.8)*

$$\mu\varepsilon \partial^2 \mathbf{H}/\partial t^2 + \mu\sigma \partial \mathbf{H}/\partial t = \nabla^2 \mathbf{H} \tag{8.32}$$

(8.31) and *(8.32)* are known as the *equations of telegraphy* because similar equations hold for waves travelling along wires. The method of getting these equations is very like that used for *Equations (8.14)* and *(8.15)*, to which the present ones reduce if σ is put equal to zero. The double curl of **E** or **H** is found and then curl **E** or curl **H** is eliminated.

For a plane wave in a conductor travelling parallel to an x axis only the components E_y, E_z, H_y and H_z remain. *Equation (8.31)* becomes

$$\mu\varepsilon \partial^2 E_y/\partial t^2 + \mu\sigma \partial E_y/\partial t = \partial^2 E_y/\partial x^2 \tag{8.33}$$

and there is a similar equation for H_z. The other two components E_z and H_y need not be considered, as no additional independent equations could be obtained. From *Equation (8.11)*

$$-\mu \partial H_z/\partial t = \partial E_y/\partial x - \partial E_x/\partial y$$

or

$$-\mu \partial H_z/\partial t = \partial E_y/\partial x \tag{8.34}$$

since E_x is zero. From *Equation (8.10)*

$$\varepsilon \partial E_y/\partial t + \sigma E_y = \partial H_x/\partial z - \partial H_z/\partial x$$

or

$$\varepsilon \partial E_y/\partial t + \sigma E_y = -\partial H_z/\partial x \tag{8.35}$$

197

because H_x also equals zero. Solutions of *Equation* (*8.33*) must also satisfy *Equations* (*8.34*) and (*8.35*). Possible solutions are

$$E_y = a \exp j\omega(t - n'x/c_0) \qquad (8.36)$$

$$H_z = b \exp j\omega(t - n'x/c_0). \qquad (8.37)$$

The wave velocity is then c_0/n'. Since the refractive index of a medium is the ratio of the wave velocity in a vacuum to that in the medium, the refractive index here is $c_0/c_0/n'$ which equals n'. n' can be shown to be complex as follows.

Substituting for E_y and H_z in *Equation* (*8.34*) we have

$$-\mu b j\omega = aj\omega(-n'/c_0)$$

or

$$b = n'a/\mu c_0 \qquad (8.38)$$

and the use of *Equation* (*8.35*) leads to

$$j\omega\varepsilon a + \sigma a = j\omega n'b/c_0$$

or

$$n' = (ac_0/b)(\varepsilon + \sigma/j\omega).$$

Thus, using *Equation* (*8.38*)

$$n'^2 = \mu c_0^2(\varepsilon - j\sigma/\omega). \qquad (8.39)$$

If $\sigma = 0, n'^2 = \mu\varepsilon c_0^2 = c_0^2/c^2 = n^2$ or $n' = n$, as would be expected. $(\varepsilon - j\sigma/\omega)$ can be regarded as a complex permittivity ε' so that

$$n' = c_0\sqrt{(\mu\varepsilon')}.$$

The use of a complex permittivity results in the electro-magnetic equations for conducting media assuming the same form as those for dielectrics, and thus analysis is aided. For example, *Equation* (*8.10*) is

$$\operatorname{curl} \mathbf{H} = \mathbf{i} + \varepsilon\delta\mathbf{E}/\partial t$$

$$= \sigma\mathbf{E} + \varepsilon\partial\mathbf{E}/\partial t$$

$$= (\sigma/j\omega + \varepsilon)\partial\mathbf{E}/\partial t$$

$$= (\varepsilon - j\sigma/\omega)\partial\mathbf{E}/\partial t$$

so that

$$\operatorname{curl} \mathbf{H} = \varepsilon'\partial\mathbf{E}/\partial t$$

which has the same form as *Equation* (*8.13*) for dielectrics.

The ratio a/b is also complex according to *Equation* (*8.38*) so there is a phase difference between E_y and H_z. This occurs because there is power dissipation, causing as well an exponential decay of E_y and H_z as the conductor is penetrated. From *Equation (8.39)*

$$n' = \sqrt{(\mu c_0^2 \varepsilon - j\mu c_0^2 \sigma/\omega)}$$

$$= n - j\chi$$

where n is the refractive index and χ is the *coefficient of extinction* or *absorption index*. By considering n' and its conjugate one gets

$$n^2 - \chi^2 = \mu c_0^2 \varepsilon$$

$$n^2 + \chi^2 = \sqrt{(\mu^2 c_0^4 \varepsilon^2 + \mu^2 c_0^4 \sigma^2/\omega^2)}.$$

Hence

$$n^2 = \tfrac{1}{2}\mu c_0^2 [\sqrt{(\varepsilon^2 + \sigma^2/\omega^2)} + \varepsilon] \qquad (8.40)$$

$$\chi^2 = \tfrac{1}{2}\mu c_0^2 [\sqrt{(\varepsilon^2 + \sigma^2/\omega^2)} - \varepsilon]. \qquad (8.41)$$

Equation (8.40) also holds for a dielectric if σ is put equal to zero. n^2 is then $\mu \varepsilon c_0^2$ which equals c_0^2/c^2 as before. *Equation (8.36)* can thus be written

$$E_y = a \exp j\omega[t - (n - j\chi)x/c_0]$$

$$= a[\exp(-\omega x\chi/c_0)] \exp j\omega(t - nx/c_0)$$

$$= a[\exp(-2\pi x\chi/\lambda_0)] \exp j\omega(t - nx/c_0). \qquad (8.42)$$

Similarly

$$H_z = b[\exp(-2\pi x\chi/\lambda_0)] \exp j\omega(t - nx/c_0). \qquad (8.43)$$

Hence E_y travels in the positive x direction with speed c_0/n and its amplitude depends on x, being reduced to $\exp(-2\pi)$ of its value at the surface of the conductor when the penetration is λ_0/χ. H_z and the other components are reduced by the same amount in the same distance. λ_0/χ is thus a convenient measure of the range or penetrating power of an electro-magnetic wave in a conductor, and is called the *depth of penetration*.

The phase difference between E_y and H_z can be found in terms of χ and n. We have written

$$n' = n - j\chi.$$

Otherwise

$$n' = \sqrt{(n^2 + \chi^2)}(\exp - j\psi)$$

where ψ is the difference in phase angle between E_y and H_z and equals $\tan^{-1}\chi/n$.

o

The preceding analysis depends on the assumption that div $\mathbf{E}$ is zero, which is true if there are no free charges present. In conductors there are many electrons which are easily detached from their parent atoms and can, for sufficiently large fields, behave as free charges. Hence generally there is poor agreement between theoretical and experimental values of n and χ.

For long waves σ/ω greatly exceeds ε. For example if λ_0 is 10^{-6} metre, which corresponds to short infra-red waves, ω is $2\pi \times 3 \times 10^8/10^{-6}$ sec^{-1}. For copper σ is $6\cdot41 \times 10^7$ farad metre sec^{-1} (amp volt metre^{-1}) so that σ/ω is $3\cdot37 \times 10^{-8}$ farad/metre whereas ε for copper may be assumed to be of the order of 10^{-12} farad metre^{-1}, that is of the order of ε_0. Hence χ is given approximately by

$$\chi = c_0\sqrt{(\mu\sigma/2\omega)}$$

from *Equation* (*8.41*) and equals n roughly. The depth of penetration of such waves is $\lambda_0/c_0\sqrt{(\mu\sigma/2\omega)}$ which is $2\sqrt{(\pi\lambda_0/\mu\sigma c_0)}$. Thus for waves much longer than those for which the preceding calculations were made, in order to justify approximations, for example one metre wavelength, the depths of penetration can be found from the last result. For one metre waves the depth of penetration is $2\cdot18 \times 10^{-4}$ metre in copper, for which μ can be assumed to equal μ_0 roughly.

Although the depth of penetration is the same for both the electric and magnetic vectors, the magnetic wave energy in many conductors, particularly those showing very weak magnetic effects, is much larger than the electric component energy. This would be expected because a conductor is usually found in practice to be far more efficient for electric than for magnetic screening. From *Equation* (*8.38*)

$$b/a = n'/\mu c_0$$

where b/a is the ratio of the amplitudes of H_z and E_y. If only the magnitudes of E_y and H_z are considered, no allowance being made for their phase difference

$$n' = \sqrt{(n^2+\chi^2)}$$
$$= c_0(\mu^2\varepsilon^2 + \mu^2\sigma^2/\omega^2)^{\frac{1}{4}}.$$

Thus the amplitude ratio b/a is given by

$$b/a = (\varepsilon^2/\mu^2 + \sigma^2/\mu^2\omega^2)^{\frac{1}{4}}. \tag{8.44}$$

For dielectrics σ is nearly zero and then

$$b/a = \sqrt{(\varepsilon/\mu)} = 1/\eta$$

as noted in section **8.2**. For conductors σ/ω may be assumed to be much larger than ε, as shown before. Hence

$$b/a = \sqrt{(\sigma/\mu\omega)}.$$

The energies per unit volume of magnetic and electric fields are shown to be $\frac{1}{2}\mu H^2$ and $\frac{1}{2}\varepsilon E^2$ in the next section, H and E being instantaneous values. Thus the ratio of the maximum energies is

$$(\mu H_z^2/\varepsilon E_y^2)_{max} = \mu b^2/\varepsilon a^2 = (\mu/\varepsilon)\sigma/\mu\omega = \sigma/\varepsilon\omega.$$

Using the preceding value of σ/ω for 10^{-6} metre waves in copper, we have for the energy ratio $3\cdot37 \times 10^{-8}/8\cdot85 \times 10^{-12}$ which equals $3\cdot81 \times 10^3$, assuming that ε is roughly ε_0 for copper. Thus the magnetic field energy is over a thousand times larger than the electric field energy at any depth in copper. •

8.5. Poynting's Vector

We have

$$\text{div } (\mathbf{E} \times \mathbf{H}) = \mathbf{H} \text{ curl } \mathbf{E} - \mathbf{E} \text{ curl } \mathbf{H}$$

$$= -\mathbf{H}.\partial\mathbf{B}/\partial t - \mathbf{E}.\mathbf{i} - \mathbf{E}.\partial\mathbf{D}/\partial t$$

using Maxwell's equations (*8.10*) and (*8.11*) for a conductor at rest. Thus for a volume V of a conductor

$$\int_V \mathbf{E}.\mathbf{i}\,dV + \int_V (\mathbf{H}.\partial\mathbf{B}/\partial t + \mathbf{E}.\partial\mathbf{D}/\partial t)dV + \int_V \text{div } (\mathbf{E} \times \mathbf{H})dV = 0$$

or

$$\int_V \mathbf{E}.\mathbf{i}\,dV + \frac{1}{2}\frac{\partial}{\partial t}\int_V (\mu H^2 + \varepsilon E^2)dV + \int_S (\mathbf{E} \times \mathbf{H}).\hat{n}\,dS = 0$$

because the associated vectors $\mathbf{H}$ and $\mathbf{B}$, $\mathbf{E}$ and $\mathbf{D}$ can be assumed to be different only in magnitudes. S is the surface area of volume V, and thus applies to a closed surface. Hence in a time t

$$\int_V (i^2/\sigma)t\,dV + \int_V \frac{1}{2}(\mu H^2 + \varepsilon E^2)dV + \int_S [(\mathbf{E} \times \mathbf{H}).\hat{n}]t\,dS = 0 \quad (8.45)$$

which is an energy equation. i^2t/σ is the electrical energy per unit volume supplied by a generator or dissipated as heat, $\frac{1}{2}(\mu H^2 + \varepsilon E^2)$ is the wave (field) energy per unit volume generated or supplied and $[(\mathbf{E} \times \mathbf{H}).\hat{n}]t$ is the energy flow normal to unit area. The signs of these three quantities must be chosen appropriately so as to achieve energy balance in any particular situation.

The wave energy thus has two components $\frac{1}{2}\mu H^2$ and $\frac{1}{2}\varepsilon E^2$ as stated in the preceding section. The vector $\mathbf{E} \times \mathbf{H}$, which is usually denoted by $\mathbf{N}$, is normal to the plane containing $\mathbf{E}$ and $\mathbf{H}$ and advances in a monochromatic wave at a speed c. It represents the rate of energy flow normal to unit area in a plane instantaneously containing $\mathbf{E}$ and $\mathbf{H}$ and is known as *Poynting's vector*.

$\int_S \mathbf{N}.\hat{n}\mathrm{d}S$ represents energy flow only when a closed surface is considered, since such an assumption is a necessary part of the analysis leading to *Equation (8.45)*. Moreover $\mathbf{N}$ may have any value without there being any noticeable energy flow. For example, if $\mathbf{E}$ and $\mathbf{H}$ are independent fields at right-angles, as in apparatus where charged particles are deflected, $\mathbf{N}$ can have very large values but div $\mathbf{N}$ may be zero and $\mathbf{N}$ does not then represent energy flow.

If $\mathbf{E}$ and $\mathbf{H}$ vary sinusoidally, $\mathbf{N}$ is given in terms of the root-mean-square values of $\mathbf{E}$ and $\mathbf{H}$. For a uniform plane sinusoidal wave travelling parallel to an x axis, the time average power flow through unit area of the yz plane is

$$\bar{P} = (1/T)\int_0^T (\mathbf{E} \times \mathbf{H}).\hat{n}\mathrm{d}t$$

where T is the period of the wave and

$$\mathbf{H} = \mathbf{H}_0 \cos k(x - ct)$$

$$\mathbf{E} = \mathbf{E}_0 \cos k(x - ct)$$

from the pairs of *Equations (8.25)* and *(8.26)*, $\mathbf{H}_0$ and $\mathbf{E}_0$ being the resultant amplitudes. That is

$$H_0 = \sqrt{(a_y^2 + a_z^2)}, \; E_0 = \eta\sqrt{(a_y^2 + a_z^2)} = \eta H_0.$$

Hence

$$\bar{P} = (E_0 H_0/T)\int_0^T \cos^2 k(x - ct)\mathrm{d}t$$

or

$$\bar{P} = \tfrac{1}{2}E_0 H_0$$

which becomes

$$\bar{P} = \tfrac{1}{2}E_0 H_0 \cos \phi$$

$$\left.\begin{array}{c} \\ \\ \end{array}\right\} \qquad (8.46)$$

$E_0/\sqrt{2}$ and $H_0/\sqrt{2}$ are the root-mean-square values of E and H for a phase angle difference ϕ between $\mathbf{E}$ and $\mathbf{H}$. This result is often useful for estimating E_0 and H_0. For example, if all the energy from a 100 watt lamp is assumed to be radiated uniformly in all directions as a sinusoidal electro-magnetic wave in air, E_0 and H_0 can be found at an appreciable distance from the source. Suppose the distance is one metre. $\bar{P}$ is then $100/4\pi$ since 100 watts is uniformly crossing a sphere of one metre radius. Because the energy flow is normal to the surface of the sphere and is there one metre distant from the source, the waves can be assumed to be plane. From *Equations* (*8.23a*) or (*8.23b*) $E_0 = \eta H_0$ and for air $\eta \simeq \eta_0 \simeq 120\pi$. Thus

$$H_0^2 = 50/120\pi^2 \text{ or } H_0 = 0.21 \text{ amp metre}^{-1}.$$

$$E_0^2 = 6000 \qquad \text{or } E_0 = 77.5 \text{ volt metre}^{-1}.$$

8.6. Skin effect

Suppose an alternating current of angular frequency ω is flowing in a straight wire of circular section. At the surface of the wire is an electric field **E** parallel to the axis of the wire and having the same sense as the current, together with a magnetic field **H** at right-angles to **E** but also parallel to the surface. These fields are the same as those due to an electro-magnetic wave of angular frequency ω entering the wire, plane polarized at right-angles to the axis of the wire, and incident normally on its surface.

When an electro-magnetic wave is incident on a conductor, the electric and magnetic components are reduced in amplitude by a factor of $\exp(-2\pi)$ for a penetration of $2\sqrt{(\pi\lambda_0/\mu\sigma c_0)}$ according to the analysis in section **8.4**. The distance corresponding to a reduction of amplitude of $1/e$ is

$$(2/2\pi)\sqrt{(\pi\lambda_0/\mu\sigma c_0)} = \sqrt{(2/\mu\sigma\omega)}$$

and is known as the *skin depth*. The current in the wire is $1/e$ of its value at the surface at a distance beneath equal to the skin depth, and if the radius of the wire is small the current density is uniform. If the radius of the wire is large compared with the skin depth, only in a thin layer near the surface—'skin'—does the current density differ appreciably from zero.

The skin effect usually becomes appreciable in wires of about 20 to 40 swg at radio frequencies greater than 100 kc/s and is reduced by using silver plated thick copper wire or tube, or 'litzendraht' wire. This consists of a large number of fine strands of copper wire insulated from each other by an enamel coating. The function of the insulant is controversial.

There is a phase difference between the current flowing at the surface, and that flowing along an inner layer distant d from the surface. The phase angle difference is a lag of $\tan^{-1}[d\sqrt{(\mu\sigma\omega/2)}]$. At the skin depth the phase angle difference is $\tan^{-1}1$ which is $\pi/4$ radians behind the phase of the current at the surface.

The skin effect is analogous to the penetration of temperature oscillations into a body whose surface is alternately heated and cooled. A phenomenon closely related to the skin effect is the heating of metals by high-frequency currents induced by suitably placed coils—induction heating. An example is a rod heated by being placed in a longitudinal magnetic field alternating at a radio frequency. The field oscillations generate in the rod an electric field which is circular and concentric with the rod, which is heated by the current flowing. At the surface of the rod is the same electro-magnetic field as that produced by a plane polarized wave incident normally, but now the wave is polarized parallel to the axis of the wire. Comparison of this wave with the one described in the explanation of the skin effect shows that the magnetic and electric fields are interchanged.

8.7. Electric Polarization

In a conductor there can be no static charge. A charge placed inside would move very quickly to the surface where it stays, as is presumed to be demonstrated by the hemispheres and butterfly net experiments. The charge of a charged conductor can be shown to be on the surface by considering the field **E** in the surrounding medium. We have from *Equation (8.4)*

$$\text{div } \mathbf{E} = \rho/\varepsilon$$

If **E** is not zero ρ is not zero, that is there must be a volume distribution of charge relating to the conductor. In section **8.4.** there has been shown to be a rapid dispersal of charge density *inside* a conductor, so for ρ not to be zero the charge must be in the limiting position which is on the surface.

In dielectrics a volume distribution of charge is possible. In some the molecules exist as individual electric dipoles randomly arranged. The effect of an impressed field is to orientate these molecules and to displace any charges, for example stray electrons, which may be present. The dielectric thus becomes *polarized*, and a field is created in opposition to the impressed one. The polarization is largely due to orientation of the molecules which are said to be *polar* and have a non-symmetrical structure, as in water.

In some dielectrics the molecular dipole moments tend to zero. The molecules are then said to be *non-polar* and the polarization

204

effect, which is usually small, is largely dependent on electrons in atoms being displaced relative to the nucleus. In ionic crystals polarization may also be partly ascribed to the relative movement of the positive and negative ions.

If the polarization is $\mathbf{P}$, which is the dipole moment per unit volume, units coulomb metre^{-2}, then that of a volume δV is $\mathbf{P}\delta V$. Since $\mathbf{P}$ depends on the applied field $\mathbf{E}$ at all points in the dielectric we write

$$P = \kappa E \qquad (8.47)$$

where κ is a constant in an isotropic dielectric and is the *dielectric susceptibility per unit volume*, units coulomb volt^{-1} metre^{-1}.

For substances with polar molecules, κ depends greatly on temperature because the increase in agitation of the molecules with a temperature increase opposes orientation. For dielectrics with non-polar molecules, κ varies slightly with temperature, the alteration being mainly due to expansion of the substance.

The origin of electric polarization in media can often be ascertained by an examination of the dependence of κ on the frequency of $\mathbf{E}$. At frequencies above the microwave band the molecular dipoles have not sufficient time to become orientated and their contribution to κ disappears. Above the infra-red region the ionic contribution, if any, is removed, and above the ultra-violet band the orbital electronic contribution vanishes. Just before their disappearance the ionic and orbital contributions pass through a resonance and κ is critically dependent on frequency. The total contribution is dependent on the origin only in respect of its magnitude for static fields and for alternating fields up to frequencies of about one megacycle per second.

Equation (8.4) is, for a dielectric of permittivity ε

$$\text{div } \varepsilon E = \rho$$

or, for a vacuum

$$\text{div } \varepsilon_0 E = \rho'$$

the difference $\rho - \rho'$ between the charge densities being caused by polarization. ρ' equals ρ if $\varepsilon_0 \mathbf{E}$ is increased to $\varepsilon_0 \mathbf{E} + \mathbf{P}$. Then

$$\varepsilon_0 E + P = \varepsilon E \qquad (8.48)$$

or

$$P = D - D_0$$

where $\mathbf{D}_0$ equals $\varepsilon_0 \mathbf{E}$ and is the displacement in vacuo. Thus $\mathbf{P}$ may be regarded as the difference between the displacement vector in a medium and that in a vacuum when the electric field is the same in both. Combining *Equations (8.47)* and *(8.48)* we get

$$\varepsilon_0 \mathbf{E} + \kappa \mathbf{E} = \varepsilon \mathbf{E}$$

or

$$\varepsilon = \varepsilon_0 + \kappa. \tag{8.49}$$

The last equation suggests a method by which κ can be measured. The dielectric whose susceptibility is required is placed between the plates of a capacitor, whose capacitance has previously been found with the space between the plates evacuated, and the new capacitance is determined. κ can be expressed simply in terms of these two capacitances. Such a method can be used from zero frequency to very high radio frequencies. For the microwave region and above the refractive index n can be found, and hence the relative permittivity ε_r by the use of *Equation (8.16)*. κ can then be easily calculated.

8.8. Lorentz Theory of Dielectrics

In the Lorentz theory of dielectrics, account is taken of molecular dipoles. The molecules are assumed to be all identical and the electric field of each is imagined to be significant in a sphere of radius R, the centre of which coincides with the centre of the molecule. The total volume of all the spheres is assumed to be the volume of the dielectric.

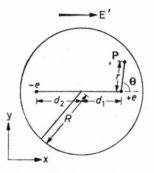

Figure 8.5. Dipole in a dielectric

A molecular dipole is shown in *Figure 8.5* and is composed of charges $+e$ and $-e$ orientated in the direction of the applied field $\mathbf{E}'$, distances d_1 and d_2 from the centre of the sphere. The field in the

x direction at a point P distance r from the positive charge due to the dipole is E_x, given by

$$E_x = (e/4\pi\varepsilon_0 r^2)(\hat{r}.\hat{\imath})$$

$\hat{\imath}$ being a unit vector in the positive x direction. The permittivity is ε_0 because most of the volume of the sphere occupies the space between the molecules. Thus

$$E_x = (e/4\pi\varepsilon_0 r^2) \cos\theta$$

and the average field in the x direction over the whole sphere of volume V is $\bar{E}_x$ where

$$\bar{E}_x = (e/4\pi\varepsilon_0 V)\int_V (\cos\theta)/r^2 dV. \qquad (8.50)$$

r and θ can vary independently hence δS, the elementary area shown in *Figure 8.6*, is $r\delta\theta\delta r$ and δV is the volume generated by this area

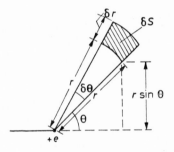

Figure 8.6. Elementary area

moving round a circular path of radius $r\sin\theta$ about the axis of the dipole. Thus

$$\delta V = 2\pi r(\sin\theta)r\delta\theta\delta r$$

or

$$\delta V = 2\pi r^2(\sin\theta)\delta\theta\delta r. \qquad (8.51)$$

Values of r for which P is on the surface of the sphere, *Figure 8.7*, are given by

$$R^2 = d_1^2 + r_s^2 + 2d_1 r_s \cos\theta \qquad (8.52)$$

207

from the cosine rule. Hence r ranges between these values and zero and we have, combining *Equations* (8.50) and (8.51)

$$\bar{E}_x = (e/2\varepsilon_0 V)\int_{r=0}^{r=r_s}\int_{\theta=0}^{\theta=\pi}(\sin\theta)(\cos\theta)\mathrm{d}\theta\mathrm{d}r.$$

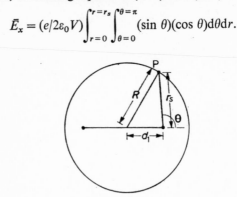

Figure 8.7. Points on the surface of a sphere

$\displaystyle\int_{r=0}^{r=r_s}\mathrm{d}r = r_s$, which must also be integrated with respect to θ. From *Equation* (8.52)

$$R^2 = (r_s+d_1\cos\theta)^2+d_1^2(1-\cos^2\theta)$$

$$= (r_s+d_1\cos\theta)^2+d_1^2\sin^2\theta.$$

Hence

$$r_s = (R^2-d_1^2\sin^2\theta)^{\frac{1}{2}}-d_1\cos\theta$$

so that

$$\bar{E}_x = (e/2\varepsilon_0 V)\int_{\theta=0}^{\theta=\pi}(\sin\theta)(\cos\theta)[(R^2-d_1^2\sin^2\theta)^{\frac{1}{2}}-d_1\cos\theta]\mathrm{d}\theta.$$

Let

$$R^2-d_1^2\sin^2\theta = \sin^2\phi.$$

Then

$$-2d_1^2(\sin\theta)(\cos\theta)\delta\theta = 2(\sin\phi)(\cos\phi)\delta\phi$$

and hence there are the two integrals

$$\int(\sin^2\phi)(\cos\phi)\mathrm{d}\phi \text{ and } \int(\sin\theta)(\cos^2\theta)\mathrm{d}\theta$$

to evaluate, which give $(\sin^3\phi)/3$ and $-(\cos^3\theta)/3$. Thus

$$\bar{E}_x = (e/2\varepsilon_0 V)\left\{-[(1/3)\mathrm{d}_1^2(R^2-\mathrm{d}_1^2\sin^2\theta)^{3/2}+\mathrm{d}_1(\cos^3\theta)/3]\right\}_0^\pi$$

$$= (e/2\varepsilon_0 V)(-2d_1/3) = -ed_1/3\varepsilon_0 V.$$

208

The average field in the positive x direction for the charge $-e$ is similarly found to be $-ed_2/3\varepsilon_0 V$ so the average field for the dipole is

$$\hat{i}[-e(d_1+d_2)/3\varepsilon_0 V] = -M/3\varepsilon_0 V$$

where M is the dipole moment. There is no average field in the y direction, because that on one side of the dipole is cancelled by that on the other. If there are N molecules per unit volume

$$\hat{i}[(\bar{E}_x)_{total}] = -MN/3\varepsilon_0 = -P/3\varepsilon_0$$

since the dipole moment per unit volume is MN which equals P.
If the net field is E

$$E = E' - P/3\varepsilon_0.$$

From *Equation (8.48)*

$$P = E(\varepsilon - \varepsilon_0) = E\varepsilon_0(\varepsilon_r - 1).$$

Thus

$$E' = E[1 + (\varepsilon_r - 1)/3] = E(\varepsilon_r + 2)/3$$

so that

$$P = 3E'\varepsilon_0(\varepsilon_r - 1)/(\varepsilon_r + 2). \tag{8.53}$$

The dipole moment can reasonably be assumed to increase linearly with the applied field, that is

$$M = \alpha E'$$

the constant α being a measure of the facility with which the molecules are polarized—the *polarizability*. For N molecules per unit volume

$$NM = N\alpha E'$$

$$= P.$$

If ρ is the density of the dielectric and m_1 is the mass of one molecule, N is ρ/m_1 and *Equation (8.53)* becomes

$$3\varepsilon_0(\varepsilon_r - 1)/(\varepsilon_r + 2) = N\alpha = \alpha\rho/m_1$$

or

$$(1/\rho)(\varepsilon_r - 1)/(\varepsilon_r + 2) = \text{a constant} \tag{8.54}$$

which is the Clausius–Mossotti relation and should be true for any dielectric. It holds for many dielectrics over limited temperature ranges, but measurements for liquids and solids, for which density changes are small, are difficult. Partial confirmation of the Lorentz theory is obtained.

The well-known Lorenz-Lorentz law can be obtained from *Equation (8.54)*. From *Equation (8.16)* the refractive index n of a dielectric is given by

$$n^2 = \varepsilon_r.$$

Thus *Equation (8.54)* becomes

$$(1/\rho)(n^2 - 1)/(n^2 + 2) = \text{a constant} \qquad (8.55)$$

or $(n^2 - 1)/(n^2 + 2)$ is directly proportional to the density of the dielectric, which is the Lorenz-Lorentz law.

8.9. Motion of Electrons

In the Lorentz theory a dielectric was assumed to contain dipoles, and when the theory was first proposed there was little basis for such an assumption. The discovery of the electron enabled the assumption to be justified and the theory to be extended to explain electromagnetic wave dispersion phenomena in substances whose susceptibility depends largely on the displacement of orbital electrons. An atom could be regarded as comprising a number of electrons having a negative charge, associated with a nucleus having a positive charge equalling in magnitude the total electronic charge. In the presence of an applied field $\mathbf{E}'$ the charged bodies are separated to form a dipole, the electrons being displaced further because of their much smaller mass. Thus in *Figure 8.5* d_2 is greater than d_1.

A further consequence of the small electronic mass is that the electrons will vibrate readily in an oscillating field $\mathbf{E}'$, while the nucleus is very little disturbed. An oscillating electric field is present when an electro-magnetic wave passes through a substance. There is also an oscillating magnetic component but this will have little effect on electronic motion if the electron velocity is small and may usually be ignored.

We assume that the equation of electronic motion is identical with *Equation (2.8)*

$$M\mathrm{d}^2\mathbf{s}/\mathrm{d}t^2 + R_m \mathrm{d}\mathbf{s}/\mathrm{d}t + S\mathbf{s} = \mathbf{F}_0 \cos pt$$

where M is now the 'particle' mass, the mass of a group of electrons, $\mathbf{s}$ the instantaneous displacement, R_m the resistance to motion per unit velocity, S the restoring force per unit displacement and $\mathbf{F}_0 \cos pt$ the applied force of angular frequency p. In the complete solution of this equation the complementary function can usually be ignored here because $\mathbf{F}_0 \cos pt$ is applied continuously. The equation is written in terms of vectors so that fields, displacements and so on can be retained in vector form later. The equation becomes

$$d^2\mathbf{s}/dt^2 + 2d\omega_0 d\mathbf{s}/dt + \omega_0^2\mathbf{s} = \mathbf{f}_0 \cos pt = \mathbf{f} \qquad (8.56)$$

where $d = R_m/2\sqrt{(SM)}$, $\omega_0^2 = S/M$ and $\mathbf{f}_0 = \mathbf{F}_0/M$, ω_0 being the natural angular frequency of oscillation of the group of electrons. We let $\mathbf{s} = \mathbf{s}_0 \exp \mathrm{j}pt$. Hence

$$d\mathbf{s}/dt = \mathrm{j}p\mathbf{s}_0 \exp \mathrm{j}pt = \mathrm{j}p\mathbf{s}$$

and

$$d^2\mathbf{s}/dt^2 = -p^2\mathbf{s}_0 \exp \mathrm{j}pt = -p^2\mathbf{s}.$$

Thus using *Equation (8.56)* we get

$$\mathbf{s} = \mathbf{f}/(\omega_0^2 - p^2 + 2\mathrm{j}d\omega_0 p) = (\mathbf{E}'e/M)/(\omega_0^2 - p^2 + 2\mathrm{j}d\omega_0 p)$$

where $\mathbf{E}'$ is the applied field. From the preceding section the net field $\mathbf{E}$ is $\mathbf{E}' - \mathbf{P}/3\varepsilon_0$ and $\mathbf{P}$ is given by

$$\mathbf{P} = Ne\mathbf{s} \qquad (8.57)$$

because the dipole moment for a displacement $\mathbf{s}$ is $e\mathbf{s}$, the movement of the nucleus being ignored, and N is the number of dipoles per unit volume. Hence

$$\mathbf{s} = (e/M)(\mathbf{E} + Ne\mathbf{s}/3\varepsilon_0)/(\omega_0^2 - p^2 + 2\mathrm{j}d\omega_0 p)$$
$$= (\mathbf{E}e/M)/(\omega_0^2 - p^2 - Ne^2/3M\varepsilon_0 + 2\mathrm{j}d\omega_0 p). \qquad (8.58)$$

The current density vector in the x direction is $\mathbf{i}_x$ and is composed largely of displacement current as the substance considered is a dielectric. The displacement current is the vector sum of the polarization current and the displacement current in vacuo, on the basis of *Equation (8.48)*. Hence

$$\mathbf{i}_x = \partial\mathbf{D}/\partial t = \sum_{n=1}^{n} \frac{\partial}{\partial t}(N_n e_n \mathbf{s}_n) + \partial\mathbf{D}_0/\partial t$$

which refers to particle groups having masses M_1, M_2, M_3, . . . , charges e_1, e_2, e_3, . . . and the numbers per unit volume being N_1, N_2, N_3, . . . *Equation (8.58)* applies generally to particle displacement so we have

$$\varepsilon_0\varepsilon_r\partial\mathbf{E}/\partial t = \varepsilon_0\partial\mathbf{E}/\partial t[1 + \sum(Ne^2/M\varepsilon_0)/(\omega_0^2 - p^2 - Ne^2/3M\varepsilon_0 + 2\mathrm{j}d\omega_0 p)]$$

since $\mathbf{D} = \varepsilon\mathbf{E} = \varepsilon_r\varepsilon_0\mathbf{E}$. Thus

$$\varepsilon_r = 1 + \sum(Ne^2/M\varepsilon_0)/(\omega_0^2 - p^2 - Ne^2/3M\varepsilon_0 + 2\mathrm{j}d\omega_0 p) \qquad (8.59)$$

the summation referring to N, M, e, ω_0 and d. Using *Equations (8.57)* and *(8.58)* we also get

$$P = E\sum(Ne^2/M)/(\omega_0^2 - p^2 - Ne^2/3M\varepsilon_0 + 2jd\omega_0 p). \qquad (8.60)$$

But from *Equation (8.47)*

$$P = \kappa E$$

so that

$$\kappa = \sum(Ne^2/M)/(\omega_0^2 - p^2 - Ne^2/3M\varepsilon_0 + 2jd\omega_0 p) \qquad (8.61)$$

which could otherwise be obtained from *Equation (8.59)*. Using *Equations (8.16)* and *(8.59)*, the refractive index n of the dielectric is given by

$$n^2 = 1 + \sum(Ne^2/M\varepsilon_0)/(\omega_0^2 - p^2 - Ne^2/3M\varepsilon_0 + 2jd\omega_0 p). \qquad (8.62)$$

For single electrons the damping of oscillations is negligible, and the summation in the preceding equations need no longer be retained. *Equation (8.62)* becomes

$$n^2 = 1 + (Ne^2/M\varepsilon_0)/(\omega_0^2 - p^2 - Ne^2/3M\varepsilon_0)$$

$$= 1 + 1/[(\omega_0^2 - p^2)M\varepsilon_0/Ne^2 - 1/3)]$$

and

$$(n^2 - 1)/(n^2 + 2) = Ne^2/3M\varepsilon_0(\omega_0^2 - p^2). \qquad (8.63)$$

This result is consistent with the Lorenz-Lorentz law, *Equation (8.55)*, because the density ρ of the dielectric is directly proportional to N, the number of dipoles per unit volume, e, M and ε_0 are constants, and ω_0 should not vary appreciably with temperature. *Equation (8.63)* can also be written in terms of the relative permittivity ε_r which is then seen to depend on the natural frequency of oscillation of the electrons, $\omega_0/2\pi$, and on the frequency at which a measurement is made, $p/2\pi$. Pure water, for example, has a relative permittivity of about 80 at low frequencies, but in the microwave region has roughly a quarter of the low frequency value.

8.10. Dispersion

From *Equation (8.63)*

$$(n^2 - 1)/(n^2 + 2) = Ne^2/3M\varepsilon_0\omega_0^2(1 - p^2/\omega_0^2)$$

212

and if p is much smaller than ω_0, which applies at infra-red frequencies for some substances

$$(n^2-1)/(n^2+2) = (Ne^2/3M\varepsilon_0\omega_0)(1+p^2/\omega_0^2+p^4/\omega_0^4+\ldots)$$

or

$$(n^2-1)/(n^2+2) = A_1+A_2/\lambda^2+A_3/\lambda^4+\ldots \qquad (8.64)$$

where $p\lambda/2\pi$ is c, the wave velocity, and A_1, A_2, $\ldots$ are constants, since N, M and ω_0 are constants for a particular substance.

Again, from *Equation (8.63)*

$$(n^2-1)/(n^2+2) = -Ne^2/3M\varepsilon_0p^2(1-\omega_0^2/p^2) \qquad (8.65)$$

and if p is much larger than ω_0, which applies at ultra-violet frequencies for some substances

$$(n^2-1)/(n^2+2) = -(Ne^2/3M\varepsilon_0p^2)(1+\omega_0^2/p^2+\omega_0^4/p^4+\ldots)$$

or

$$(n^2-1)/(n^2+2) = B_1\lambda^2+B_2\lambda^4+B_3\lambda^6+\ldots \qquad (8.66)$$

where B_1, B_2, $\ldots$ are constants. The results (8.64) and (8.66) agree with various empirical dispersion formulae, including that due to Cauchy.

At very high frequencies p is very much larger than ω_0 and *Equation (8.65)* becomes

$$(n^2-1)/(n^2+2) = -Ne^2/3M\varepsilon_0p^2$$

or

$$n = (1-Ne^2/3M\varepsilon_0p^2)^{\frac{1}{2}} \qquad (8.67)$$

which shows that, at very high frequencies, n can become less than unity, the condition for the total reflection of waves at a boundary. The same equation as (8.67) is obtained if the electrons have no free period, for then ω_0 is zero. This occurs for electrons in layers such as space charges if there is no magnetic field present.

According to *Equation (8.65)*, $(n^2-1)/(n^2+2)$ should become very large if p approaches ω_0. No such effect occurs practically. The discrepancy arises because the damping of vibrations has been ignored. A return must be made to *Equation (8.59)* in which ε_r is replaced by $(n-j\chi)^2$ which equals n'^2, as in section **8.4.** χ is the coefficient of extinction and n' is the complex refractive index. Thus for single electrons

$$(n-j\chi)^2 = 1+(Ne^2/M\varepsilon_0)/(\omega_0^2 - p^2 - Ne^2/3M\varepsilon_0 + 2jd\omega_0 p)$$

and equating real and imaginary parts yields

$$n^2 - \chi^2 = 1 + \frac{(Ne^2/M\varepsilon_0)(\omega_0^2 - p^2 - Ne^2/3M\varepsilon_0)}{(\omega_0^2 - p^2 - Ne^2/3M\varepsilon_0)^2 + 4d^2\omega_0^2 p^2} \qquad (8.68)$$

$$2n\chi = (Ne^2/M\varepsilon_0)(2d\omega_0 p)/[(\omega_0^2 - p^2 - Ne^2/3M\varepsilon_0)^2 + 4d^2\omega_0^2 p^2]. \qquad (8.69)$$

Equation (8.69) shows that χ becomes larger as p approaches ω_0. n^2 and χ can be plotted against the frequency $p/2\pi$ or the corresponding wavelength λ, as shown in *Figure 8.8*, which applies to substances having a main absorption band in the visible region of the electromagnetic wave spectrum.

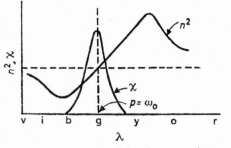

Figure 8.8. Graph of n^2 *and* χ *against* λ

With many transparent substances the refractive index decreases as λ increases over the visible region, and light having short wavelength components is refracted more than light having components of longer wavelengths. Dispersion occurs in suitable circumstances and white light is split into the components indicated in *Figure 8.8* along the λ axis. If n^2 varies as shown in the figure, orange light, for example, is refracted more than green, and the usual order of the components of white light becomes reversed in the portion over which n increases as λ increases. The phenomenon is known as *anomalous dispersion* and is shown by substances having absorption bands within the range of wavelengths of radiation passed through them, that is by all substances for a sufficiently wide wavelength range. Thus the term is a misnomer unless limited to dispersion within the visible region or other narrow bands of wavelengths. In the visible region, substances such as solutions of some inorganic salts including cobalt chloride, solutions of aniline colouring matters like cyanin, and glasses coloured with, for example, cobalt oxide show anomalous dispersion. If there are several appreciably different natural frequencies of vibration of electron groups and single electrons, there will be several corresponding absorption bands with the accompanying dispersion effects. The electron theory leads to a satisfactory qualitative explanation of dispersion, but quantitative theoretical results show some disagreement with experimental ones.

8.11. Reflection, Refraction and Polarization

E and D alter as they pass from one dielectric to another, but certain components are unchanged. Consider two points A and B on the interface, the position vector of B relative to A being δx, that is the vector δx is drawn from A to B. If the tangential components of electric field at the boundary are E_1 and E_2 the potential difference between A and B on one side is $E_1.\delta x$ and on the other side $E_2.\delta x$. Normal components of E have no effect on the potential difference between A and B. The potential difference between points on the boundary is the same on both sides, so that $E_1.\delta x$ equals $E_2.\delta x$ or E_1 equals E_2, that is the tangential component of E is continuous. This result is unaffected by charges on the boundary because tangential components of field leaving them result in equal quantities or zero being added vectorially to both E_1 and E_2.

Suppose D_1 and D_2 are the normal components of displacement at the interface. Imagine a flat elementary volume drawn with its side normal to the boundary and its ends parallel to and just on either side of the boundary. If δS is the area of either end, the charge enclosed in the volume is, according to Gauss' theorem, $D_1.\hat{n}_1\delta S + D_2.\hat{n}_2\delta S$ where $\hat{n}_1$ and $\hat{n}_2$ are the outward drawn unit normals to the ends. The flux through the side of the volume involving tangential components of D can be ignored as the area of the side is vanishingly small. If there is no charge on the boundary inside the volume, $D_1.\hat{n}_1$ equals $-D_2.\hat{n}_2$. The normals are drawn in opposite senses which accounts for the minus sign, so that D_1 and D_2 are in the same sense and are equal in magnitude. Thus the normal component of D is continuous if there is no charge on the boundary through where it passes. If there is a charge the normal component of D is discontinuous, since the flux leaving the charge normal to the interface is added to the normal component of D in one dielectric and subtracted in the other, although a charge is more easily allowed for by applying Gauss' theorem as indicated earlier.

The tangential component of **H** and the normal component of **B** are also continuous if no dipoles are present on the boundary. If there are dipoles on the boundary, continuity or otherwise depends on their dispositions relative to the boundary and to the point at which **H** and **B** are considered. Fortunately only an interface devoid of charges and dipoles need be considered in an analysis of the reflection, refraction and polarization of electro-magnetic waves.

In *Figure 8.9* suppose that the boundary between two dielectrics passes through the x axis shown and is normal to the plane of the diagram. Thus the boundary coincides with the xy plane, to which the z axis is normal. IO, OR and OT are the directions of the incident, reflected and transmitted waves but they are not necessarily in the same plane. IO can be assumed, for convenience, to lie in the xz plane, that of the diagram.

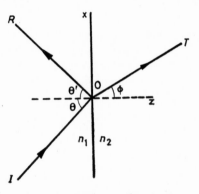

Figure 8.9. Incident, reflected and
transmitted waves

Equation (8.18b) is

$$\mathbf{s} = \mathbf{a} \exp jk(Lx + My + Nz - ct)$$

where **s** represents **E** or **H**, k is $2\pi/\lambda$ and L, M and N are direction cosines. If θ is the angle of incidence $L = \sin\theta$, $M = 0$ and $N = \cos\theta$ since IO lies in the xz plane. Both **E** and **H** can be imagined to be composed of three vectors parallel to the x, y and z axes, and each of these components will, in the incident wave, be directly proportional to

$$\exp jk(x \sin\theta + z \cos\theta - c_1 t).$$

c_1 is the wave velocity in the dielectric of refractive index n_1 and is

216

c_0/n_1, where c_0 is the wave velocity in a vacuum. Similarly c_2, the wave velocity in the dielectric of refractive index n_2, is c_0/n_2.

The reflected and transmitted waves move in directions specified by L_R, M_R, N_R and L_T, M_T, N_T, where $N_R = \cos(\pi - \theta') = -\cos\theta'$ and $N_T = \cos\phi$. Thus the components for these two waves are proportional to

$$\exp jk_R(L_Rx + M_Ry + N_Rz - c_1t)$$

and

$$\exp jk_T(L_Tx + M_Ty + N_Tz - c_2t).$$

The tangential components of **E** are the same on both sides of the boundary, which is the plane $z = 0$. Thus

$$\mathbf{a} \exp jk(x \sin\theta - c_1t) + \mathbf{a_R} \exp jk_R(L_Rx + M_Ry - c_1t)$$

$$= \mathbf{a_T} \exp jk_T(L_Tx + M_Ty - c_2t)$$

where $\mathbf{a}$, $\mathbf{a_R}$ and $\mathbf{a_T}$ are the amplitudes of the incident, reflected and transmitted waves. This equation holds for all values of x, y and t only if the indices are all equal

$$k(x \sin\theta - c_1t) = k_R(L_Rx + M_Ry - c_1t)$$

$$= k_T(L_Tx + M_Ty - c_2t).$$

Equating coefficients of x, y and t one finds

$$k \sin\theta = k_R L_R = k_T L_T$$

$$0 = k_R M_R = k_T M_T$$

$$kc_1 = k_R c_1 = k_T c_2.$$

The second relation shows that M_R and M_T both equal zero since k_R and k_T do not equal zero, so that the reflected and transmitted waves OR and OT lie in the same plane, the xz plane, as the incident wave IO. The third relation shows that the frequencies f_R and f_T of the reflected and transmitted waves equal the frequency f of the incident wave since

$$kc_1 = 2\pi c_1/\lambda = f$$

$$k_R c_1 = 2\pi c_1/\lambda_R = f_R$$

$$k_T c_2 = 2\pi c_2/\lambda_T = f_T.$$

217

Because, also from the third equation, k_R equals k the first equation becomes

$$\sin \theta = L_R.$$

But

$$L_R = \cos (\pi/2 - \theta') = \sin \theta'.$$

Hence

$$\theta' = \theta \tag{8.70}$$

since the simplest solution applies here. Thus the angle of reflection equals the angle of incidence. Furthermore, from the first equation

$$k \sin \theta = k_T L_T$$

or

$$(\sin \theta)/\lambda = L_T/\lambda_T$$

since $k = 2\pi/\lambda$ and $k_T = 2\pi/\lambda_T$.

But the frequencies of the waves are all the same so that

$$(\sin \theta)/c_1 = L_T/c_2$$

or

$$n_1 \sin \theta = n_2 L_T$$

because $c_1 = c_0/n_1$ and $c_2 = c_0/n_2$.

We have

$$L_T = \cos (\pi/2 - \phi) = \sin \phi$$

so that

$$n_1 \sin \theta = n_2 \sin \phi \tag{8.71}$$

which is *Snell's law*.

Phase and amplitude relations are obtained simply if the incident wave is plane polarized. If not the analysis is difficult. We thus consider first an incident wave polarized in the xz plane, the plane of incidence, which has been shown to contain also the reflected and transmitted waves. In accordance with the convention used in section **8.3.** the magnetic vector lies in the xz plane and is perpendicular to IO. The electric vector is normal to this plane and is thus parallel to the y axis. The positive part of the y axis is directed up out of the plane of *Figure 8.10* if the axes follow a right-hand screw rule. The direction in which the wave is advancing, **E** and **H**, in that order, also conform to a right-hand screw rule, as noted in section **8.2.** Hence

218

with **H** as shown in *Figure 8.10* **E** must be in the negative y sense. Thus

$$\mathbf{H}_x = \mathbf{H} \cos \theta \; ; \; \mathbf{H}_y = 0 \; ; \; \mathbf{H}_z = -\mathbf{H} \sin \theta;$$
$$\mathbf{E}_x = 0 \; ; \; \mathbf{E}_y = -\mathbf{E} \; ; \; \mathbf{E}_z = 0.$$

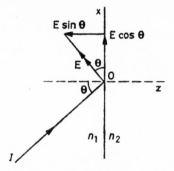

Figure 8.10. Incident wave polarized in the plane of incidence

Using the preceding exponential functions for **H** and **E** and assuming that the amplitude of **H** is **a** we get

$$\mathbf{H}_x = \mathbf{a}(\cos \theta) \exp jk(x \sin \theta + z \cos \theta - c_1 t)$$
$$\mathbf{H}_y = 0$$
$$\mathbf{H}_z = -\mathbf{a}(\sin \theta) \exp jk(x \sin \theta + z \cos \theta - c_1 t)$$
$$\mathbf{E}_x = 0$$
$$\mathbf{E}_y = -\eta_1 \mathbf{a} \exp jk(x \sin \theta + z \cos \theta - c_1 t)$$
$$\mathbf{E}_z = 0$$

because, according to *Equation (8.24)*, $\mathbf{E} = \eta\mathbf{H}$ generally, where $\eta = \sqrt{(\mu/\varepsilon)}$.

Similar reasoning holds for the reflected and transmitted waves for which θ, where it occurs in the preceding equations for the components of **H** and **E**, is replaced by $\pi - \theta$ and ϕ in turn. Thus for the reflected wave

$$\mathbf{H}_x = -\mathbf{a}_R(\cos \theta) \exp jk(x \sin \theta - z \cos \theta - c_1 t)$$
$$\mathbf{H}_y = 0$$
$$\mathbf{H}_z = -\mathbf{a}_R(\sin \theta) \exp jk(x \sin \theta - z \cos \theta - c_1 t)$$
$$\mathbf{E}_x = 0$$
$$\mathbf{E}_y = -\eta_1 \mathbf{a}_R \exp jk(x \sin \theta - z \cos \theta - c_1 t)$$
$$\mathbf{E}_z = 0$$

219

and for the transmitted wave

$$\mathbf{H}_x = \mathbf{a}_T(\cos\phi)\exp jk_T(x\sin\phi+z\cos\phi-c_2t)$$
$$\mathbf{H}_y = 0$$
$$\mathbf{H}_z = -\mathbf{a}_T(\sin\phi)\exp jk_T(x\sin\phi+z\cos\phi-c_2t)$$
$$\mathbf{E}_x = 0$$
$$\mathbf{E}_y = -\eta_2\mathbf{a}_T\exp jk_T(x\sin\phi+z\cos\phi-c_2t)$$
$$\mathbf{E}_z = 0.$$

The boundary conditions are that $\mathbf{H}_x$, $\mathbf{H}_y$, $\mu\mathbf{H}_z$, $\mathbf{E}_x$, $\mathbf{E}_y$ and $\varepsilon\mathbf{E}_z$ are continuous at $z = 0$ for all values of x and t but these reduce to two independent relations which are, for example, that $\mathbf{E}_y$ and $\mathbf{H}_x$ are continuous. Thus, if only magnitudes are considered

$$\eta_1 a + \eta_1 a_R = \eta_2 a_T$$

$$a\cos\theta - a_R\cos\theta = a_T\cos\phi.$$

Multiplying the first by $\cos\theta$ and the second by η_1 we get

$$\eta_1(a+a_R)\cos\theta = \eta_2 a_T\cos\theta$$

$$\eta_1(a-a_R)\cos\theta = \eta_1 a_T\cos\phi$$

and adding and subtracting

$$2\eta_1 a\cos\theta = a_T(\eta_2\cos\theta+\eta_1\cos\phi)$$

$$2\eta_1 a_R\cos\theta = a_T(\eta_2\cos\theta-\eta_1\cos\phi)$$

so that

$$a/(\eta_2\cos\theta+\eta_1\cos\phi) = a_R/(\eta_2\cos\theta-\eta_1\cos\phi)$$

$$= a_T/2\eta_1\cos\theta.$$

But Snell's law is

$$(\sin\theta)/c_1 = (\sin\phi)/c_2$$

where

$$c_1 = 1/\sqrt{(\mu_1\varepsilon_1)} \text{ and } c_2 = 1/\sqrt{(\mu_2\varepsilon_2)}$$

or

$$c_1 \simeq 1/\sqrt{(\mu_0\varepsilon_1)} \text{ and } c_2 \simeq 1/\sqrt{(\mu_0\varepsilon_1)}$$

because the relative permeabilities are nearly unity in most dielectrics which can transmit light. Also

$$\eta_1 \simeq \sqrt{(\mu_0/\varepsilon_1)} \text{ and } \eta_2 \simeq \sqrt{(\mu_0/\varepsilon_2)}$$

$$\simeq \mu_0 c_1 \qquad\qquad \simeq \mu_0 c_2.$$

Thus

$$\eta_2/\eta_1 = c_2/c_1 = (\sin\phi)/\sin\theta$$

so that, on dividing the denominators of the amplitude ratios by η_1 and multiplying them by sin θ we find that

$$a/\sin(\theta+\phi) = -a_R/\sin(\theta-\phi) = a_T/\sin 2\theta \qquad (8.72)$$

which gives the amplitude ratios and the phase relations of the magnetic vectors belonging to the incident, reflected and refracted waves.

If the dielectric into which the waves pass has a greater refractive index than the one in which the incident and reflected waves travel, ϕ is less than θ and a_R/a is negative. There is thus a phase angle change of π radians in both the E and H vectors when reflection occurs in the medium of smaller refractive index. This is described as reflection at an unyielding boundary, as mentioned in section **6.2.** If reflection occurs in the medium of greater refractive index a_R/a is positive because ϕ exceeds θ and there is no phase change in both vectors. The boundary is then said to be yielding. The amplitude ratios for the electric vectors can be found from *Equation (8.72)* by introducing the appropriate values of η. The amplitudes become $a\eta_1$, $a_R\eta_1$ and $a_T\eta_2$. The ratio η_2/η_1 can be eliminated as before.

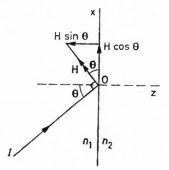

Figure 8.11. Incident wave polarized normal to the plane of incidence

When the incident wave is polarized normally to the plane of incidence a similar analysis can be devised. Then the electric vector is as shown in *Figure 8.11* and the magnetic vector is normal to the plane of the diagram but in the positive *y* sense, its amplitude being put equal to *b* since it is in general not the same as in the preceding

221

case. In effect $\mathbf{E}$ and $\mathbf{H}$ here are interchanged with those preceding. For the incident wave

$$\mathbf{H}_x = 0$$
$$\mathbf{H}_y = \mathbf{b} \exp jk(x \sin \theta + z \cos \theta - c_1 t)$$
$$\mathbf{H}_z = 0$$
$$\mathbf{E}_x = \eta_1 \mathbf{b}(\cos \theta) \exp jk(x \sin \theta + z \cos \theta - c_1 t)$$
$$\mathbf{E}_y = 0$$
$$\mathbf{E}_z = -\eta_1 \mathbf{b}(\sin \theta) \exp jk(x \sin \theta + z \cos \theta - c_1 t).$$

For the reflected wave

$$\mathbf{H}_x = 0$$
$$\mathbf{H}_y = \mathbf{b}_R \exp jk(x \sin \theta - z \cos \theta - c_1 t)$$
$$\mathbf{H}_z = 0$$
$$\mathbf{E}_x = -\eta_1 \mathbf{b}_R(\cos \theta) \exp jk(x \sin \theta - z \cos \theta - c_1 t)$$
$$\mathbf{E}_y = 0$$
$$\mathbf{E}_z = -\eta_1 \mathbf{b}_R(\sin \theta) \exp jk(x \sin \theta - z \cos \theta - c_1 t)$$

and for the transmitted wave

$$\mathbf{H}_x = 0$$
$$\mathbf{H}_y = \mathbf{b}_T \exp jk_T(x \sin \phi + z \cos \phi - c_2 t)$$
$$\mathbf{H}_z = 0$$
$$\mathbf{E}_x = \eta_2 \mathbf{b}_T(\cos \phi) \exp jk_T(x \sin \phi + z \cos \phi - c_2 t)$$
$$\mathbf{E}_y = 0$$
$$\mathbf{E}_z = -\eta_2 \mathbf{b}_T(\sin \phi) \exp jk_T(x \sin \phi + z \cos \phi - c_2 t).$$

If $\mathbf{H}_y$ and $\mathbf{E}_x$ are continuous at $z = 0$ for all values of x and t

$$b + b_R = b_T$$

and

$$\eta_1 b \cos \theta - \eta_1 b_R \cos \theta = \eta_2 b_T \cos \phi.$$

Multiplying the first by $\eta_1 \cos \theta$ yields

$$\eta_1 b \cos \theta + \eta_1 b_R \cos \theta = \eta_1 b_T \cos \theta$$

and adding to and subtracting from this the second relation we get

$$2\eta_1 b \cos \theta = b_T(\eta_1 \cos \theta + \eta_2 \cos \phi)$$

and

$$2\eta_1 b_R \cos \theta = b_T(\eta_1 \cos \theta - \eta_2 \cos \phi).$$

Thus

$$b/(\eta_1 \cos \theta + \eta_2 \cos \phi) = b_T/2\eta_1 \cos \theta$$
$$= b_R/(\eta_1 \cos \theta - \eta_2 \cos \phi).$$

As before

$$\eta_2/\eta_1 = (\sin \phi)/\sin \theta$$

so that on dividing the denominators by η_1 and multiplying them by $\sin \theta$ we have

$$b/(\sin 2\theta + \sin 2\phi) = b_R/(\sin 2\theta - \sin 2\phi)$$
$$= b_T/2 \sin 2\theta \qquad (8.73)$$

which again gives the amplitude ratios and the phase relations for the magnetic vectors. Those for the electric vectors can be found from this equation by introducing the relevant values of η.

b_R is zero if $\sin 2\theta$ equals $\sin 2\phi$. Since θ is not equal to ϕ

$$\phi = \pi/2 - \theta$$

for the simplest relation. Then Snell's law gives

$$n_1 \sin \theta = n_2 \sin \phi = n_2 \cos \theta$$

or $\qquad\qquad \tan \theta = n_2/n_1 \simeq \sqrt{(\varepsilon_2/\varepsilon_1)}. \qquad (8.74)$

Such an angle of incidence is known as *Brewster's angle*, for which there is no reflected ray when the incident ray is polarized normally to the plane of incidence, that is when the magnetic vector is normal to the plane of incidence. The incident wave is often unpolarized. *Equations (8.72)* and *(8.73)* show that if the incident amplitudes in and normal to the plane of incidence are equal, the reflected amplitudes will not be and thus even an unpolarized incident wave will, after reflection, be partially plane polarized. When the angle of incidence is given by *Equation (8.74)* the reflected wave is completely polarized in the plane of incidence, even if the incident wave is unpolarized. The angle given by $\tan^{-1} n_2/n_1$ is hence sometimes called the *polarizing angle*, and is about 56° at an air–glass interface. The effect can be utilized for obtaining plane polarized light but any other reflections, for example those from the back surface of a glass block, must be eliminated.

Because reflected light is partially polarized, the glare of sunlight reflected from polished surfaces and water can be reduced by using spectacles fitted with a polarizing material such as 'Polaroid'. If unpolarized light is passed through such a material the emergent light is substantially plane polarized in a particular direction. Very little light is transmitted if the incident light is polarized at right-angles to this direction. The material can thus be suitably orientated in the spectacle frame, and is usually arranged to attenuate considerably the polarized component in the light reflected from horizontal surfaces, other light being only slightly affected.

From the preceding analyses the amplitude relations can be found for an incident wave plane polarized in any direction. The magnetic vector can be resolved into a component of amplitude a in the plane of incidence and one of amplitude b normal to this plane, and the *Equations* (8.72) and (8.73) can then be applied to these components. a and b can be assumed to be known. We then get, from *Equations* (8.72) and (8.73)

$$\left.\begin{array}{l} a_R = -a\,[\sin\,(\theta-\phi)\,]/\sin\,(\theta+\phi) \\[2pt] a_T = a(\sin\,2\theta)/\sin\,(\theta+\phi) \\[2pt] b_R = b(\sin\,2\theta-\sin\,2\phi)/(\sin\,2\theta+\sin\,2\phi) \\[2pt] \quad = b\,[\tan\,(\theta-\phi)/\tan\,(\theta+\phi)\,] \\[2pt] b_T = b(2\sin\,2\theta)/(\sin\,2\theta+\sin\,2\phi) \\[2pt] \quad = b(\sin\,2\theta)/\,[\sin\,(\theta+\phi)\,]\cos\,(\theta-\phi) \end{array}\right\} \qquad (8.75)$$

which are Fresnel's equations for the amplitudes of the magnetic field components. A similar set for the electric field components can be got from these. The amplitudes become $a\eta_1$, $a_R\eta_1$, $a_T\eta_2$, $b\eta_1$, $b_R\eta_1$ and $b_T\eta_2$. The ratio η_2/η_1 can be eliminated as before.

When the incident wave is in the denser of the two dielectrics *total* (*internal*) *reflection* can occur. ϕ is greater than θ, and if θ is increased from zero ϕ increases until it becomes $\pi/2$ radians. If θ is increased still further ϕ becomes imaginary, and although no refracted wave is found experimentally there can be shown to be an attenuated wave theoretically.

Suppose the incident wave is polarized in the plane of incidence. The incident and reflected waves can be expressed in component form as shown previously, exponential wave functions being used for convenience. In the exponential term for the transmitted wave $\sin\,\phi$ is real because

$$\sin\,\phi = (c_2/c_1)\sin\,\theta$$

but $\cos\,\phi$ is imaginary since

$$\cos\,\phi = \sqrt{(1-\sin^2\phi)} = \sqrt{[1-(c_2/c_1)^2\sin^2\theta]}$$

and $\sin\,\theta$ exceeds the ratio c_1/c_2 when there is total reflection. Let $\cos\,\phi$ equal $\pm j\alpha$, where α is real. The electric field component of the transmitted wave parallel to the y axis is then given by

$$\mathbf{E}_y = -\eta_2\mathbf{a}_T\exp jk_T(x\sin\,\phi\pm j\alpha z-c_2 t)$$
$$= -\eta_2\mathbf{a}_T(\exp\pm k_T\alpha z)\exp jk_T(x\sin\,\phi-c_2 t).$$

Experimentally no transmitted wave is observed at optical frequencies, and at those of microwaves only a highly attenuated refracted wave has been found in, for example, prisms made of pitch. The plus sign in the preceding equation can thus be assumed not to apply. Hence

$$\mathbf{E}_y = -\eta_2\mathbf{a}_T(\exp- k_T\alpha z)\exp jk_T(x\sin\,\phi-c_2 t).$$

For light waves $k_T \alpha$ is so large that the penetration is only a few wavelengths. $k_T \alpha$ increases as λ_T decreases (k_T is $2\pi/\lambda_T$) so the penetration of high frequency waves is negligible. In practice there is not an abrupt transition from a refractive index n_1 to n_2 but the preceding results, except those which apply in the region of the polarizing angle, are not significantly affected unless the change occurs over a distance of the same order as the wavelength of the incident radiation. Experiments have indicated that the thickness of the layer in which the transition from n_1 to n_2 occurs is about $1/50$ of the mean wavelength of the sodium doublet for a polished glass surface in air.

At normal incidence the transmitted energy is smaller than the incident energy by a few per cent. The energy loss may be decreased by a layer having a refractive index $\sqrt{(n_1 n_2)}$ and of thickness one quarter that of the mean wavelength of the incident radiation, as noted in section **6.3**. The waves reflected from the two surfaces then interfere. Many of the lenses used in cameras, binoculars and so on are thus 'coated', for the amount of light reflected and hence lost is then only about one per cent. Reflection and transmission coefficients for electro-magnetic waves at a particular interface can be calculated from the time average power flow normal to unit area for the various waves, the result for $\bar{P}$ expressed in *Equation (8.46)* being used.

Reflection at a dielectric–conductor interface is considerably different from that examined already, but the foregoing results can be used if the refractive index n_2 is replaced by the complex refractive index n_2' and the permittivity ε_2 by its complex counterpart. The penetration of the transmitted wave is very small, as was found in section **8.4**. Another kind of wave is that travelling in a dielectric parallel and near to the boundary between the dielectric and a conductor having finite conductivity. The amplitude of such a wave varies inversely with the distance of travel along the boundary and with conductivity. If the wave is originally polarized there is a change in polarization. The 'ground wave' from radio transmitting stations is an example of this kind of wave and follows the earth's surface, thus deviating from the optical path. Signals are received at places beyond the horizon seen from the transmitter, even though diffraction effects may be negligible as they are for medium and short radio waves. There is a detailed examination of such a wave in 'Electromagnetic Theory' by J. A. Stratton, McGraw-Hill, 1941, on pages 573 to 587.

WAVE VELOCITY

9.1. Phase, Wave and Group Velocities

The waves emitted by sources of acoustic or electro-magnetic disturbances cover a range of frequencies. This is true even for 'monochromatic' sources, although the frequency range is small when associated with particular lines. If the medium through which the waves are travelling is *dispersive*, that is if waves of different frequencies travel at different speeds in the medium, waves of nearly the same frequency are sorted into groups as the waves advance. The groups have a different speed from the individual waves as will be shown later.

When an ocean wave approaches a sea wall so that the wave-front is inclined to the wall, the splash set up at the region of contact of the wave crest and the wall is seen to travel along the wall much faster than the incoming waves. The splash velocity is an example of *phase velocity*, the rate of travel of a particular phase, here the crest. In the preceding pages the term *wave velocity* has been used to describe the phase velocity in the direction in which the waves are travelling, for the rate of advance of a certain phase, for example a crest or a trough, has been implied.

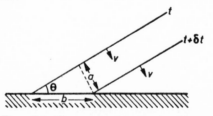

Figure 9.1. Wave approaching barrier obliquely

Figure 9.1 depicts two successive positions of a wave-front approaching a barrier obliquely. In a time δt the wave-front moves a distance a, so that its velocity v is $a/\delta t$. The phase velocity along the barrier is u which equals $b/\delta t$. Thus

$$u/v = b/a = 1/\sin \theta$$

where θ is the angle between the wave-front and the barrier. Hence

u increases as θ decreases, becoming infinite when θ is zero, so that for plane waves the phase velocity parallel to the wave-front is infinite.

v is the *group velocity*. The waves observed on the sea are usually gravity waves whose velocity depends on their wavelength, according to *Equation (4.30)*. Hence as the waves travel those of roughly the same wavelength become grouped, if the original disturbance contained waves of many lengths. The rate of advance of, for example, the maximum of the combined effect is the group velocity, which here is less than that of any of the individual waves.

Suppose a wave contains two components

$$s_1 = a \cos 2\pi(t/T_1 - x/\lambda_1)$$

and

$$s_2 = a \cos 2\pi(t/T_2 - x/\lambda_2)$$

where a is the displacement amplitude and

$$\lambda_2 = \lambda_1 + \delta\lambda_1 = \lambda + \delta\lambda$$

and

$$T_2 = T_1 + \delta T_1 = T + \delta T.$$

The resultant wave is, since the principle of superposition applies in the absence of non-linearities in the medium through which the waves are travelling, $s_1 + s_2$ which equals s given by

$$s = 2a \cos \pi[t(1/T_1 + 1/T_2) - x(1/\lambda_1 + 1/\lambda_2)]$$
$$\times \cos \pi[t(1/T_1 - 1/T_2) - x(1/\lambda_1 - 1/\lambda_2)].$$

But

$$1/\lambda_1 + 1/\lambda_2 \simeq 2\lambda/\lambda^2 = 2/\lambda$$

and

$$1/\lambda_1 - 1/\lambda_2 \simeq \delta\lambda/\lambda^2.$$

Similarly

$$1/T_1 + 1/T_2 \simeq 2/T$$

and

$$1/T_1 - 1/T_2 \simeq \delta T/T^2.$$

Thus the resultant wave equation is

$$s = 2a[\cos 2\pi(t/T - x/\lambda)] \cos \pi(t\delta T/T^2 - x\delta\lambda/\lambda^2). \qquad (9.1)$$

The wavelength of the second term is $2\lambda^2/\delta\lambda$ which greatly exceeds λ. The resultant wave is indicated in *Figure 9.2* and has a frequency close to those of the original waves, but its amplitude varies slowly as with beats, mentioned in section **2.5**. The progression of this amplitude variation is observed, instead of that of the component waves whose velocity may differ from that of the group.

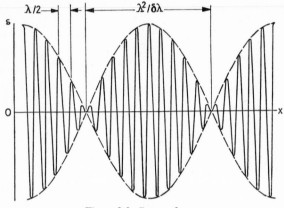

Figure 9.2. Group of waves

In the second function in *Equation (9.1)* an increase of $2\lambda^2/\delta\lambda$ in x makes the function repeat, as does an increase of $2T^2/\delta T$ in t. Thus the group velocity v is given by

$$v = (2\lambda^2/\delta\lambda)/(2T^2/\delta T).$$

But $T = \lambda/c$ so that $T^2 = \lambda^2/c^2$ and $\delta T = (c\delta\lambda - \lambda\delta c)/c^2$. Hence

$$v = (\lambda^2/\delta\lambda)(c\delta\lambda - \lambda\delta c)/\lambda^2$$

$$= c - \lambda\delta c/\delta\lambda$$

or in the limit

$$v = c - \lambda dc/d\lambda \qquad (9.2)$$

which is known as Rayleigh's equation. It can be written in the form

$$v = (1-p)c$$

if the relation between the wave velocity c and wavelength λ is

$$c = k\lambda^p$$

where k and p are constants since

$$dc/d\lambda = kp\lambda^{(p-1)} = cp/\lambda.$$

228

Values of p and the corresponding relations between group and wave velocity are given in *Table 9.1*.

Table 9.1. Relations between group and wave velocities.

Longitudinal sound waves and transverse waves on strings, both of small amplitude.	$p = 0$	$v = c$
Gravity waves.	$p = \frac{1}{2}$	$v = c/2$
Ripples.	$p = -\frac{1}{2}$	$v = 3c/2$
Transverse waves on bars.	$p = -1$	$v = 2c$

For light waves the observation of separate components has not yet been possible so that all direct experimental methods for determining wave velocity up to the present give in fact the group velocity, although the wave velocity can be found by using *Equation (9.2)* or another form of it. In air at STP the difference between wave and group velocities is about 6×10^3 metre/sec which cannot be ignored in accurate velocity determinations. *Equation (9.2)* can be put in a more appropriate form for light waves by introducing the refractive index n. If c and c_0 are the velocities of electro-magnetic waves in a medium and in a vacuum, the refractive index of the medium is c_0/c. Hence dc/dn is $-c_0/n^2$. We have

$$\frac{dc}{d\lambda} = \frac{dc}{dn} \cdot \frac{dn}{d\tau} = \frac{c_0}{n^2} \cdot \frac{dn}{d\tau}$$

$$= -\frac{c}{n} \cdot \frac{dn}{d\tau}.$$

Thus *Equation (9.2)* becomes

$$v = c\left(1 + \frac{\lambda}{n} \cdot \frac{dn}{d\lambda}\right). \tag{9.3}$$

From his early direct measurements of the velocity of light in carbon disulphide, Michelson deduced that its refractive index was $1\cdot758$ whereas from the usual experiments giving refractive indexes the value was $1\cdot635$. The discrepancy occurred because the first result is the ratio v_0/v, which equals c_0/v since the group velocity v_0 in a vacuum is identical with the wave velocity c_0 there, while the second result is c_0/c.

229

Signal velocity, the velocity with which intelligence may be transmitted, is often identified with group velocity. Usually the two velocities are the same, but if dispersion occurs such that the group velocity of waves is greater than the wave velocity, as with anomalous dispersion (section **8.10.**), there is a difference which may be difficult to calculate. Intelligence cannot be transmitted at a velocity exceeding the wave velocity according to the special theory of relativity, and the supposed equality between signal and group velocities led to early objections to the theory. Signal velocities are examined in 'Electromagnetic Theory' by J. S. Stratton, McGraw-Hill, 1941, on pages 333 to 340.

9.2. Experimental Determination of Electro-magnetic Wave Velocity

The velocity of light waves in air is about 3×10^8 metre/sec so that in any direct measurement the path length of the waves must be very large, if time intervals relating to the travel of the waves are to be actually or effectively measured with any precision in order to obtain an accurate result. Thus in the early determinations of the velocity of light, effects which occur in astronomy were utilized, as in Römer's (1676) and in Bradley's (1727) methods. Fizeau's (1849) experiment was the first in which terrestrial distances were used, followed by Foucault's (1850), Michelson's (1879) and further experiments due to Michelson and others. In these experiments the light waves were emitted in pulses from a rotating wheel or mirror, but in 1925 a more elegant method of modulating the light beam at much higher frequencies was used by Karolus and Mittelstaedt. This was the Kerr cell optical shutter, described later, and was used in many of the more recent determinations including those by Hüttel (1940), Anderson (1937, 1940), Bergstrand (1950, 1951), Schöldröm (1955) and Edge (1956). Houstoun (1949) used a quartz diffraction grating of the kind described in section **6.7.** in which the maxima, other than the zero order maximum, could be pulsed at about 100 Mc/s. An indirect determination had been made by Rosa and Dorsey (1906, 1907) depending on the ratio of electro-magnetic and electro-static units, while Mercier (1923) had measured the velocity of short radio waves on Lecher wires. There have also been some measurements at microwave frequencies—Essen and Gordon-Smith (1947, 1950), Aslakson (1949, 1951), Hanson and Bol (1950) and Froome (1951, 1954, 1958), and some from band spectra—Rank and others (1952-1957).

Many transparent substances, when placed in a strong electric field between two parallel plates, behave as uniaxial crystals whose axes are normal to the plates. Thus plane polarized incident light generally becomes elliptically polarized on passing through the substance, for the light is resolved into two components—ordinary and extraordinary rays—which travel at different speeds so that there is a phase difference ϕ between them on emergence. This is the *Kerr effect* and was discovered in 1895. A Kerr cell usually consists of a rectangular glass container, in which two parallel metal plates are held in position by their connecting wires passing through opposite walls, filled with a liquid showing a strong Kerr effect, such as nitrobenzene. Light is passed between and parallel to the plates through

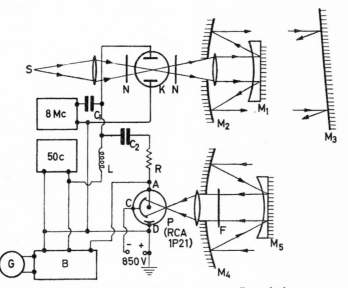

Figure 9.3. Velocity of light by Bergstrand's method

sides which are parallel. If such a cell is placed appropriately between two crossed Nicol prisms or 'Polaroid' screens the light emerging from the system is directly proportional to $\sin^2\phi/2$. Usually a linear part of the transmitted intensity–potential difference characteristic is employed by superposing a zero-frequency bias potential on any alternating potential applied across the cell. The transmitted intensity then varies about a mean value at the frequency of the alternating component.

A Kerr cell was used in Bergstrand's method of velocity determina-

231

tion, a similar method being employed by Schöldröm and later by Edge. *Figure 9.3* indicates the experimental arrangement, the Kerr cell and photomultiplier circuits being considerably simplified to aid explanation. The source S is a 30 watt projection filament lamp. K is a Kerr cell containing nitrobenzene arranged suitably between Nicol prisms N. The mirrors M_2 and M_4 are concave spherical surface silvered mirrors having 75 cm focal lengths and 46 cm apertures, M_3 is plane while M_1 and M_5 are plano-concave lenses silvered on the plane surfaces. The spherical aberration of M_2 and M_4 is cancelled by that of M_1 and M_5. The chromatic aberration of M_1 and M_5 is unimportant since only the yellow component of the transmitted light is detected by the photomultiplier P, F being a yellow-green filter. The Kerr cell is modulated by a signal of frequency 8·3 Mc/s from an oscillator, the potential difference of amplitude 2 kV being superposed on another of 5 kV amplitude and frequency 50 c/s derived from the mains. The latter potential has a rectangular wave form which is produced by peak clipping, and acts as a bias. A potential V_A for the photomultiplier anode A is obtained from the high-frequency oscillator, so that the sensitivity of P varies at the same frequency as the intensity of the transmitted light. The dynode D of the photomultiplier nearest the anode A is at earth potential, while across the others and the cathode is divided 850 V, the cathode C being at the lowest potential. The inductor L and the capacitor C_1 prevent the high and the low frequency supplies from mutually short-circuiting. C_2 prevents 50 c/s pulses from appearing at the anode of P directly from the supply, but the photocurrent contains pulses of this frequency arising from the modulated light beam, its phase being changed at 100 times per second as indicated in *Figure 9.4* which is not to scale. A linear part of the I–V characteristic is used, and the transmitted intensity is independent of the sign of V so that the two curves on either side of the V axis are the same.

The output of P is amplified and passes to the control grids of two identical EF 50 pentodes forming part of a balancing device B. The suppressor grids of these pentodes are provided with a sufficient potential from the low frequency supply to render the valves alternately conducting. Across their anodes is connected a microammeter G filled with oil in order to increase the damping of the moving coil, and hence increase the period of oscillation to ten seconds. When the outputs from the two pentodes are the same, G indicates zero current if the zero has been previously set with the plane mirror M_3 screened. The frequency of the alternate pulses through G is too high for the moving coil to respond to them. The outputs of the pentodes are identical if successive pulses from the photomultiplier P are the same. This occurs only if the phase angle lag, produced mainly by the light travelling along a path of length $2d$, is an odd multiple of $\pi/2$, as shown by the following analysis.

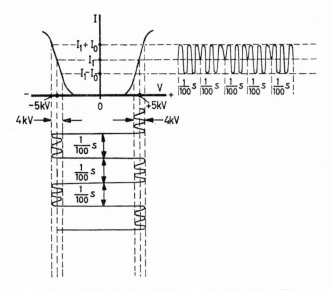

Figure 9.4. Variation of light transmitted by Kerr cell and Nicol prisms

The intensities of light emerging from the Kerr cell arrangement during the positive and negative half-cycles of the low frequency bias potential are

$$I_+ = I_1 + I_0 \sin \omega t$$

and

$$I_- = I_1 + I_0 \sin (\omega t + \pi)$$

where I_1 is a constant intensity and I_0 is the amplitude of the variable intensity. The phase angle π is required because the phase angle of the light passing during the negative half-cycle is advanced by π radians.

The light then travels into P which passes current when the anode is positive, as it is every alternate half-cycle of the potential of high frequency $\omega/2\pi$ which is f, the duration of each half-cycle being

233

$1/2f$. The currents i_+ and i_- corresponding to intensities I_+ and I_- are given by

$$i_+ = 2kf \int_{t_1}^{t_1+1/2f} [I_1 + I_0 \sin \omega(t-2d/v)]dt$$

$$i_- = 2kf \int_{t_1}^{t_1+1/2f} \{I_1 + I_0 \sin [\omega(t-2d/v)+\pi]\}dt$$

because the time taken for the light to travel from the Kerr cell arrangement to P is $2d/v$, $2d$ being the path length and v the group velocity of the waves. k is principally the photoelectric conversion constant of P but also includes an allowance for the attenuation of the light beam during its travel. The currents i_+ and i_- have opposite effects on the balancing device B, the deflection of G being directly proportional to $i_+ - i_-$, which equals i, given by

$$i = -(4fkI_0/\omega) \left[\cos \omega(t-2d/v) \right]_{t_1}^{t_1+1/2f}$$

$$= (2kI_0/\pi)[\cos \omega(t_1-2d/v) - \cos \omega(t_1+1/2f-2d/v)]$$

$$= (2kI_0/\pi)\{\cos \omega(t_1-2d/v) - \cos [\omega(t_1-2d/v)+\pi]\}$$

$$= (4kI_0/\pi) \cos \omega(t_1-2d/v)$$

$$= 0 \quad \text{if} \quad \omega(t_1-2d/v) = \pi/2 - p\pi$$

where p is an integer. t_1 includes the delay between changing the potential across the Kerr cell and the emergence of the corresponding wave intensity from the second Nicol prism, the time difference between the potential appearing at the Kerr cell plates and at the anode of P and the transit time of electrons in P. There may also be some error in the measurement of the beam path length, particularly in the region of the Kerr cell and of the photomultiplier P. Any such error can also be included in t_1. We now have

$$\omega(t_1-2d/v) = \pi/2 - p\pi$$

or

$$d = (v/\omega)(2p-1)\pi/4 + vt_1/2.$$

Thus

$$d = (2p-1)\lambda/8 + K \tag{9.4}$$

where K equals $vt_1/2$ and can be assumed to be constant for any changes in atmospheric conditions that are likely to occur while an experiment is being conducted. K can be eliminated by measuring two values of d, d_1 and d_2. Then

$$d_2 - d_1 = (p_2 - p_1)\lambda/4. \qquad (9.5)$$

p_1 and p_2 are the values of p corresponding to d_1 and d_2. $(p_2 - p_1)$ is integral and can be found by using an approximate value of λ in *Equation (9.5)*. Then λ can be found accurately (36 metres when f was 8·332 Mc/s) and hence the velocity v. The wave velocity c_0 in a vacuum can be found by using *Equation (9.3)*.

Many determinations were made with M_3 fixed at 7 km, the frequency f being adjusted to give a zero deflection in G, and then with a movable convex mirror at 90 m, the frequency being un-

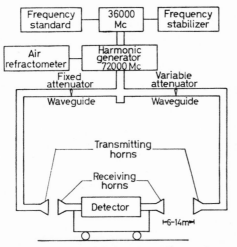

Figure 9.5. Simplified diagram of Froome's interferometer

altered. The convex mirror gave an image at P the same as that given by the plane mirror, and was adjusted to give a zero deflection in G once more. The final result for the velocity of light in a vacuum was

$$299793 \cdot 1 \pm 0 \cdot 2 \text{ km sec}^{-1}.$$

A more recent (1957) value is

$$299792 \cdot 85 \pm 0 \cdot 16 \text{ km sec}^{-1}.$$

In agreement with this latter value is Froome's result[1]

$$299792 \cdot 50 \pm 0 \cdot 10 \text{ km sec}^{-1}$$

which was obtained with a millimetre wave interferometer, indicated schematically in *Figure 9.5*, operating at about 72,000 Mc/s, the

235

corresponding wavelength being 4 mm. The principle of the method is the same as that of Hebb's experiment for sound waves, mentioned later. Bergstrand's result is also in accord with Essen's earlier micro-wave cavity resonator result, unlike other experiments in which light waves were used. A possible reason for the disagreement has been advanced by Miller and Lopez[2] who assert that reflection from mirror surfaces cannot be instantaneous, because free electrons are forced into oscillation by the incident wave and re-emit energy in a time of the order of 10^{-10} sec. Such a delay does not occur or is of no effect in interferometer or resonant cavity measurement, while in Bergstrand's experiment the delay would be included in t_1 and hence in K.

A method has recently been proposed by Sanders[3] which depends on the development of a suitable optical maser emitting two very narrow lines of nearly the same frequency. The two waves would be combined in a photosensitive device, and the amplitude of the differ-ence frequency signal would depend on the path and frequency differences and upon the velocity of light. Direct modulation of the light beam would not be necessary because the correlation of photons in coherent light, as discussed in section **6.1.**, would be used. Thus an optical standard of length could be employed instead of the relatively large distances, several kilometres, required at present even with high modulation frequencies.

A maser (a term derived from the initial letters of the description—microwave amplification by stimulated emission of radiation) can comprise a pair of optically flat plates sufficiently close together to form a resonant cavity. In the cavity is a mixture of gases, for example helium and neon, excited so as to generate electro-magnetic waves. These waves are coherent, the absence of phase fluctuations being caused by feedback from the electric field of the waves, and have a spectrum of very intense and narrow lines, their wavelengths depend-ing on the dimensions of the cavity. In some recent kinds of optical maser or laser (light amplification by stimulated emission of radia-tion) the resonant cavity is formed by an artificially-grown crystal, such as ruby, having machined and aluminized ends. Excitation is produced by intense flashes of light from, for example, a photographic flash tube. The emitted light has the previously mentioned character-istics, its intensity being claimed in some instances to exceed a million times that of sunlight.

In section **9.1.** Michelson's measurement of the velocity of light in carbon disulphide has been mentioned. This measurement was made in 1885 together with the velocity of light in water and was based on a method used qualitatively by Foucault (1850), devised originally to test whether the velocity of light in a medium denser than air was greater or less than that in air. Foucault found that the velocity of light in water was less than in air as predicted in the wave theory of light, the contrary being expected according to the corpuscular theory. Michelson's results were confirmed by Gouy (1885) and Gutton (1912).

Recent measurements of the velocity of light in media other than air are those of Houstoun (1944) and Bergstrand (1954), both of whom used the ultrasonic diffraction grating for modulating the light. Their results confirm the theoretical relation between group and wave velocity, *Equation (9.3)*.

9.3. Experimental Determination of Acoustic Wave Velocity

The velocity of acoustic waves in air, about 330 metre/sec, is very much lower than that of light. The wave path length in large scale velocity measurements could thus apparently be made smaller than that in optical experiments by a factor of 10^{-6} without loss of accuracy, if the time of travel or its phase angle equivalent could be measured or allowed for as accurately as in optical determinations. Because the much smaller path lengths could be measured more precisely a greater accuracy would in fact be expected. Unfortunately, although time intervals can now be found very accurately and time delays in the sending or receiving apparatus can be measured or eliminated from the velocity determination, atmospheric conditions have a much greater effect on sound than on light velocities.

The factors affecting the velocity of sound c_0, which equals $\sqrt{(\gamma P_0/\rho_0)}$ for small amplitude waves, in air and in gases generally are:

(*i*) Temperature. c_0 is nearly directly proportional to the square root of the absolute temperature of the gas over a temperature range depending on the gas. The increase in velocity is about 1/546 or 0·2 per cent per ° C increase in temperature.

(*ii*) Changes in density ρ_0 when not balanced by corresponding changes in pressure P_0. These occur if the composition of the gas can vary because of the alteration in the amounts of, for example, carbon dioxide or water vapour present, or if the pressure is altered so much that there is no longer a linear relation between pressure and density. Because of changes in composition there is also an alteration in γ but the accompanying effect on c_0 is much smaller. The overall effects are for the velocity to be increased by 0·52 metre/sec if the water content increases by one molecule per cent, and decreased by

0·6 metre/sec for a similar increase in carbon dioxide content. The velocity of sound in saturated air at 20° C and 760 mm of mercury pressure is 0·35 per cent greater than in dry air at the same temperature and pressure.

(*iii*) Wind velocity. The effective sound velocity is the algebraic sum of the wave velocity and the component of the wind velocity in the direction of the sound wave, if the wind speed is small in comparison with the speed of the waves. Although a constant wind velocity can be eliminated from measurements by allowing the sound wave to travel along a fixed path in opposite senses, the wind velocity may change appreciably even during a short time because of a change in magnitude or direction or both.

The wave velocity is increased when the wave amplitude is increased, as shown in section **7.1.** Thus near a source of intense sound, which may be required if the wave path is long to allow for attenuation, the waves travel at a higher speed than when they are further away. If waves having a wide frequency range are emitted, dispersion occurs to an extent depending on wave amplitude and also has to be taken into account. Hence the accuracy of large scale open-air experiments is severely limited because of the insuperable difficulty of making allowances for all these factors which may change as the wave is travelling. There have thus been no recent large scale determinations but the results available, which are very inaccurate compared with those for light waves, are sufficiently accurate for most purposes. Furthermore, the determination of the velocity of sound waves in air, in contrast with that of light waves, does not lead to the evaluation of a physical constant of great importance.

In the stationary wave method of Hebb[4], suggested by Michelson, the estimation of time delays, usually difficult to allow for as they may vary, was avoided in the sending and receiving apparatus. Two telephone transmitters, carbon granule microphones, were each placed at the focus of a parabolic plaster of Paris reflector of about 152 cm radius and 38 cm focal length. These reflectors were situated coaxially so that sound waves emitted by a whistle of frequency 2376 c/s at the focus of one were collected at the focus of the other. The microphones were each connected in series with batteries and with the separate primaries of a telephone transformer. Across the secondary was a potential difference which was the vector sum of the potentials induced from the primaries, and was estimated by ear with the aid of a telephone receiver. As one of the reflectors with its microphone was moved, the sound heard passed through maxima and minima, the distance moved between successive ones being a quarter wavelength. Over 200 successive settings covering a distance of about 30 m were made of the movable reflector for minima. The whistle frequency was accurately found by comparison with a tuning fork which was ultimately rated against a standard clock. The relevant atmospheric conditions between the two mirrors were accurately evaluated and the result was

$$331 \cdot 29 \pm 0 \cdot 04 \text{ m/sec}$$

at $0°$ C, amended later (1919) to $331 \cdot 44$ m/sec, which led to a value of γ agreeing well with that obtained by direct determinations.

There have been very few small scale measurements recently made at sonic frequencies. In such determinations a resonance tube has usually been employed, as in a method described by Shafter[5] for measuring underwater sound speeds at a frequency of 570 c/sec. A circular tube about $1 \cdot 2$ m long and 4 cm in diameter with a hydrophone probe mounted at its centre for detecting resonance was employed, the vibrations being generated by a piezo-electric transducer. The tube was open at both ends and the conditions for resonance, discussed in section **5.4.**, apply to this and the following experiment.

In earlier measurements of sonic velocities in gases Kaye and Sherratt[6] used a resonance tube of variable length. Vibrations in the gas column were caused by a moving-iron or crystal transducer at frequencies ranging from 500 to 27,000 c/s and resonance was detected by reaction on the transducer. The potential difference across the transducer passed through a series of maxima and minima as the tube length was altered over a range of values, differing by about 60 cm between extremes, by moving a piston. The displacement was half the wavelength of the sound at a particular frequency for successive maxima or minima. The temperature of the various enclosed gases was held constant at 18 or $100°$ C and tubes of several diameters and materials were used.

In all measurements of velocities of sound in fluids contained in tubes, a correction has to be made to measured values which are lower than those in the free fluid. The reduction is thought to be due to the combined effects of friction at the wall of the tube and heat conduction through the tube material tending to equalize the temperatures of compressions and rarefactions. The correction cannot be calculated precisely, but a formula derived by Helmholtz and Kirchoff is usually sufficiently accurate. The formula is

$$c = c_0[1 - k/2r\sqrt{(\pi f)}] \qquad (9.6)$$

where c is the speed of sound in the fluid contained in the pipe of

239

radius r, c_0 the speed in free fluid, f the frequency of the sound, and k a constant which has roughly the value given by

$$k = \sqrt{(\mu)} + (\gamma - 1)\sqrt{(\nu/\gamma)}$$

μ being the kinematic viscosity and ν the thermal diffusivity, although it also depends on the nature of the surface of the tube. For a pipe of one metre diameter the retardation is about 0·5 m/sec in the audio-frequency range. There may also be corrections to allow for the yielding of the tube wall and for end effects, mentioned in section **5.4.** These corrections, which are appreciable and necessarily impre-cise, lower the experimental accuracy attainable. For this reason, and because much smaller quantities of media having only one pair of accurately aligned faces are required, ultrasonic velocity measure-ments have recently been of much greater prominence than sonic determinations.

At frequencies exceeding 1 Mc/s resonance methods of velocity measurement involving the first few modes of vibration are not generally used, because the size of the specimen required would have to be inconveniently small. Fortunately ultrasonic waves can easily be transmitted into specimens of sizes equivalent to many wave-lengths by the use of suitable transducers, of thin quartz crystal or barium titanate for example, and free field velocities can be calculated from measured ones.

In the *pulse method* short rectangular pulses of waves originating from a transducer acting as a transmitter and a receiver are reflected back and forth in the specimen, and the velocity is obtained from the delay time t between echoes, which are caused by waves reflected from a face parallel to the one from which the waves are transmitted. If the distance between the faces is d, the wave velocity is $2d/t$. t is usually measured between the leading edges of successive pulses displayed on a cathode-ray tube screen, but measurement may be difficult because of distortion of the pulses due to reflections at the transducer-specimen interface. Furthermore an appreciable correc-tion to the measured time may be required. The correction can be evaluated by using a symmetrical pair of transducers, one being used as a transmitter and receiver. By measuring t with and without the second transducer in position on the specimen the correction can be evaluated.

The '*sing-around*' *method* is also widely used. The principle appears to have been devised in 1937 and the description to have been coined by Hanson[7]. In this method separate transducers are used for trans-mitting and receiving. The pulse, of short duration compared with the time taken to cross the specimen, is passed between parallel faces, received, converted back into an electrical signal and used to trigger another pulse from the generator. The pulse repetition frequency can be accurately measured and used to determine the delay time and wave velocity.

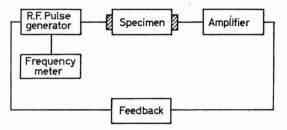

Figure 9.6. Block diagram of 'sing-around' method

Figure 9.6 indicates the principle of the 'sing-around' method. Electrical pulses leave the generator at a frequency just below the minimum frequency f required for stable operation. The pressure pulses leaving the transducer pass through the specimen in a time d/c, where d is their path length and c is the wave velocity. The received pressure pulses are converted into electrical pulses and, after being amplified and shaped, are used to synchronize the pulse generator. If t_e is the sum of the electrical and any other delays

$$1/f = t_e + d/c. \tag{9.7}$$

t_e can be found by measuring f for known values of d or, more accurately, calibrating the apparatus by using a specimen in which the wave velocity is known. Then, by measuring f, the unknown velocity can be found.

Errors can arise from echoes. They are not synchronous because each set is derived from a different primary pulse. They can be eliminated by tilting the transducers slightly or by matching the impedance of the transducers to that of the medium, thus making the echo amplitudes negligible in comparison with the main pulse amplitude. Alternatively the transducers can be mounted on the same face and the main pulse received after one reflection. The other pulses are then reflected three or more times and their amplitudes are made negligible as before, particularly if the reflector is a material like hard rubber or a perforated metal plate.

The ultrasonic diffraction grating is often used for the determination of wave velocities in transparent liquids. In the usual method the

241

wavelength is found by using *Equations* (*6.30*) or (*6.31*) so that, if the frequency of the waves is known, their velocity can be calculated. In a recent method due to Terry[8] the ultrasonic waves passing through the liquid have been amplitude modulated, as mentioned in section **3.7.**, at a lower frequency. The central image of the diffraction pattern is suppressed and light from the higher order spectra, having an intensity varying at the modulation frequency, is collected and passed on to a photocell. The frequency of the amplitude modulating signal corresponding to minimum output from the photocell is related simply to the ultrasonic wave velocity, attenuation in the liquid, and to the length of the light beam parallel to the ultrasonic waves. A similar principle has been used in the Scophony television system and in other devices. Thus a velocity measurement can rapidly be made by finding the corresponding frequency of the amplitude modulation.

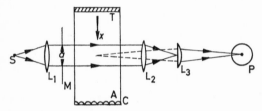

Figure 9.7. Optical diffraction arrangement

The experimental arrangement is shown in *Figure 9.7.* S is a white light horizontal slit source placed at the focus of a convex lens L_1, and the parallel beam limited by a rectangular hole in the mask M passes through the vertical ultrasonic light cell C into another convex lens L_2. L_3 is a small plano-convex lens with a thin stop across its horizontal diameter, placed so that the central image falls on the stop. Thus only light from the diffraction spectra can pass on to the photocell P, adjusted so that the image of the aperture in M is accommodated on its cathode. The transducer T is a quartz crystal of resonant frequency 9·65 Mc/s from which the ultrasonic beam of this frequency passes through the liquid to an absorber A. Very little energy is reflected, so that the ultrasonic waves are substantially progressive.

In a preliminary experiment the light was modulated by a fan blade revolving in the light beam so as to produce from P an alternating output which could be amplified. A linear relation was found between the photocell amplifier output and the amplitude of the potential difference across the crystal, ranging from 35 to 115 V rms. The amplitude of the ultrasonic signal was thus set at 70 V and there was found to be a linear relation between the photocell amplifier output and the depth of modulation up to about 50 per cent, the fan having been removed. Such a result would be anticipated because, for 50 per cent amplitude modulation, the carrier potential would vary between 35 and 105 V if it were 70 V when unmodulated.

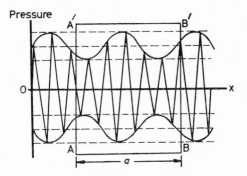

Figure 9.8. Amplitude modulated ultrasonic waves

Figure 9.8 indicates a modulated ultrasonic wave in the liquid. The diffraction pattern intensity at any time depends on the length a, nearly 1 cm, of the rectangular aperture, and on the pressure distribution in this length of liquid illuminated through the aperture. Thus the area enclosed between the envelope of the modulated wave and the ordinates AA′, BB′ in *Figure 9.8* gives a measure of the diffraction pattern intensity. This area is constant with time only if a is $m\lambda'$, where m is an integer and λ' is the modulation wavelength. a is fixed so that for values of λ' not satisfying this equation the diffracted amplitude will vary with time, and some output will be obtained from the photocell amplifier. The wave velocity c equals $f\lambda'$, where f is the frequency of the amplitude modulating signal. Hence

$$c = f\lambda' = fa/m \qquad (9.8)$$

from which c can be found. For heptane at $18 \cdot 8°$ C a first minimum amplifier output was obtained when f was $124 \cdot 3$ kc/s and further minima at $248 \cdot 0$ and $371 \cdot 0$ kc/s. These frequencies are not quite in the ratio 1:2:3. The discrepancy can be removed by allowing for attenuation of the modulated waves in the liquid. Attenuation also accounts for minimum amplifier outputs instead of the zero ones predicted from the simple analysis. Dispersion is negligible, if present at all, for small amplitude waves in liquids, and the wave velocity c in heptane was found to range from $1 \cdot 188$ and $1 \cdot 081 \times 10^3$ m/sec for temperatures varying between $16 \cdot 05$ and $39 \cdot 10°$ C. The claimed accuracy was better than $0 \cdot 5$ per cent.

Various kinds of ultrasonic interferometers have been designed for measurements of wavelengths, and hence velocities in fluids, of both the fixed and variable path types. The wave source is usually a quartz, barium titanate or magneto-strictive transducer whose dimensions can be chosen to correspond to a particular frequency at which the oscillations are stabilized in the variable path interferometer. In this respect, and in dimensions generally, the ultrasonic interferometer differs from the resonance tube velocity measurements of Kaye and Sherratt, but is similar in that the action of the reflected waves on the transducer is often used to detect maxima or minima. In the fixed path type the frequency is varied over a small range usually centred about the frequency of the fundamental mode of vibration of the transducer. The fixed path interferometer is much more limited in application than the variable path kind but is useful for measuring small changes in velocity with, for example, pressure variations[9]. An accuracy of $0 \cdot 03$ per cent in wavelength measurements can easily be attained with both kinds.

Several phase comparison methods have recently been developed for velocity measurements in solids and fluids. In these the phases of successive echoes of a pulse in a specimen are studied. There is a phase difference corresponding to the time required for the later echo to travel twice the length of the specimen. The phase difference depends on the frequency of the wave forming the pulse, and the frequency can be adjusted so that two successive echoes arrive at a transducer when they are, for example, at maxima. Then the phase angle difference is $2m\pi$, where m is an integer. The wave velocity can be found in terms of frequency, $2m\pi$ and the phase angle change produced by two reflections. This phase angle is sometimes difficult to determine accurately, but may be found if a 'buffer rod' of quartz or fused silica is used through which waves are transmitted to the specimen sealed to one end of the rod[10]. Other methods and references are quoted in this paper, in which there is also a brief note on the effect of diffraction on wave velocity which is increased when the waves are diverging from a finite source. At ultrasonic frequencies waves in specimens having rough lateral surfaces can be assumed to be propagated in free field conditions and, since they come from a finite source, their velocity is greater than that of waves from a point source. The excess velocity is about 0·04 per cent for longitudinal waves in a fused silica block if $\sqrt{(D^2 d/\lambda^2)}$ is 200, where D is the diameter of the transducer, d the distance from the transducer and λ the wavelength, falling to 0·01 per cent or nearly zero if $\sqrt{(D^2 d/\lambda^2)}$ is 6000 or 10^5.

References

[1] K. D. FROOME *Proc. Roy. Soc., A*, 1958, **247**, 109.
[2] R. A. MILLER and A. LOPEZ *J. opt. Soc. Amer.* 1959, **49**, 930.
[3] J. H. SANDERS *Nature, Lond.* 1959, **183**, 312.
[4] T. C. HEBB *Phys. Rev.* 1905, **20**, 91.
[5] J. D. SHAFTER *Rev. Sci. Instrum* 1960, **31**, 1318.
[6] G. W. C. KAYE and G. G. SHERRATT *Proc. Roy, Soc., A* 1933, **141**, 123
[7] R. L. HANSON *J. Acoust. Soc. Amer.* 1949, **21**, 60.
[8] N. B. TERRY *Acustica* 1956, **6**, 521.
[9] R. I. TAIT *Acustica* 1957, **7**, 193.
[10] H. J. MCSKIMIN *J. Acoust. Soc. Amer.* 1961, **33**, 606.

NAME INDEX

SUBJECT INDEX